HORNET

HORNET
The Inside Story of the F/A-18

Orr Kelly

Airlife
England

To the late Rev. Edward Shipsey, S. J. . . . . Jesuit, teacher, friend and wise man.

Copyright © 1990 by Orr Kelly

First published in the United States of America
by Presidio Press.

This edition first published in the United Kingdom
in 1991 by Airlife Publishing Ltd.

British Library Cataloguing in Publication Data
Kelly, Orr
    Hornet.
    1.   United States, Navy, Fighter aeroplanes, history
    I.   Title
    623.74640973

    ISBN 1-85310-226-1

Printed in the United States of America.

Airlife Publishing Ltd.

101 Longden Road, Shrewsbury SY3 9EB, England.

Contents

Photographs appear following page 92

Preface

Throughout my reporting and research on this book, I had a good deal of help both from the navy and from the companies that manufacture the plane or provide major components.

They provided their assistance freely although they had no way of knowing whether the book, in its final form, would reflect favorably on the navy and its contractors, which it does, or whether it would highlight serious faults, which it also does.

Rear Adm. Jimmie Finkelstein, an old friend who was then the navy's chief of information, got me started. Vice Adm. Robert F. Dunn, deputy chief of naval operations for air warfare, suggested a number of people to interview and bases to visit and okayed my request for a flight in the F/A-18.

In Finkelstein's office, Lt. Comdr. Sheila Graham, Lt. Bruce Cole, Lt. Frank Thorp, and Lt. Robert Fallon helped me to make appointments and gather information from naval sources. Bob Fallon became my personal guide through the bureaucratic labyrinth, time after time making the impossible become possible. Also helpful were Denny Kline and Grace Green of the Naval Air Systems Command's public affairs staff.

At Patuxent River Naval Air Station, Bill Frierson, the public affairs officer, was both helpful and sympathetic as I went through the ordeal of the flight physical and the physiological training described in the Appendix.

At Cecil Field, Florida, the East Coast training base for Hornet pilots, Nick Young, a veteran navy public affairs officer, put me in the hands of Lt. Casey Albert, who introduced me to many of the instructor pilots and then arranged for me to spend several hours in the simulators so I could gain some appreciation of what it is like to land on a carrier at night, what it is like to attack targets on the surface, and what it is like to come up against a skilled foe in a dogfight.

During my visit to Lemoore Naval Air Station, California, where I flew in the F/A-18, Dennis McGrath, the air station's public affairs officer, put me in touch with the pilots in VFA-125, the first Hornet training squadron.

At the Fallon Naval Air Station, Comdr. William Shepherd, the Strike University's executive officer, found time in his schedule to fill me in on how entire air wings are trained there before they are deployed and how senior officers go through an intensive course to prepare them for war at sea.

When I visited the *Coral Sea,* during training exercises in the Atlantic north of Puerto Rico, Lt. Robert Rivera and JOC(SW) James P. McKane III ran me up and down ladders from the top of the ship to the deepest engine rooms to help me undeistand how the Hornet operates aboard a carrier. At Norfolk, Lt. Comdr. Mike John helped arrange for my visit to the ship.

At the Top Gun school at Miramar, Lt. Jim McAloon, an F-14 back-seater—a naval flight officer and not a pilot—not only described the training in aerial combat but helped me to understand how air crews are learning to use the Tomcat and the Hornet together to take advantage of their unique capabilities.

My visits to the factories where the Hornet, its radar, and its engines are made began at the McDonnell Douglas plant in St. Louis, where Timothy J. Beecher, director of communications, and his assistant, Thomas J. Downey, arranged for me to interview a parade of engineers, managers, and test pilots who had been involved in designing, manufacturing, and testing the plane—and who had suffered through the difficult days when everything seemed to go wrong.

From St. Louis, I went on to southern California. At Northrop, Tony Cantafio and Gregory A. Waskul, of the company's public affairs staff, filled me in on Northrop's role in development of the F/A-18 at the corporate headquarters in Century City. Then I went to the plant in nearby Hawthorne for a tour of the plant under the guidance of Terry Clawson and visits with officials involved in development and production of the plane.

A short distance away, at Hughes Aircraft's Radar Systems Group, Kearney Bothwell, director of public relations, introduced me to three of the executives involved in development and production of the radar and then took me on a tour through the plant.

Later, on the East Coast, I spent two days at the General Electric jet engine plant in Lynn, Massachusetts, where the engines for the F/A-18 are made. My guide there was Kent Schubert, an independent public relations consultant who works under contract for G.E.

Much of my preliminary research for the book was carried out at the Pentagon library, the library of the Smithsonian Institution's Air and Space Museum, and the Montgomery County library branch in Bethesda. The files of the *Current News,* the Pentagon's daily summary of newspaper and magazine articles, were an important source of background information. Earlier, when I was an associate editor and Pentagon correspondent for *U.S. News & World Report* magazine, I did some research on the history of the F/A-18 with the help of members of the magazine's library staff.

My reporting on the history of the F/A-18 provided a fascinating opportunity to see a major Pentagon weapons procurement program whole— from the early debates over whether the navy needed a new plane and what kind it should be to the plane's first use in combat. Robert Tate, my editor at Presidio Press, patiently helped me to organize this complex story, covering a period of nearly two decades and involving politics, billions of dollars, high technology, tactics, and strategy. Because it is a complex story, the reader may benefit from a brief guide to the way the book is put together.

The first chapter covers the early controversy over the kind of plane that was needed. The second provides some perspective with a review of the history of military and, especially, naval aviation. The third picks up again with the development of the plane and the early decisions on what it should be expected to do.

The next four chapters describe the technology that makes the Hornet the unique plane that it is. Chapter 4 covers the all-important radar, the computers, the cockpit, and the controls. Chapter 5 covers the development of the engine. Chapter 6 brings these elements together with the airframe to make an airplane. Chapter 7 is devoted to the largely untold story of the critical problems associated with the tall vertical tails and how the manufacturers and the navy struggled to fix them.

The final two chapters cover the training of the pilots and ground crews and the first use of the plane by the marines and navy, including an account of the Hornet's first use in combat in the 1986 raid against Libya. The book ends with a description of how the F/A-18 would be used in the ultimate test: a major war with the Soviet Union.

The reader may be puzzled to find that every fighter pilot has a nickname, often an exotic one. The reason is that each pilot is given a distinctive call sign by his squadron mates to help avoid confusion during aerial operations, and many pilots are known better by their nicknames than by the names their mothers gave them.

When the manuscript was complete, John M. Elliott of the aviation branch of the Naval Historical Center and Dr. Robert Goulard, an aeronautical engineer and professor of engineering at George Washington University, were kind enough to read it for technical accuracy. I owe them both a debt of gratitude for helping to protect me from error, although any remaining errors are, of course, my responsibility.

Throughout the research and writing of *Hornet* I enjoyed the patient encouragement and support of my wife, Mary.

CHAPTER ONE

The Battle of the Admirals

In July 1970, an American Big Bird satellite passed silently over the Soviet Union, as it did routinely every hour and a half. Through superb lenses capable of photographing an item the size of a tennis ball, cameras aboard the satellite recorded the scene 120 miles below.

A short time later, as Big Bird crossed the Pacific, a trapdoor opened and a canister of exposed film plummeted downward. As it entered the lower atmosphere, a parachute deployed automatically and the canister drifted toward the sea near Hawaii, a radio beacon signalling its position. Before it hit the waves, an airplane with a large boom extended behind it snagged the parachute, and the canister was quickly reeled in.

For photo analysts examining miles of film, the challenge was to find change: anything that wasn't there yesterday or the week before; anything that was there before, but was gone today.

What caught the eyes of the analysts on this particular day was a new shape, the shape of an airplane they had never seen before. It was spotted at an airfield near the city of Kazan, at the confluence of the Kama and Volga rivers, about 400 miles east of Moscow. For years, there had been speculation that the Soviet Union was working on a new bomber, and in the previous year, rumors about such a bomber had become more frequent. Now, the speculation ended. Here was a picture of the bomber.

Skilled photo interpreters with a background in aeronautical engineering can reach some remarkably accurate conclusions about the probable performance of a plane by studying a photo, without ever seeing the plane itself or watching it fly. The length of the wings and the dimensions of the fuselage tell a good deal about a plane's range and payload. The engine inlets and exhaust ports provide clues to engine performance and thus tell something about speed and altitude.

In this case, as more information came in, it was clear that the shape seen on the ground at Kazan was indeed something quite new. The West gave the plane the code-name of Backfire. The Soviets, it was later learned, called it the Tu-26, a product of the Tupolev design bureau.

This is what it looked like: With its wings capable of moving backward and forward in flight, its appearance was much like that of the American F-111 fighter-bomber that had been in service for several years. But it was bigger and it carried a crew of four, rather than the two in the F-111. Its wings, swung full forward, as they would be for landing or takeoff, spread nearly 113 feet and it was almost 130 feet long. With a weapon load of 26,450 pounds, its maximum takeoff weight was 286,600 pounds. Its two engines, originally developed for the Soviets' abortive effort to build a supersonic transport plane, hurled it through the air at better than twice the speed of sound at high altitude and just under the speed of sound on the deck.

As word of this new bomber spread from the intelligence community to the Pentagon, the White House, and Capitol Hill, one question dominated all others. Did the Backfire have the range to attack targets in the U.S. and return home again? If it did, then it might be a dangerous new strategic threat to the U.S. homeland, requiring large amounts of money to be spent on air defenses. As more information about range came in, the answers to the questions about the purpose of this new plane were ambiguous. With an unrefueled combat radius of 2,485 miles, a Backfire attacking under U.S. radar would have to be refueled coming and going. Perhaps it could go on to land in Cuba or—and this was not entirely unthinkable in a nuclear war—it might be used in one-way suicide attacks.

Through most of the 1970s, the Backfire was at the center of a continuing debate between those who considered the plane both a new threat to the U.S. and proof of ill-will on the part of the Soviet Union, and those who argued that its relatively limited range ruled it out as a strategic bomber.

This was the issue that was debated in the White House, Congress, and the Pentagon and, increasingly, in public. But the navy's top admirals, in their offices on the outermost ring of the Pentagon's fourth floor, looked at the Backfire and saw something quite different and much less ambiguous. They didn't at all like what they saw.

For years, the admirals had worried about massed bomber attacks on their ships, especially the big aircraft carriers. Those worries, based on their experience in the great naval war with Japan, had been largely hypothetical. The Soviets had never put together a naval bombing force capable of a knockout blow. But the Backfire could change all that. Whether or not the new plane threatened the continental U.S., it could, in sufficient numbers, inflict major damage on the American fleet.

If a war with the Soviet Union broke out in Europe, the existence of a regiment or two of Backfires could vastly complicate what was seen then as the navy's primary job of keeping open the sea lanes between the U.S. and European ports.

The navy's strategy has evolved since that time, but this is how such a conflict might have unfolded in the early 1970s:

With the opening of hostilities, much of the Atlantic Fleet would move quickly toward the line that stretches from Greenland to Iceland, to the Faeroe Islands, and on to the United Kingdom—the G-I-UK Gap, as it is called. Destroyers and submarines would form a picket line to prevent Soviet submarines and surface raiders from sailing down into the North Atlantic. Carriers would move into place to provide air cover and aid in the search for submarines. In effect, the plan was to bottle up the Soviet Navy north of the Gap, in the Norwegian Sea.

The Red Navy already outnumbered the U.S. in submarines. Add to this a new threat from the air, and even strong defenders of the navy strategy began to wonder if it would work.

Each Backfire could carry two big AS-4 Kitchen missiles under its wings. Taking off from bases in the northern Soviet Union near Murmansk, the bombers would fly high over Finland, Sweden, and Norway, passing out to sea above the Arctic Circle. Then, to avoid radar detection, they would swoop down close to the waves and aim toward the American carriers at just below the speed of sound. At about 200 miles out, they would pop up, launch their missiles (doubling the number of targets the Americans would have to contend with), and then turn for home.

The Kitchen missile, first seen in the early 1960s, looks like a little airplane, with stubby wings and a cross-shaped tail. Its rocket motor propels it faster than the speed of sound and its own radar set guides it to the target. In its nose it carries either a nuclear or conventional warhead. Even the 2,200 pounds of ordinary high explosive is enough to sink a merchant ship or a destroyer. A hit from even one Kitchen would be powerful enough to cause serious damage to a carrier, at least disrupting flight operations for a number of hours.

If a combined bomber-submarine assault succeeded in breaking the American barrier at the Gap, then the whole Western strategy for the defense of Europe might quickly unravel. Submarine packs would be free to swing down into the mid-Atlantic or gather off ports in the U.S. and Europe. Backfire bombers and older Soviet Bears and Badgers—perhaps already operating out of bases in Norway—could wreak havoc with shipping. While the pilot of a Backfire would be foolhardy to come close to the warplanes of a carrier, he could freely attack cargo and troop ships with his twelve 1,100-pound bombs once the threat from fighters and interceptors had been removed.

It is against this background that two admirals emerge, representing conflicting views on the nature of the threat from Backfire and on what to do about it. The planes that fill the decks of America's carriers in the 1990s are what they are because of the decisions made while these two men—Vice Adm. William Houser and Vice Adm. Kent Lee—held the two top posts in naval aviation in the mid-1970s.

Houser, a fighter pilot who had commanded carriers and entire carrier divisions, became deputy chief of naval operations [DCNO] for air warfare in August 1972. That made him the navy's senior aviator, responsible for advising the chief of naval operations [CNO] on all matters relating to aviation: pilots, airplanes, weapons, training, carriers and bases. In effect, he was the representative in the Pentagon of the carrier navy.

His chief rival in the battle to shape the future of carrier aviation was Kent Lee, who had shot down one Japanese plane as a World War II fighter pilot and later served as commander of an attack squadron. In the late 1960s, while serving as commander of the nuclear-powered carrier U.S.S. *Enterprise,* Lee became deeply discouraged with the quality of the planes the navy was flying. He had two maintenance crews working twelve-hour shifts, and they still couldn't keep up with the workload. It was not unusual for the crews to put in forty or fifty manhours for every hour a plane spent in the air.

Lee made a deliberate decision to spend the rest of his career in the nuts and bolts world, trying to change this situation. This was an unusual career decision. Normally a captain who had achieved command of a carrier would look forward to promotion to rear admiral and to flying his flag at sea as commander of a group of carriers. Lee's decision, some of his colleagues felt, had been influenced by a tragic accident aboard the *Enterprise.* On 14 January 1969, while Lee was the skipper, an explosion aboard the ship set off a chain reaction in which rockets, bombs, and ammunition went off, tearing three large holes in the deck, destroying fifteen planes and killing twenty-four sailors. Instead of seeking a command at sea, Lee set as his goal the job of commander of the Naval Air Systems

Command [NAVAIR], responsible for designing and building the navy's airplanes and aerial weapons.

Although little known to the public, or even to many in the navy, the Air Systems Command, which was formed in 1921 as the Bureau of Aeronautics, should probably be considered the world's most successful weapons design bureau. Together with the navy's weapons laboratory at China Lake, California, NAVAIR has been responsible for the development of most of the aerial missiles in use by the U.S. Navy and Air Force and many of their allies: the Sidewinder, Sparrow, Phoenix, and Walleye, as well as the cruise missile. It was also responsible for a series of successful airplanes, many of them used by the U.S. Air Force and other nations. They include the F-4, the A-7, and the E-2C airborne battle station. Lee couldn't have chosen a position with better leverage from which to try to make the changes he thought were needed. In January 1973, five months after Houser had become DCNO for air warfare, Lee reached his goal and settled into his office at NAVAIR, in the new Crystal City complex about a mile down the Potomac from the Pentagon. Houser and Lee had once been good friends. But for the next three years they became locked in a bitter debate over the future of naval aviation.

The conflict had actually begun to fester several years earlier when Lee headed the office of program appraisal for the secretary of the navy. Houser had been director of aviation plans and requirements under Vice Adm. Thomas Connolly, then the DCNO for air warfare. The issue was the F-14, named the "Tomcat" to honor both Tom Connolly and Admiral Thomas Moorer, another aviator who was chief of naval operations during the plane's formative years.

The F-14, built by Grumman in Bethpage, Long Island, was the navy's answer to the Backfire before the Backfire came into existence. A big fighter-interceptor, it carried a two-man crew, a large, very powerful radar, and six Phoenix missiles capable of knocking down a target as small as a fighter plane more than a hundred miles away. It also had wings that could be moved in flight. When the crew wanted to fly slowly and loiter far from the carrier or when they wanted to slow down for landing, the wings would be fully extended. But if the Tomcat ran into enemy fighters, the wings would automatically swing back close to the fuselage, turning the plane into a formidable dogfighter.

Navy Secretary John Chafee, concerned about reports of cost and technical problems with the F-14—the navy's biggest aviation program—asked Lee and a civilian official to study the situation for him. They reported to Chafee that the problems were much worse than anyone had acknowledged, that he had "a monster" on his hands. The engines were underpowered and sometimes exploded in flight. Dogfight maneuvers had to be limited because the engines tended to stall. Grumman was in such shaky financial condition that the company's president even threatened during a congressional hearing to close his doors, and this situation was reflected in poor reliability and discouraging instances of shoddy workmanship.

When Connolly heard about this attack on the plane for which he had fought so hard, he stormed into Lee's office, read him his charter as the navy's senior aviator and stomped out.

Houser, who had been involved in the early work on the F-14, thought then, and continued to believe, that the F-14 was the plane the navy needed. He feared growing sentiment on Capitol Hill, and even within the Pentagon, to abandon the Tomcat because of its numerous problems or to supplement it with a cheaper and smaller fighter. Even Houser, the navy's staunchest defender of the F-14, had to admit that it "wasn't doing many things well." But the proper thing to do, he felt, was to fix the problems and keep the F-14 in the fleet.

At the heart of the dispute between Houser and Lee was the threat from the Backfire force. Lee vividly recalls one meeting when he and Houser made their cases before the chief of naval operations. Houser argued that the most serious threat to the fleet was a massive bomber attack, and the only way to handle it was with an all–F-14 force. The plan was that the F-14s would be able to knock out the Soviet bombers before they launched their missiles. "Shoot at the archer rather than the arrows," the argument went.

"I didn't think the bomber threat was all that real," Lee says. "I felt we could put a bunch of F/A-18s out there and they would do just as well against the bombers. Houser convinced everybody the only way to handle this was with the F-14. We were kind of laughed out of the room."

Lee was then giving serious thought to a new type of plane for the navy—a plane that would be both a fighter and a light bomber. At that time, of course, the F/A-18 was still little more than a concept in Lee's imagination. It had not been built, nor flown, nor even given a number. A small group of aviators had begun studies of such a plane in the mid-1960s, but the navy, even more than most tradition-bound organizations, is slow to take to new ideas. Few in the navy took this new idea very seriously. And when they thought about it at all, they tended to see it as a threat to the F-14.

The attachment that officers like Houser and Connolly had to the F-14 is understandable. In the early 1960s, Defense Secretary Robert S. McNamara, in his zeal to rationalize the defense business, decided the country needed one basic airplane—he called it the TFX—that would serve as a fighter and bomber for the air force, and a fighter, long-range interceptor, and bomber for the navy.

The air force actually developed the TFX into the F-111, which is flying today as a fighter-bomber, long-range bomber, and radar jammer. The navy publicly went along with McNamara, even up to the point of carrier trials of the swing-wing plane. But it also quietly worked with Grumman to develop the F-14, which was waiting in the wings when the naval version of the TFX faded away.

The TFX did not do well in carrier trials, but what really finished things off was a brief comment by Connolly at the end of a day-long session of the Senate Armed Services Committee. After listening to civilian officials defend the plane, the committee chairman, Sen. John Stennis (D-Miss.), finally asked Connolly whether more powerful engines would make the TFX a suitable plane.

Tired and frustrated after the long session, Connolly gave the kind of candid answer seldom heard from a three-star: "Senator Stennis, there's not enough thrust in all Christendom to make a fighter out of this airplane."

That was the background from which the supporters of the F-14 came. After the long fight to protect the navy from what they considered a grievous mistake, many senior admirals had committed so much time and emotional energy to the cause of the F-14 that, as Lee later put it, "they had F-14 religion."

The feud between Houser and Lee cannot be explained entirely by looking at the issues that divided them. In fact, it can only be understood by a look at internal navy politics and at the personalities of the two men.

Houser was an Annapolis graduate and had risen to his three-star rank through the normal career path followed by a bright young officer, in which candidates are singled out for promotion by review boards of other officers.

Lee, on the other hand, had joined the navy as an enlisted man fresh out of high school in 1940 and earned his commission and his wings in 1944 after a special wartime cadet program was opened to high school graduates. It was not until after the war, when the navy sent him to Columbia University, that he earned his college degree in mathematics and physics. He later went on to graduate school in nuclear engineering and physics. But he never wore the Naval Academy ring.

Many other officers felt that Lee would never have become an admiral if he had not had the help of friends in high places, and there is probably some truth in this. Lee himself credits Navy Secretary Chafee and Adm. Elmo Zumwalt, who was an unorthodox and controversial chief of naval operations, for giving him his third star. And he credits Zumwalt for giving him the job on which he had set his sights: head of the Naval Air Systems Command.

Perhaps because of his earlier brush with Connolly, Lee felt that the office held by Connolly and then by Houser had come to dominate naval aviation, including the Naval Air Systems Command, far more than it should. He was determined to change that by asserting his independence. Under the conditions in the past, that would have been difficult. NAVAIR had traditionally been a two-star billet filled by a rear admiral. The DCNO for air warfare—an office known in naval jargon as OP 05—was a vice admiral, outranking the head of the systems command.

But when Lee was selected to NAVAIR, he was already a three-star, so the rank for that job was raised one notch to permit him to fill it. That would seem to put Lee on the same level as Houser. But in the navy, as in the animal farm, some vice admirals are more equal than others. Although Houser had been awarded his commission from the academy two years before Lee earned his in the wartime cadet program, Lee had become a vice admiral a few months before Houser. He thus outranked Houser, and he did not neglect this modest advantage in his effort to shore up his position at NAVAIR.

Lee said: "We're going to have no more OP 05 running NAVAIR. I'm running NAVAIR. I'm going to hire and fire the program managers and do business with the contractors. OP 05 can do the financial part and so forth, but I'm running NAVAIR." And that, he feels, was what led to the hard feelings between him and Houser. There was also a difference in personality between the two men. Houser is, as Lee describes him, "personable, charming." Lee, as a colleague recalls, was "a nuts and bolts guy, not a people person, and he threw his weight around a lot." For the next two or three years, Lee says, he and Houser had "a good wrestling match."

Perhaps if they had not been so busy grappling, they would have recognized that there were more things on which they agreed than on which they disagreed.

As a result of his experience at sea, Houser was concerned about the proliferation of different types of airplanes on the carrier deck, certainly some of the highest-priced real estate in the world. When he was skipper of the *Constellation* in 1966, he counted nine different kinds of aircraft on his deck, each designed for a specific purpose and each requiring its own stock of spare parts and its own crew of mechanics. In some cases, two models of the same plane required different engines. It almost seemed as though the navy would have to build a fleet of "caddy carriers" to go along with the big carriers, to carry spare parts and provide room for the maintenance crews to work, eat, and sleep.

Houser wrote Tom Connolly to tell him "we've got to simplify the deck load; we've got to have planes do more things in fewer models." He later felt that the F-14 had gone part way toward this goal by combining in one plane a long-range interceptor, a dogfighter, and an air combat control center. The F-14 had even been designed as a bomber, but it was never tested in that role because it didn't make much sense to fly one of the world's most expensive aircraft down the barrel of a 37-mm gun.

Lee was an even more fervent believer in the multipurpose airplane, although, for him, the expensive, problem-plagued F-14 definitely wasn't it.

While the two men were close to agreement, in concept, on what the navy needed in its future planes, they also agreed on what it didn't need: a small, lightweight, cheap fighter to supplement, or even replace, the F-14.

There were many, however, both within the navy and elsewhere in Washington, who thought that was exactly what was needed.

Fighter pilots were, and continue to be, divided on the issue. Drawing on their Vietnam experience, many pilots insisted on a plane with two cockpits. That extra pair of eyes to look for enemy fighters and missiles and that extra pair of hands to operate the plane's electronic gear, they felt, were the difference between life and death in aerial combat.

But other pilots were equally insistent on a small, single-cockpit plane. They called it a "wrap-around fighter," and that term had two meanings. It meant the plane was so small that preparing to fly it was more like slipping into a form-fitting suit than climbing into a machine. And, in the air, it was so maneuverable that it could "wrap around" the enemy and shoot him down. In Vietnam, navy pilots often envied the North Vietnamese pilots their sleek, maneuverable little MiGs—at least until the U.S. developed tactics to lengthen the odds against the MiGs.

To many in Washington, the appeal of the lightweight fighter was not so much its fighting abilities as that it was supposedly cheap. Theoretically, this meant the country could afford to buy more of the smaller planes, which would be less expensive but also less capable.

Both Houser and Lee rejected the "wrap-around" fighter, for somewhat different reasons.

For Houser, buying a lightweight fighter to supplement the F-14 would add one more plane to the already overcrowded carrier deck. Furthermore, it would probably be a plane incapable of "shooting the archer" in the event of a massive bomber attack. Also, with money diverted into another production line, the F-14s would be bought at such a slow and expensive rate that there would certainly be pressure to end the F-14 once and for all. In Houser's view, the new plane not only couldn't do the job, but it posed a serious threat to the only plane that could. All of his studies showed that the navy should put its money into F-14s and, when the time came, develop a new model to replace the aging A-7 attack planes.

Lee wasted no worries on the fate of the F-14. But he, perhaps even more than Houser, worried about the many different types of planes on the carriers. And he was beginning to see what a true multirole plane might look like and how it might be built. It did not look like the cheap lightweight fighter, but it didn't look like the F-14 either.

These issues were being debated in 1973 and 1974. At the same time, the navy was facing some very difficult questions whose answers would determine the kinds of ships and aircraft that would put to sea through the end of the century and on into the early years of the next century.

At the height of the Vietnam War, the fleet numbered about 900 ships, but many of them were of World War II vintage. The carriers had taken a fearful beating from the pace of operations during their tours of duty at Yankee Station, off the South Vietnamese coast, even though they had never come under attack. They were tired and in need of major overhaul, if not outright replacement. Zumwalt, as chief of naval operations, saw that the navy could use whatever money was available to keep its ships sailing until they just wore out. Or it could cut back on the number of ships in the fleet and use the money saved to build new ships and weapons.

He chose the latter course. By 1974, the fleet had shrunk in five years from 900 ships to 500, and the decline was expected to continue. The shrinkage in the number of carriers was the most worrisome. During the Vietnam War, the fleet included twenty-four carriers. With the cuts ordered by Zumwalt, the number dropped to fourteen big attack carriers and two smaller anti-submarine carriers. Projections showed that, as the World War II-era ships wore out, the total would drop from sixteen to twelve.

All of the calculations of the number of carriers needed for a major war indicated that a minimum of sixteen was required. In peacetime, that number would permit deployments of reasonable length to ease the burden of separation on the crews and their families. It also allowed time in port and drydock for adequate maintenance. The navy thus faced a carrier gap that could be expected to continue for years, perhaps decades. The problem was complicated by the retirement of most of the anti-submarine carriers. This meant the attack carriers had to take on the added responsibility of providing their own protection against submarines, crowding the decks even more with different types of planes and helicopters. The navy was moving in exactly the opposite direction from that in which both Houser and Lee felt it should be headed.

One obvious answer to this dilemma was to build smaller carriers and to build more of them for the same money the navy proposed to spend on its favored 95,000-ton supercarriers. Zumwalt, in fact, proposed a fleet of small sea control ships to carry helicopters and so-called jump jets capable of taking off and landing vertically.

Zumwalt is the only surface warfare officer, part of the "black shoe" navy as distinguished from the "brown shoe" aviators, to serve as chief of naval operations between 1961 and the present. It is not surprising that his proposals were greeted with some suspicion by the carrier advocates, especially after the concept of smaller ships was adopted by critics as a substitute for the big carriers. Zumwalt himself saw the sea control ships as a move toward a more balanced navy, and not as a rival to the carriers. His first priority, in fact, was to purchase the navy's fourth nuclear-powered supercarrier, and the keel for that ship, the U.S.S. *Vinson,* was laid in November 1973.

To those who had "F-14 religion," the argument over big versus small carriers had special significance. The Tomcat was designed to operate from and protect the big carriers built in the 1960s and 1970s. It certainly could not take off from or land on anything as small as a sea control ship, and it could operate only inefficiently and with difficulty from the ships of 50,000 to 60,000 tons advocated by the critics of the behemoths. The arguments over carrier aircraft thus involved not only the qualities of the planes themselves, but the size and qualities of the carriers from which they would operate.

It was against this background that the navy found itself looking at a variety of different kinds of planes that might someday operate from the ships that would emerge from the debate over carrier size. But it should not be forgotten that few in the navy felt a great sense of urgency to move ahead quickly on the design and production of a new plane. With the planes then in service—the F-14 interceptor backed by the older F-4 Phantom fighter, plus the A-6 all-weather bomber and the A-7 light attack plane—the navy could get along fairly comfortably for the next few years.

But there were pressures for haste, and most of them came from outside the navy.

A good deal of the pressure stemmed from the problems with the F-14. William H. Clements, Jr., who was later to serve twice as governor of Texas, was then deputy defense secretary, responsible for development and procurement of new weapons. Responding to urging from Congress, he ordered the navy to come up with proposals for a smaller, lower-cost alternative to the F-14. The admirals proposed a modified F-14, taking out some of the expensive hardware. Clements said, ''No, that's not what I want.'' They tried again, and again it looked like an F-14. Clements sent them away once more with stern instructions: ''Don't come back with another F-14!''

Reluctantly, the navy did some work with a navalized version of the F-15 Eagle, then coming into service with the air force. The twin-engined F-15 was already a big, complex, expensive plane. To modify it for carrier service would add to both weight and cost. The only advantage to adapting the air force plane for carrier service would be to increase the number of F-15s to be purchased and thus to lower the price per plane.

The navy rightly concluded that navalizing the F-15 wouldn't save money and probably would result in a plane less useful than the F-14. It had little difficulty justifying its rejection of the F-15.

Largely due to Lee's prodding, Clements gave the navy permission to have several aircraft companies do studies of what was known as a VFAX. In this case, ''V'' stood for fixed wing; ''F'' stood for fighter; ''A'' stood for attack, and ''X'' stood for experimental, although no actual plane would be flown. In other words, the study focused on a carrier plane that would do both the fighter and attack tasks. Except for Lee and a small group of colleagues in NAVAIR, the VFAX concept had little support.

Most of the other admirals considered it impractical—"Lee's pipe dream."

The VFAX was part of the navy's rather relaxed approach to the question of what plane to buy next. But other forces were at work, moving inexorably toward forcing unwanted and untimely choices on the navy. A few years earlier, David Packard, Clements's predecessor as deputy defense secretary, had provided a few million dollars apiece to a couple of aircraft companies to do some experimental work in fighter design. A major purpose was to keep experienced design teams together and demonstrate, in actual flying prototypes, innovations in technology.

Production of a new fighter was not contemplated. But suddenly, before anyone had had time to make a conscious decision, these technology demonstrators were being seen as prototypes for the lightweight fighter then coming into favor.

The air force was in the midst of a major modernization program. If they had had their choice, the generals would have bought a fighter force made up entirely of various models of the F-15, just as most of the admirals favored an all–F-14 force. But, under pressure to hold down costs while increasing the number of planes available, they began looking seriously at the possibilities offered by a lightweight fighter. What they decided upon was, in the jargon of the time, a Hi-Lo mix of big, complex, highly capable, twin-engined F-15s and a larger number of smaller, lightweight fighters that would be cheaper than the F-15s, but also less capable.

Suddenly it occurred to a lot of people in Washington that the thing to do would be for the navy to buy the same lightweight fighter as the air force. This would have the advantage of providing for a larger production run and a higher production rate, thus cutting the cost for each plane. To many in Congress, this seemed an ideal way to hold down the defense budget, not only taking advantage of production efficiencies but also eliminating the need for separate navy spending on research and development.

For the moment, the navy moved doggedly ahead. In June 1974, Lee sent out his request for comments from the aircraft industry on the VFAX. The responses came back in July.

In August, the Senate and House Armed Services Committees agreed that $30 million should be allocated for the VFAX. Acting on this favorable signal, Clements gave the navy the okay to ask industry for proposals for full-scale development of the VFAX. Lee was elated.

Action by the armed services committees is not the final word, however, and the navy aircraft program was in far more serious trouble than anyone dreamed. Nothing happens until the appropriations committees actually vote to provide the money. In this case, the Senate Appropriations Committee agreed on $20 million for the VFAX. But the House Appropriations Committee, following the lead of its powerful defense subcommittee, balked.

That subcommittee had become the center of opposition to Lee's plan for a combined fighter and attack plane, and for years to come there would be opposition to the F/A-18 from that source. Reasons for the opposition ranged from simple politics—two of the key members had rival aircraft plants in their districts—to deeply held beliefs on the part of staff members about the type of planes needed in future wars.

One of those who worked closely with the committee was a former navy pilot to whom the lightweight fighter was especially appealing. His name was Charles Meyers and he was then serving as a deputy assistant secretary of defense for research. "Chuck Meyers thought we ought to wear leather helmets and still have just a day fighter," Lee recalls. Actually, Meyers's argument was more sophisticated than that. He thought it was foolish to send multimillion-dollar, manned aircraft to attack heavily defended targets. Instead, he favored using missiles for that purpose. But he also foresaw large-scale dogfights where sheer numbers would count. By that reasoning, lightweight fighters in large numbers were what the services needed, and there was no place for a new attack plane.

How much credit or blame he deserves is not entirely clear, but the admirals thought Meyers and his allies on Capitol Hill were largely responsible for one of the most difficult bits of congressional language they had ever had to deal with. It came about this way:

When the House and Senate failed to agree, leaders of the committees involved met in conference. They quickly agreed on the Senate's $20 million figure. But then they inserted the language that was to send a shock wave through the Pentagon and Crystal City. Because it was later to prove so important, it is worthwhile to look at the exact words contained in their report:

> The managers are in agreement on the appropriation of $20 million as proposed by the Senate instead of no funding as proposed by the House for the VFAX aircraft. The conferees support the need for a lower cost alternative fighter to complement the F-14A and replace F-4 and A-7 aircraft; however, the conferees direct that the development of this aircraft make maximum use of the air force lightweight fighter and Air Combat Fighter technology and hardware. The $20 million provided is to be placed in a

new program element titled "Navy Air Combat Fighter" rather than VFAX. Adaptation of the selected air force air combat fighter to be capable of carrier operations is the prerequisite for use of the funds provided. Funds may be released to a contractor for the purpose of designing the modifications required for navy use. Future funding is to be contingent upon the capability of the navy to produce a derivative of the selected air force air combat fighter design.

The requests for proposals to begin full-scale development of a fighter/ attack plane were about to go out when word of the surprise action on the Hill reached the Pentagon. Although the law itself did not include the restrictions contained in the conference committee report, the navy prudently decided to limit its request to the industry to derivatives of the planes involved in the air force competition. The plain language of the congressional orders seemed to commit the navy to a cheap little "wraparound" fighter rather than the bigger, more expensive strike-fighter the Pentagon leadership and the House and Senate Armed Services Committees had agreed on.

Lee's elation suddenly turned to gloom. But for Houser and the others within the navy who were dubious of Lee's VFAX, there was little to be pleased about, either. At worst, they could see the navy forced to use a totally unsuitable air force fighter. At best, they could foresee a long battle with Congress and the defense bureaucracy to turn the decision around.

This was certainly not the first setback in the navy's long and frequently difficult effort to take aircraft to sea. But problems in the past had most often been technical ones—such as learning how to fly in the first place, or learning how to take off from the deck of a ship and come back aboard in one piece.

CHAPTER TWO

Wings Over the Ocean

To the pilot and observer in a German observation plane flying safely above the muddy death in the trenches down below, the war might have been a million miles, rather than a few thousand feet, away. The first faint green touches of spring were visible where the ground had been plowed by high explosive shells, and it all looked almost peaceful.

They were above the range of bullets from the ground, and their only worry was the possibility of engine failure. And even if that happened, the prevailing wind would carry them safely back to their own side of the lines.

As their Albatross flew in lazy circles near the village of Epernay, the observer tapped the pilot's shoulder and pointed to a French Morane-Saulnier single-seater. The pilot shrugged and continued calmly on his course. The Morane turned toward them, approaching from the rear. But there was nothing to worry about. The worst the Frenchman might do would be to pull alongside and try to shoot at them with his service pistol.

One can imagine the surprise and panic that gripped the observer, peering back over his shoulder, as a stream of machine-gun bullets suddenly poured at them *through the propeller* of the French plane. The pilot died instantly. But the observer—flying, in those days, without a parachute—clung helplessly to the sides of his cockpit as the plane went into a spin and crashed.

The date was 1 April 1915.

On that day, the airplane ceased to serve merely as an aerial observation post for the forces on the ground and became a fighting machine in its own right. The era of aerial combat had begun.

Piloting the French plane on that historic day was Roland Garros, who was both a concert pianist and an exceptionally skilled flier before World War I began. He was also the inventor of the device that permitted him to fire his machine gun through the propeller.

The problem he faced was that, without some means to protect the propeller, the pilot would, sooner or later—and probably sooner—shoot himself down by blowing away his own prop. Garros calculated, however, that fewer than seven percent of the rounds from a Hotchkiss gun, which was capable of 300 rounds a minute, would hit the prop. The others would fly between the blades. In a ten-second burst, he only had to worry about three or four bullets. Garros directed his mechanic to bolt a machine gun between the cockpit and the engine and then to protect the blades with a shield of armor plate shaped so that the few bullets that hit the shield would be deflected.

Although his invention was dangerously defective, Garros and his secret weapon went on a rampage, destroying four more planes in the next two weeks. But on 19 April, on a bombing mission, he made a crash-landing after his engine failed, and his plane fell into German hands.

Within five days, Anthony Fokker, a young Dutch airplane designer and builder employed by the Germans, had analyzed and rejected Garros's design and worked out his own system for shooting through the propeller. Despite the armor plate on Garros's prop, Fokker reasoned, the blades would soon be battered out of balance and the engine would tear itself from the plane. His solution was an interrupter gear that permitted the gun to fire only when a blade was not in the line of fire. Within the next few months, pilots flying planes fitted with the new device virtually drove the Allied pilots from the air over the front. They called it the "Fokker scourge."

The British and French scrambled to meet the challenge. They sent planes into combat with shields of the type developed by Garros, but Fokker was right. The impact of even a few bullets destroyed propellers and engines. They tried mounting a machine gun on the top of the wing so it could fire over the propeller. But with the weapon in that position, the pilot found it difficult to clear a blockage or change ammunition drums. Unfastening the seatbelt, holding the control stick between the knees, and standing up to work on the gun was not a formula for longevity. Another effort involved putting the engine in the rear, in a pusher arrangement, but that made for a clumsy flying machine.

Without enemy observers lurking overhead, the German generals were able to move troops into position for surprise attacks, and they eagerly began planning an early victory. But a Fokker plane fell into Allied hands and the balance of power in the air was restored.

Thus, by late 1915, barely a dozen years after Orville Wright's first twelve-second, powered flight on 17 December 1903, all the elements of combat aviation were in place. Pilots had dropped small bombs from their cockpits as early as 1912. Planes had also proved their usefulness on reconnaissance missions. And, with the addition of forward-firing guns, fighter planes could attack or defend bombers and reconnaissance craft as well as attack targets on the ground.

It was in the final three years of the four-year war that the great aerial battles that have become part of aviation legend took place. Infantrymen watched in fascination as the German flying circuses, complex formations numbering fifty to sixty planes, collided with equally large Allied formations. Arch Whitehouse, who flew many missions as an observer and gunner in the British Royal Flying Corps and who later became a prolific writer, claims to have coined the word "dogfight" to describe these mass engagements.

Typically, a dogfight began with a large formation descending out of the sun to attack a group of enemy planes. If the attack was undetected, the air was quickly filled with the debris of shattered planes. The survivors twisted and turned their planes, trying to avoid being shot while catching an enemy in their sights. Mid-air collisions added to the destruction. When the wood and fabric planes were hit, they often lost wings or tails and burst into flames. Flying without parachutes, crew members of stricken machines had a deadly choice: stay with the plane and burn, or jump to escape the flames. One eyewitness reported observing a pilot standing on the wing of his burning plane, trying to slip the plane so the flames would stream off to the other side. When the observer glanced back, the pilot was gone and the plane was spinning violently toward the earth.

By the end of the war, well over 100,000 planes had been built by the belligerents, and aviation had become an integral and important part of modern warfare.

While the war in the air over Europe evolved rapidly from reconnaissance to full-scale aerial combat, the development of naval aviation was much more tentative. No one seemed to be quite sure how airplanes fitted in with the naval forces' traditional role of controlling the seas, and there was little enthusiasm for this newfangled contraption.

Fortunately, the United States Navy had been blessed with one far-seeing advocate of naval aviation. He was Capt. Washington Irving Chambers, a battleship skipper who was assigned to Washington in 1910 and, in addition to other duties, was given the responsibility of keeping track of developments in aviation. He was ordered "to gradually provide the navy with suitable equipment for aerial navigation and to instruct the navy personnel in its use." Chambers became not only the most forceful advocate of taking planes to sea, but virtually the only one within the navy itself. At one point, even his cubbyhole office was taken from him and he was forced to work out of his home.

Eventually, he felt, every cruiser should carry a scout plane that could be launched from the ship's deck, land on the sea, and be hoisted aboard for another flight. But, since planes capable of landing on water had not yet been perfected, he pushed ahead with experiments that took land planes to sea.

He set out to prove that a plane could take off successfully from a ship. The forward deck of the cruiser U.S.S. *Birmingham* was fitted with a wooden platform eighty-three feet long and twenty-four feet wide, sloping downward by five degrees. Since the navy had no aviators of its own, Chambers prevailed on Eugene Ely, a civilian aviation pioneer, to make the flight in a biplane built by Glenn Curtiss. It looked little different from the delicate craft in which Orville Wright had first flown seven years before.

The plane was hoisted aboard in Baltimore and the ship proceeded down the Chesapeake Bay through rain squalls and gusty winds on 14 November 1910. At about three o'clock in the afternoon, there was a break in the weather. Ely took his seat on the flimsy outrigger, which seemed to be perched out on the end of nowhere, revved up his four-cylinder pusher engine, and signaled his mechanic to activate the release mechanism.

Although the platform was eighty-three feet long, Ely had only a fifty-seven foot run before he went over the edge, thirty-seven feet from the surface of the bay. As the sailors watched, the plane dropped from sight. They could picture Ely, with the engine at his back, being driven to the bottom of the bay. The wheels hit the water. The tips of the propeller splintered on the whitecaps. And then the plane gained power and rose into the view of those watching anxiously from the deck of the ship. An "aircraft carrier" had launched its first aircraft successfully. Ely, disoriented and nearly blinded by the salt spray on his goggles, landed safely a few minutes later on a nearby beach.

Less than two months later, the navy, under prodding from Chambers, set out to test the other half of the equation: Could a plane land on a ship, as well as take off? Again, the plane was a Curtiss, and Ely was the pilot. The ship chosen for the experiment was the U.S.S. *Pennsylvania,* then anchored in San Francisco Bay. A wooden platform 120 feet long and thirty-two feet wide was erected above the after gun turret at the stern of the ship. Twenty-two pairs of fifty-pound bags of sand were attached to lines stretched across the deck at intervals of three feet to act as arresting gear, and three hooks were attached to the plane to catch the lines.

Curtiss and Ely recommended that the ship sail into the wind, but the captain felt this would be dangerous in the relatively narrow confines of the bay. Instead, the ship was at anchor and a five-knot wind was blowing down the bay. This meant that Ely would have a tail wind as he approached the ship, a violation of the most basic rule in the pilot's book.

Ely flew out toward the Golden Gate, then turned and headed toward the ship. As he came in over the stern, the tail wind kept him airborne, floating above the arresting lines that were set twelve inches above the deck. He passed over half the lines before one caught. As the weight of the bags dragged at the plane, it quickly stopped, fifty feet from the end of the platform. A short time later, Ely took off from the *Pennsylvania* and flew safely ashore.

Chambers had demonstrated that planes could take off from ships and land again. The one additional thing he needed was a reliable catapult so that seaplanes could be launched from battleships and cruisers without covering the decks with wooden platforms. That missing ingredient was supplied on 12 October 1912 when Lt. Theodore G. ("Spuds") Ellyson, the navy's first aviator, and his plane were successfully launched at Annapolis, Maryland, by a catapult powered by compressed air.

Probably to Chambers, and certainly to most ship captains, the cumbersome wooden platforms used in the demonstrations aboard the *Birmingham* and *Pennsylvania* were an undesirable inconvenience, and little thought was given to developing a true aircraft carrier capable of taking large numbers of planes to sea. Instead, the navy focused on perfecting the seaplane as a scout and gun-spotter for the ships. Such planes were first used in combat during the American intervention in Mexico in 1914.

When the U.S. entered the war in Europe in April 1917, the navy had fifty-four training planes and thirty-nine aviators. By the time the war ended in November 1918, they had 1,656 aviators, as well as 2,127 aircraft—purchased at a cost averaging about a million dollars apiece.

Becoming a naval aviator in those days was a brief and dangerous process. Cadets received preliminary flight training and then went to Pensacola, Florida, still a center for advanced naval aviation training today.

To earn his wings, a pilot had to fly at least fifteen hours solo; operate a service airplane satisfactorily; navigate a sixty-mile, cross-country hop; spend at least fifteen minutes at 6,000 feet, and make a "dead stick" landing. He was also required to make at least two night landings with flares. That all took twenty-five to fifty hours in the air, after which he either was sent overseas or became an instructor.

During the war, twenty-five students died in accidents at Pensacola, and another 208 pilots and crew members were killed in accidents in the U.S. and overseas. The wonder is that more men did not die, considering the brevity of the training and the trickiness of the planes they flew.

One of the greatest hazards was a stall followed by a spin. Student pilots were told that they should always keep up enough air speed to cause the wires to whistle sharply. "If the wires don't sing to you, the angels will," they were warned.

Despite the dangers, naval aviation drew a steady stream of volunteers, stimulated by the thrill of flying and the propaganda coming from the European battlefronts.

The French, Germans, and Americans, and to a much lesser extent, the British, deliberately glamorized aerial combat as part of their effort to attract recruits. The propaganda campaign was launched after soldiers, watching the carnage in the air, decided that life in the trenches, bad as it was, was preferable to death in the air.

The French lionized Garros after his spectacular string of victories and made him the first "ace." His five victories became the standard, still observed in the U.S., for a journeyman air fighter. The British refused to adopt the ace system and the Germans set their own standard: A flier who shot down ten planes became a *kanone* and could look forward to the award of the *Pour le Merite* medal, or Blue Max, as it was known.

The propagandists created and glamorized the "knights of the air" and a new stream of recruits came, not from among the soldiers who had seen the air battles from below, but from among youths who had not. Despite the persisting glamor that has been associated with aerial combat, the fact is that most of those made famous during World War I—the "Red Baron" Manfred von Richtofen, Max Immelmann, Oswald Boelcke, Norman Prince, Frank Luke, Georges Guynemer, Albert Ball—died young in combat.

The glamor of aerial combat was particularly appealing to a group of men at Yale University. They learned to fly on their own, studied aviation, and enlisted in the navy together as the U.S. entered the war. Two more Yale units followed them into the service, together forming a significant number of the navy's first 100 aviators.

By the fall of 1917, Americans were patrolling the English Channel and the approaches to European ports. When the war ended a year later, they had flown 22,000 patrols and carried out more than thirty attacks on submarines. Although none of the subs was known to have been sunk by air attack, the air crews were credited in a number of instances with helping destroyers to find and sink German submarines.

The Yale students and others who volunteered to fly with the navy may have been enticed by the prospect of dogfights over the trenches and the chance to join the select company of aces, but the majority of navy and marine pilots spent most of the war airborne in lumbering flying boats and bombers. A few, however, volunteered to help out British and French units and found themselves flying Nieuport, Spad, and Sopwith Camel fighters on combat patrols.

Throughout the war, America's naval aviation was land based even though the U.S. Navy had been the first, by many years, to demonstrate that a plane could take off from and land on a ship. Ely's first landing on the U.S.S. *Pennsylvania,* did, in a rudimentary way, utilize the same technology used today to stop planes after they have touched down on a modern carrier. But, having carried out these dramatic demonstrations, the navy turned to other things.

It was not until the midst of the war that Britain's Royal Navy resumed the attempt to send planes to sea as part of a desperate effort to find some way to prevent German lighter-than-air ships from bombing London and other parts of England.

The concept of using gas-filled balloons in warfare was not new. As early as 1793, the French used captive balloons for reconnaissance, and Napoleon took along a balloon company on his invasion of Egypt. Nearly a century later, when Paris was besieged during the Franco-Prussian War, the French used balloons to carry passengers and mail out of the city— and the Germans responded by developing the first antiaircraft gun to shoot at them. Before Paris finally capitulated on 28 January 1871, the balloon airline had made sixty-six out-bound flights carrying nine tons of mail and 155 passengers.

Across the Atlantic, during the Civil War, the North successfully used captive balloons to observe troop movements. Count Frederick von Zeppelin, a young German army officer serving as a military attaché in Washington, was permitted to go aloft in one of the balloons. He saw how a man raised 200 feet above the earth could, with a telescope, study enemy troop formations five miles behind the front lines.

But he also saw something more: a balloon would be able to do far more if it were made rigid and provided with power to move from one place to another. When he returned home, he set to work to develop such a craft. The result was a large dirigible with a rigid frame and engines to propel it. The first Zeppelin—a 420-foot-long monster—flew successfully from a floating hangar on Lake Constance on 2 July 1900.

In the years immediately before the war, Germany poured money into the construction of dirigibles. On 31 May 1915, a Zeppelin, flying at more than 20,000 feet, bombed London, killing seven persons and injuring thirty-five more. In the next year, they carried out fifty-one raids, dropping 196 tons of bombs, and killing 557 persons. The British responded with a massive anti-Zeppelin defense that pulled 110 planes from duty on the Western front.

Much of the effort fell to the Royal Navy. In one early attempt to deal with the dirigible menace, a fighter plane was placed on a barge. The barge was then towed into the wind by a destroyer, and the plane took off. During one of these tests, word came that a Zeppelin was in the vicinity. The pilot took off, fired a stream of incendiary shells into the craft, and dodged out of the way as it exploded in flame and fell into the sea. Despite this success, the barge concept was abandoned as too dangerous, especially in the rough seas often encountered in the North Sea and English Channel.

The Royal Navy then turned to a system similar to the early American experiments. Wooden platforms were built on cruisers and battleships so land planes could be taken to sea. The pilots were able to take off from the thirty-foot platforms, but were not able to land again. If they could not make it to shore, they were ordered to come down in the water alongside a ship and hope to be rescued before the plane sank.

After one Zeppelin was shot down by a fighter launched from a ship, the Germans were careful to avoid flying over British ships. The scheme thus served as a deterrent. But it was clearly not a very satisfactory way to take planes to sea, and the British turned their efforts to the construction of a true aircraft carrier. A 200-foot platform was added forward of the bridge of H.M.S. *Furious,* a cruiser then under construction. Planes were launched successfully, but landing proved difficult and dangerous, even after a 300-foot landing platform was added aft of the superstructure.

Despite these problems, seven Sopwith Camels were launched from the *Furious* while she was cruising sixty miles off the German coast on 19 July 1918, and they succeeded in destroying two Zeppelins in their hangars. This was the first successful bombing raid launched from an aircraft carrier.

With air currents eddying around her superstructure, *Furious* was far from being a fully satisfactory carrier. By the time the war ended, H.M.S. *Argus* was ready to go to sea with forty planes. She had a flush deck and horizontal funnels. Later, a temporary "island" was added at the side of the deck as a navigating bridge and the *Argus* assumed the now-familiar shape of an aircraft carrier.

It was not until 1922 that the U.S. Navy, which had pioneered taking planes to sea more than a decade before, commissioned its first aircraft carrier, the U.S.S. *Langley*. The ship, converted from the hull of a coal-carrier while it was still under construction, had a displacement of 11,050 tons and could carry twelve one-man fighter-spotter planes, twelve two-man spotter planes, and ten torpedo planes. It was equipped with one elevator to move planes between the hangar deck and the flat, unobstructed flight deck.

The *Langley* reflected general agreement among naval officers in the period immediately after World War I that control of the air at sea was an essential part of their effort to build a fleet second to none. But there was much less agreement on the extent to which airplanes might be used successfully to attack ships and not just to fight other planes and serve as spotters for the fleet. Many admirals were certain that large warships were far too heavily armored to be sunk by aircraft. In 1921, tests were set up in which U.S. Navy pilots carried out carefully controlled attacks on captured German vessels to determine how much damage could be inflicted on a warship by bombers.

In the midst of these tests, Brig. Gen. William ("Billy") Mitchell, the army's most outspoken and controversial proponent of air power, challenged the navy to let his pilots have a crack at an anchored battleship. His goal was to prove that bombers could effectively guard the U.S. and its possessions from attack from the sea. Beyond that, he wanted to show that the U.S. should spend its money on airplanes, not warships.

Ignoring the rules laid down by the navy, Mitchell's pilots roared in over the former German battleship *Ostfriesland*, anchored in the Atlantic off the mouth of the Chesapeake Bay, and bombarded it with eleven 1,000- and 2,000-pound bombs. The ship sank. Mitchell's demonstration, details of which he promptly leaked to the press, was a sensation. And it foreshadowed what would become of powerful warships two decades later, if they found themselves under attack without friendly aircraft to protect them. Practically, however, his demonstration probably did more to strengthen the case of the naval aviators than it did to bolster his own case for a fleet of bombers.

In the winter of 1921–22, the United States, Great Britain, Japan, Italy, and France met in Washington in the first of a series of arms control meetings. They agreed to reduce their navies according to a complex formula that limited shipbuilding by the powers until the eve of World War II. For the U.S., the treaty involved scrapping a number of older battleships and stopping construction on new ones. But it also permitted conversion of two cruisers, then under construction, into aircraft carriers.

When these sister ships, the *Lexington* and the *Saratoga*, went into service in 1927, they were the supercarriers of their day. They displaced 33,000 tons, were 888 feet long and carried ninety planes apiece—about the same number as today's 95,000-ton supercarriers. They were also fast: a top speed of more than thirty-four knots or forty statute miles an hour, also matching today's big carriers.

Over the next fourteen years, the U.S. built five more carriers, none of them as big or powerful as the *Lexington* and *Saratoga*. The Washington Treaty provided some restraint on size, but budget pressure played an even more important role. The first two big carriers cost $46 and $44 million respectively. When the U.S.S. *Ranger* was approved in the last days of the presidency of Calvin Coolidge in February 1929, Congress held the cost at $19 million. This meant a ship of only 14,500 tons, capable of less than thirty knots and carrying only eighty-six aircraft, none of them the bigger torpedo planes.

But, despite budget constraints, the navy was not as hard up for money as the army, which was reduced to drilling with wooden guns even as the war clouds billowed in Europe and Asia. In 1922, when the *Lexington* and *Saratoga* were approved, Congress also okayed a five-year program to increase the naval air arm to 1,000 modern planes. In 1933, in the heart of the depression, the navy won approval to increase its force to 1,625 planes. Funding was also voted for more carriers. Three were virtual sister ships, at 20,000 tons, carrying ninety planes and capable of thirty-four knots. They were the *Yorktown, Enterprise,* and *Hornet,* which entered service in 1937, 1938, and 1941. The smaller 14,700-ton *Wasp* was commissioned in 1940.

During the two decades before World War II, there was an obvious fascination with aviation throughout much of the navy. As early as the mid-1920s, a new policy went into effect requiring all Naval Academy graduates to undergo flight training.

For the aviation enthusiasts, the concept of mobile air bases didn't stop with ships. The navy built two huge dirigibles—the *Akron* and the *Macon*— and used them as flying aircraft carriers. Experiments with the *Los Angeles* had already demonstrated that tiny fighter planes could be launched from an airship and recovered with a hook hanging down below the hangar bay. Both the *Akron* and *Macon* were lost in accidents, however, and the idea of flying aircraft carriers faded away.

Even as the powerful new carriers came into service, there was still considerable uncertainty among the senior battleship admirals as to how this new force would be used. Their tendency was to keep the carriers safely back behind the battleship battle line with the supply ships and other support vessels.

Younger officers, fascinated by the advantages offered by their high-speed carriers, put on a series of demonstrations of how sea-based air power might be used in combat.

In January 1929, the brand-new *Saratoga* moved in south of the Panama Canal and launched an early morning raid in which eighty-three planes "destroyed" the locks and air bases in the Canal Zone. As the war game played out, however, the carrier was, in turn, knocked out by battleships and army planes.

An even more impressive demonstration took place on a Sunday morning three years later. Two of the fast carriers took up a position northeast of the Hawaiian Islands and launched 152 planes for a devastating surprise attack on Pearl Harbor. The date was 7 February 1932, nearly a decade before the Japanese launched their own assault with real bombs.

In July 1940, after war had broken out in Europe, but a year and a half before the U.S. entered the conflict, Congress passed the Two-Ocean Navy Act, which not only provided for more ships, but called for an increase in navy aircraft strength from 1,741 to 15,000.

Until it got enough ships and planes for a true two-ocean force, however, there was no doubt about the navy's orientation. The navy, as it was then shaping up, was specifically designed for battle against another major sea power. The only potentially hostile major sea power was Japan. As soon as the new carriers entered service, the biggest and fastest of them— *Lexington, Saratoga, Enterprise,* and *Yorktown*—were sent to the Pacific. The two smaller carriers, *Wasp* and *Ranger,* were based at Norfolk as part of the Atlantic Fleet. The old *Langley* became a floating base for seaplanes. In exercises, the navy showed its flexibility by sending ships through the Panama Canal to beef up strength in the Atlantic. But as soon as the exercises ended, the ships returned to their proper places in the Pacific. In the months before Pearl Harbor, the *Yorktown* was sent to the Atlantic, but she was soon back in the Pacific to play a vital role in the early battles of the Pacific war.

Just as there was no doubt about the navy's Pacific orientation, there was little doubt either, at least among the more senior admirals, about the most important ships in the fleet. While the fast carriers were sent to the Pacific, they were thought of as an adjunct to the twelve battleships, not a replacement for them.

By this time, of course, the carriers did have a potent offensive capability. The four big carriers in the Pacific each carried four squadrons of fighters, four squadrons of torpedo planes, and eight squadrons of scout bombers. This practice of assigning a separate type of plane to each role and making the crews experts in that one task became a deeply embedded navy tradition. Although some of the bombers were fitted with the new Norden bomb sights to see if they could drop bombs while flying horizontally high above their targets, the planes were designed and used primarily as dive-bombers. Large air brakes permitted them to dive almost straight down toward the target, in a tactic developed by the marines in Nicaragua in 1924. They were extremely accurate bombers.

Despite the attacks on the Panama Canal and Hawaii during peacetime battle games, and despite Billy Mitchell's early demonstration of what planes could do to a surface ship, the true offensive power of sea-based air had not been demonstrated in actual warfare at the time World War II broke out in the fall of 1939. The war had been underway for more than a year when the British put on such a demonstration: On the night of 11–12 November 1940, twenty-one aged biplanes from the carrier *Illustrious* attacked the Italian fleet at anchor in the harbor of Taranto, on the western side of the Italian boot. With the loss of only two planes, the British knocked out three battleships, burned the harbor's oil depot, and succeeded in putting half the Italian fleet out of business.

The British onslaught proved one important point for the Japanese, who were even then thinking of the possibility of an attack on Pearl Harbor. A major concern was that torpedoes could not be used effectively in the relatively shallow waters of Pearl Harbor. But torpedoes had worked at Taranto, where the maximum depth of the water was forty-two feet, three feet shallower than that of Pearl Harbor. While the Japanese learned from the British success, however, the Americans didn't. The U.S. officers decided against rigging anti-torpedo nets at Pearl Harbor because of the congestion it would cause and because they considered the water too shallow for torpedo attack.

The task of planning the Japanese attack fell, ironically, to Adm. Isoroku Yamamoto, who had studied at Harvard, served as a military attaché in Washington, and knew the United States better than any other Japanese military man. He was adamantly opposed to any policy that would bring his country into war with the United States. But if there was to be war, he reasoned, the only chance for a Japanese victory was to go for a quick kill, avoiding a drawn-out war in which Japan would surely lose.

During his time in Washington, Yamamoto was deeply impressed by Mitchell's sinking of the *Ostfriesland,* and upon his return to Tokyo, he became one of the most outspoken advocates of taking air power to sea. Before the conflict with the U.S. broke out, the Japanese built ten carriers, as big or bigger than the seven modern American carriers, and as fast or faster. But they did not abandon the navy's traditional faith in the power of large battleships. The *Yamato* and three other new dreadnoughts were nearing completion. With eighteen-inch guns, they were the largest warships the world had ever seen.

Planning for the attack on Pearl Harbor began a full year before it was carried out. For weeks, pilots practiced their tactics at Kagoshima Bay, whose harbor is similar enough to Pearl Harbor to provide realistic training. Finally, on 10 November 1941, the orders were given and one ship after another weighed anchor and steamed northward. Under strict radio silence, they gathered in Hitokappu Bay, in the Kurile Islands, far to the north of Tokyo. If a modern satellite had been able to photograph that gathering, it would have showed an awesome striking force: six carriers, two battleships, two heavy cruisers, one light cruiser, nine destroyers, three submarines, and eight supply vessels.

On 26 November, the task force steamed out of Hitokappu Bay, staying far to the north of the normal shipping routes across the Pacific. American intelligence specialists puzzled over their failure to detect radio signals to and from a large part of the Japanese fleet. Something was up, but there was little reason to believe a powerful striking force was moving stealthily into position for its surprise attack. Only in recent years has the U.S. Navy rediscovered the art of emission control—turning off electronic signals that might tell the enemy where a fleet is—that the Japanese used so effectively.

Just after 6 A.M. on 7 December, the six Japanese carriers—*Kaga, Akagi, Shokaku, Zuikaku, Hiryu,* and *Soryu*—turned eastward into a brisk wind about 200 miles north of Oahu and began to launch the first of two waves of planes. On each ship, the planes were crowded together on the stern to provide as much deck space as possible for the takeoff run. Unlike today's carrier planes, which are hurled into the air by catapults, the Japanese pilots stood on their brakes, ran their engines up to full throttle and then careened down the pitching deck on their own power.

Within fifteen minutes, the six carriers launched 183 planes: first, forty-three fighters, then forty-nine high-level bombers, followed by fifty-one dive bombers, and forty torpedo planes.

For the next hour, crews worked frantically to bring more planes up from the hangar decks. At 7:15 A.M., the second wave of the attack began its takeoff. In this group were thirty-six Zero fighters, fifty-four horizontal bombers and seventy-eight dive bombers.

The attackers achieved a stunning surprise. Before the morning was over, their bombs, torpedoes, and machine gun bullets had destroyed or badly damaged eight battleships, three light cruisers, three destroyers, and four auxiliary craft; destroyed or damaged 164 American planes, and heavily damaged many supply and maintenance facilities. The cost in lives had also been high: 2,403 dead and another 1,178 wounded. The Japanese lost twenty-nine planes, with another seventy-four damaged.

Looking at the list of vessels destroyed or damaged, it is tempting to conclude that the Japanese focused on battleship row because they thought the battleships were more important than aircraft carriers. The fact is that the Japanese officers responsible for planning the attack on Hawaii (though not the admiral selected to carry it out) fully understood the new reality of warfare at sea. They knew how powerful and how flexible a weapon the carrier could be—as their ability to move their own floating air bases halfway across the Pacific to within striking distance of Hawaii demonstrated—and they had made the destruction of the American carrier force their number one priority. But, when the time came for the takeoff from the carriers north of Oahu, the Japanese simply didn't know where the American flattops were.

After the victorious Japanese had returned to their carriers, senior aviators urged two courses of action: First, send another strike back to knock out the American fuel tanks and other remaining targets; and, additionally, search for the missing American carriers and destroy them.

But Vice Adm. Chuichi Nagumo, who led the First Air Fleet in its surprise attack, had been picked almost entirely on the basis of seniority. The result was to put a traditional battleship admiral with no experience or interest in the use of air power in charge of this large-scale use of air power at sea. Moreover, he was a cautious man, reluctant to risk an attack on his ships and unwilling to go beyond the exact letter of his orders.

Instead of completing the devastation of the American forces in Hawaii and seeking out the American carriers, Nagumo turned his task force toward home.

Where were the American carriers? The *Saratoga* and *Hornet* were on the West Coast and the *Yorktown* was still in the Atlantic, along with the smaller *Ranger* and *Wasp*. That left two carriers to be accounted for. Days before the Japanese attack, the *Lexington* and *Enterprise* had managed to slip off undetected to ferry reinforcements of aircraft to Wake Island. When the attack came, they were returning to Hawaii but were still hundreds of miles to the west, while the Japanese fleet was about 200 miles to the north of Oahu. The American carriers thus were not in a position to disrupt the Japanese attack, but they were also spared the destruction suffered by much of the rest of the fleet.

If the surprise attack demonstrated the ability of a carrier task force to move large numbers of aircraft into position to attack a fixed target, something else that happened in the very first hours of the Pacific war proved, if anything, even more unsettling to those who still clung to the belief that a major warship could not be successfully attacked from the air.

On 10 December, a Japanese submarine reported two British warships in the South China Sea north of Singapore. At 6 A.M., nine planes took off from Saigon in search of the ships. At 7 A.M., thirty-four high-level bombers and fifty-one torpedo planes followed in nine waves. Just as they were running short on fuel, a scout plane spotted the British formation, and the bombers and torpedo planes attacked.

Their targets were H.M.S. *Prince of Wales,* a 36,717-ton battleship, the most modern of its type in the world, and H.M.S. *Repulse,* a 33,250-ton World War I–era ship. With the loss of only four planes, the Japanese sank both ships, and 840 British sailors died. It was one thing to knock out a row of battleships anchored at their base in Pearl Harbor. It was another to attack and sink a battleship able to maneuver in the open seas. Winston Churchill later wrote, when he was informed of the loss, "In all the war, I never received a more direct shock."

The lesson of the vulnerability of surface ships to air attacks was reinforced for the U.S. (and the Japanese) soon again in the Battle of the Coral Sea, 3–7 May 1942. The *Lexington,* one of the two biggest, fastest carriers in the U.S. Navy, was attacked from the air and sunk. The smaller *Yorktown* was so badly damaged in the same battle that the Japanese counted her as having been sunk. The U.S. sank a small Japanese carrier and damaged the *Shokaku,* one of the two big Japanese carriers involved in the fight. The *Zuikaku* herself was not hit, but she lost the majority of her aircraft and many pilots.

The Battle of the Coral Sea was part of a desperate effort by the U.S. to halt, or at least slow, the progress of the Japanese offensive through the western Pacific and Southeast Asia, toward Australia and a possible linkup with Hitler's forces in the Indian Ocean. For the Japanese, the worry was that the remnants of the American fleet remained on their flank as they sped toward the south and west.

It was this concern, plus what was later ruefully labeled the "victory disease," that set the stage for one of history's great decisive battles.

For decades, the U.S. Navy had based its plans for fighting in the Pacific on War Plan *Orange.* When that plan was first drawn up in 1907, America's naval buildup, dramatized by President Theodore Roosevelt's "Great White Fleet," was well underway, and Japan was building its own modern navy. *Orange* was revised regularly at the Naval War College in Newport, Rhode Island, but its basic structure remained the same: in the event of war, the American battle line would confront the Japanese fleet in the mid-Pacific, and destroy it in a major showdown.

Admiral Yamamoto knew War Plan *Orange* almost as well as the Americans. A copy had been purloined from the safe of the secretary of the navy and sent to Tokyo in the mid-1930s, and Japanese intelligence had managed to keep track of revisions. Yamamoto decided on a bold operation that would play out the *Orange* strategy, but do it at a time and place of Japan's choosing. Well before the Pearl Harbor attack, Yamamoto had reasoned that the U.S. Navy would not come out to fight a major engagement until it had rebuilt its strength. But perhaps he could stack the cards so the American admirals had no choice. The scenario he devised involved an invasion of the tiny island of Midway. Situated some 1,500 miles to the west of Hawaii, Midway in Japanese hands would pose a constant threat of renewed attacks on Hawaii and on American ships and aircraft that might try to threaten Japanese operations in the South Pacific.

If the Americans didn't come out to fight, Yamamoto would have a base within striking distance of Hawaii. If they did come out to fight, he would outnumber them and destroy them.

By analyzing Japanese radio traffic, American intelligence officers learned that a major operation was afoot. They suspected Midway was the target but couldn't be sure. In a classic ruse, the defenders on Midway were ordered to report by radio that they were running short of fresh water. Within hours, the Japanese had reported this broadcast and associated it with their code word for Midway, thus confirming the target for the attack.

The Japanese plans involved an attack in three waves: First came Admiral Nagumo, the same man who had led the Hawaiian attack, with the carriers *Hiryu, Soryu, Kaga,* and *Akagi.* From the southwest came the invading force carrying some 5,000 troops. And finally—and this was not discovered by American intelligence before the battle—Admiral Yamamoto himself commanded a powerful surface fleet built around the battleships *Yamato* and *Musashi* to administer the coup de grace.

Preparations for the battle had two other facets. Between Hawaii and Midway, along the line that the Americans would have to come when they learned the island was under attack, a picket line of submarines was to be placed, but they arrived two days late. And far to the north, another fleet would make a diversionary attack on the Aleutian Islands.

It was an artfully contrived trap, with irresistible bait and powerful jaws ready to clamp shut. In all, there were 145 Japanese ships at sea, opposed by thirty-five American vessels.

The one significant advantage the Americans had was their foreknowledge of the Japanese plans, which enabled them to move their outnumbered force into position to surprise Nagumo. They also had one more carrier than the Japanese credited them with. The *Yorktown* had not been sunk in the Coral Sea. Despite severe damage, she had been able to limp back to Pearl Harbor, trailing a ten-mile-long oil slick. Salvage experts estimated it would take three months to make her battleworthy again. They were given three days. The *Yorktown* entered the harbor on 27 May and sailed off to war again on 30 May.

Already at sea were the two other available American carriers, the *Enterprise* and the *Hornet,* the same ship from which General Jimmy

Doolittle's B-25 bomber force had been launched to bomb Tokyo a short time before.

Nagumo's attention was focused on his attack on Midway and possible retaliation by planes based there. So far as he knew, the *Yorktown* was at the bottom of the Coral Sea, and deceptive radio signals broadcast by another ship had convinced him the other two American carriers were a thousand miles away in the South Pacific. Early on 3 June, Nagumo launched his planes for an attack on Midway. They were returning when he received the shocking word that at least one American carrier was in the vicinity.

Instead of launching the planes remaining on his decks to attack the American carrier, Nagumo chose to change the bomb load on his planes as he retrieved the returning aircraft. This made him terribly vulnerable to attack, with the decks of his carriers filled with planes, bombs, ammunition, and torpedoes. And through it all snaked the hoses carrying high-octane aviation fuel.

He managed to get a swarm of Zero fighters into the air as the first wave of American carrier-based planes—torpedo craft without fighter escort—began their attack. In the years just before the war, the navy had replaced its older torpedo planes with new models capable of more than 200 miles an hour. But, to make his attack successfully, the pilot had to drop down to eighty feet above the sea, slow to eighty knots and bore in until he was within 1,000 yards of the target.

Lumbering slowly toward their targets, the planes were defenseless against gunfire from the ships and from the tiny, agile Zero fighters that swarmed around them. Only one of the first wave of American torpedo bombers survived to return to its carrier.

But the Zeros were either being refueled or flying at wave-top altitude looking for more torpedo planes when a formation of American bombers flying at 19,000 feet arrived undetected and went into their screaming dives. Within six minutes, three Japanese carriers had been so badly damaged that they sank or had to be scuttled. The fourth was found later in the afternoon and also fatally damaged, but not before its planes had damaged *Yorktown* so badly that she, too, sank.

As night fell, it was clear the U.S. had won a crucial victory. It had lost a carrier and a destroyer, 150 aircraft, and 300 men. The Japanese had lost four carriers, a cruiser, 322 aircraft, and some 5,000 men. The American commander was later criticized for failing, just as Nagumo had seven months before, to follow up his advantage and chase down the fleeing Japanese. But in this case his caution was well placed. If he had gone blundering off through the darkness, he might well have fallen under the guns of the *Yamato* and *Musashi*, leading the powerful fleet of surface ships that, unknown to the Americans, formed the other jaw of the trap.

Land-based aircraft from Midway played some part in the battle, although the four-engined, B-17 Flying Fortresses, which seemed incapable of finding or hitting their targets, proved a grievous disappointment. Submarines also played a role, finishing off the sinking *Yorktown*. But Midway remains in the history books a battle of carriers, the first battle in which the fate of nations hung on the outcome of a battle between these new weapons.

Two months after Midway was the opening of another battle that to this day exerts a powerful influence on American military forces. On 6 August 1942, 16,000 men of the 1st Marine Division landed on the beaches of Tulagi and Guadalcanal, two small islands north of Australia in the South Pacific. With air cover from the *Saratoga, Wasp,* and *Enterprise,* the marines made a successful landing, catching the Japanese by surprise. But on 8 August, while transports were still unloading supplies, the naval commander sent all three of his carriers south for refueling. This left the 6,000 marines on Tulagi and the 10,000 on Guadalcanal stranded without air cover and with only a few hand tools and one captured bulldozer.

Within a week, the marines scratched out an airfield so marine fighter planes could come to their aid, but they have never forgotten that experience. Ever since they were abandoned by the navy, the marines have insisted on control of their own powerful air force—a full air wing for each division—to support their troops on the ground.

As Yamamoto had correctly foreseen when he warned so strenuously against becoming involved in war with the United States, the tide would begin to turn against his homeland as American military and economic might was brought to bear. But he probably did not believe that tide would turn so early, and he may even have believed that a successful battle of Midway would make possible an eventual Japanese victory. But that was not to be.

In 1944, the Japanese became so worried about the increasing strength of the American fleet and the growing threat to their home islands that they seized upon a desperate means of stopping the Americans. Young men were given rudimentary flight training and then sent out to crash their explosives-laden planes into the American ships. They were called kamikaze, after a typhoon—the "divine wind"—that saved Japan from invasion by a Mongol fleet in 1281. In a little less than a year, some 2,000 Imperial Navy volunteers died in these attacks, sinking forty ships and damaging at least 300 others. One result of this assault was the creation of the U.S. Navy's first force of strike-fighters—the early ancestors of the F/A-18. This is how it came about:

The new F-6F Grumman Hellcat—a tough, easy-to-fly fighter with six machine guns—was just coming into service in large numbers. The navy also had the gull-winged F-4U Vought Corsair, although it was at first not deemed suitable for carrier service. The threat from the kamikazes meant that the carriers needed more fighter protection—lots more—and these two planes provided it.

Kent Lee, then a young fighter pilot aboard a new carrier, the U.S.S. *Essex*, remembers being sent ashore on Eniwetok for nine hours of training in the Hellcat. Then he was back on his carrier flying combat missions.

The fighters began to turn the tide against the suicide planes. But with their decks filled with fighters, the carriers lost much of their offensive punch. With their increasing ability to defend themselves and other ships in the fleet, the carriers' ability to harm the enemy sharply declined.

Frederick ("Mike") Michaelis, then a young squadron commander who was later to become an admiral and serve as chief of naval matériel, recalls how the crew members noted that the Hellcats had been fitted with "hard points" from which bombs could be hung, although they were not intended as bombers. With a little ingenuity, it was found that the Hellcats, when not needed as fighters, could do a creditable job as bombers. Because they lacked the speed brakes of the dive-bombers, however, they attacked in a fairly shallow dive. As soon as they had dropped their bombs, they became fighters again.

A similar transformation turned the Corsairs into strike fighters. Jury-rigged bomb racks were first used on 26 February 1943, when eight Corsairs of VF-17 attacked a former British officers' club on Rabaul that had been converted into a brothel for use by Japanese officers.

Together, the Hellcats and Corsairs gave the American carriers the capability of a one–two punch during the final year of the war against Japan. They were able not only to defend the fleet and themselves but to hit enemy ships and targets ashore as well. Years later, as senior admirals, men like Michaelis and Lee were to remember the fighting power those improvised strike fighters had given them. Houser had his own experience with the Corsair as a squadron commander later, during the Korean War.

The Japanese began to build their modern navy in 1895, and by 1941 it had become one of the world's most formidable fighting forces. But by the fall of 1945, when World War II ended, the Imperial Japanese Navy had, for all practical purposes, ceased to exist.

The U.S. set out to build a great modern navy a few years after the Japanese, and by the war's end, it was the most powerful naval force the world had ever seen. But it was a force designed to fight a war at sea against another powerful navy. When the war ended, the U.S. Navy was, unlike the Imperial Navy, totally victorious. But it was also without a purpose. With the defeat of the Japanese, there was no other major navy with which the U.S. might conceivably come into conflict.

In the years immediately after the war, the navy struggled to find a satisfactory answer to this basic question: Now that the only hostile fleet capable of challenging American control of the seas had been sent to the bottom, what future role did a big, expensive navy have? To many Americans, the Soviet Union was a dangerous potential foe. But the Russian empire was a great land power with a negligible fleet, not at all like pre-war Japan, an island nation with one of the world's most powerful navies.

The debate over this issue, which has not yet been settled to the satisfaction of all those involved, spawned the most bitter, open battle between two military services in American history.

The air force, newly independent of the army, insisted that a fleet of bombers capable of massive destruction of the Soviet Union was not only the best, but the most economical way to deal with the threat from Moscow. This left little strategic role for the navy and, perhaps of even more practical import, little money for ships, especially big carriers and their fleets of planes and escort ships.

The navy was dominated by the carrier admirals and they favored the construction of a new supercarrier, the U.S.S. *United States,* big enough to carry bombers capable of direct nuclear attacks on the Soviet Union. For a few months, it seemed there would be enough money for both bombers and the new carrier. In 1948, Congress approved construction of the ship. At 60,000 tons and nearly 1,100 feet long, she would be the largest warship ever built. But in 1949, draconian budget cuts were ordered. The *United States* was cancelled, the number of heavy carriers was reduced from eleven to eight, and the number of naval aircraft was slashed by forty percent. As the admirals saw it, the nature of the debate had changed. It was no longer a question of the navy's proper future role, but whether the navy had a future at all.

The issue came to a head in the second week of October 1949, in what quickly became known as the "revolt of the admirals." Senior admirals, their chests bedecked with ribbons symbolizing their recent great victory at sea, took their places in a congressional hearing room and bluntly condemned air force strategy and tactics. They heaped particular scorn on the air force's favorite weapon, the six-engined B-36 intercontinental bomber. The admirals may have enjoyed the opportunity to vent their spleen, but the whole affair was a debacle for the navy, culminating in the firing of Adm. Louis Denfield, the chief of naval operations.

Out of this disaster, however, came the strategy that served as the rationale for a large carrier navy. It is the strategy that, in somewhat modified form, was revived in the late 1970s and still defines the navy's role today. This maritime strategy was largely the brainchild of Adm. Forrest P. Sherman, who sketched its outlines as a senior staff officer shortly after World War II and then put it into effect as chief of naval operations between November 1949, when he succeeded Denfield, and 22 July 1951, when he died unexpectedly during a visit to Naples.

Sherman had wisely avoided involvement in the "revolt of the admirals." A brilliant and ambitious officer, he honestly disagreed with his fellow admirals in their hard-ball, winner-take-all battle with the air force. He favored unification of the services under a strong defense secretary. He respected the air force's role in strategic bombing and said that if the B-36 couldn't do the job, then they should get one that did. But he also championed a broad concept of the navy's role in any war with the Soviet Union.

In the event of hostilities, he said, carrier task forces should be prepared to strike Soviet targets, both at sea and ashore, in the Far East, in Norway, and in Germany. A vital element of this strategy was naval control of the Mediterranean, from which carrier-based planes could reach targets in the Soviet Union, as well as in other parts of Europe and the Middle East. It was a concept that gave the navy an important worldwide role in any future war, but it also represented an historic shift of the navy's traditional center of gravity from the Pacific to the European theater, and especially the Mediterranean.

While the Navy was struggling to determine its strategic and political roles in the postwar world, it was also attempting to find solutions to some serious technical problems that might doom it, regardless of the outcome of political battles over its future.

Jet airplanes were clearly the wave of the future. The new technology had been developed by the United States and Britain during the war, and the Germans had actually flown jet planes in combat against the Allied bombers. But flying those early jets from an air base with long, uncluttered runways and flying them from the short, crowded deck of an aircraft carrier were two quite different things.

The first jet engines were, by modern standards, seriously underpowered. Jet-propelled planes were much faster than those powered by conventional engines. But the new engines were so unresponsive that they gave the pilot little room for error as he approached a carrier deck. He had to get "in the groove" at the proper position astern the carrier and then fly a flat path toward the ship.

A landing signals officer stood near the stern and guided the pilot in by waving large colored paddles. It was a colorful, dramatic process, but it was also subject to human error, especially at the faster approach speeds of the jets. Almost as soon as the pilot turned onto his final approach to the carrier, the officer manipulating the paddles had to decide whether to permit him to land or wave him off. (The Japanese had used a different system, which relied entirely on the judgment of the pilot. He had only a steam jet to indicate the direction of the wind across the deck, a row of lights to indicate the centerline of the deck, and another string of lights on the edge of the deck to help him judge his height.)

With the early jets, the navy festooned the deck with eleven arrester cables, and then erected a thirty-two-foot-high web barrier across the deck to protect the parked planes. If the pilot failed to catch one of the cables with his tailhook, he didn't have enough power to clear the barrier. With luck, the barrier would stop him with relatively little damage. But the plane might also burn or, even worse, break through the barrier into the other aircraft lined up on the deck.

At the other end of the process, the navy also faced serious problems operating jets aboard carriers. One concern was that when the early jet engines were started, they spat out a plume of flame hot enough to ignite other planes. Before engines were started, the planes were doused with water and carbon tetrachloride to prevent fires.

Getting the new planes into the air was also a problem. In the first few moments of takeoff, a jet engine moves less air over the wing than the big fan of a comparable prop plane. This meant the jets had difficulty building up flying speed in the short distance available on a carrier deck. By that time, the carriers had catapults, but they were operated by gunpowder. In effect, the plane was shot into the air like some giant missile. These older catapults proved unsatisfactory for the new planes.

"We went through a very difficult period. We were very goosey about our future," says Admiral Michaelis. "The Brits pulled our fat out of the fire with the angled deck, the mirrored landing system, and the steam catapult."

The angled deck was first proposed in 1951 at a conference of the British Royal Aircraft Establishment. The following year, a portion of the deck of the U.S.S. *Antietam* was widened so planes could land at an eight-degree angle to the centerline of the ship. With this system, if a pilot failed to catch an arresting cable, he was able to take off and go around again. It is now standard procedure for a pilot to push his throttles full forward as he hits the deck so he will be able to leap back into the air if he fails to catch the cable. Four thousand successful landings on the *Antietam* proved the new system and it was quickly adopted for all American carriers.

A British officer was also responsible for a new catapult system in which steam from the ship's boilers is used to drive a piston. The plane is attached to the piston through a slot in the deck, and the steam pressure is adjusted to match the weight and flying speed of the plane. The steam catapult proved capable of taking any plane aboard the carrier from a standing start and hurling it into the air in a couple of seconds. The first of the new catapults was installed on the U.S.S. *Hancock* and tested in June 1954.

The third improvement suggested by the British at this time was a system of mirrors reflecting a beam of light along the approach path as a plane comes in for a landing. By keeping his eye on this light—the "meatball"—set off to the left side of the deck, the pilot can tell whether he is high or low and adjust his approach. Landing systems officers still monitor each landing, but they no longer wave paddles, and often they don't even have to talk to the pilot as he comes aboard.

The navy later credited the angled deck and the new system of landing lights with cutting in half the number of accidents involved in carrier landings.

Adoption of the angled deck and steam catapults also had another beneficial effect. On the old straight-deck carriers, planes landed at the rear of the ship and parked at the bow end. Then they had to be moved to the other end of the ship in preparation for launch. Now, planes can often be left where they were originally parked, so long as they are not on the narrow portion of the angled deck actually used for landings. Then they can be moved directly to the catapults and launched in rapid-fire order. This makes possible the navy's "flex-deck" system in which the ship is prepared to launch or recover planes at any time.

With new carriers incorporating these vital improvements and with the older carriers modified to accept them, the navy by the mid-1950s had solutions to the three technical problems that had threatened its ability to continue to operate an effective carrier fleet.

While the navy worked to overcome its technical problems, the new strategy was being put into effect. The navy's center of gravity shifted heavily toward the Atlantic, and especially the Mediterranean. But Sherman, although he was the father of this strategic shift of forces, remained deeply worried about the scarcity of American naval forces in the wide expanses of the Pacific. He personally saw to it that the U.S.S. *Valley Forge,* one of the fifteen carriers then in service, was assigned to the western Pacific. When North Korea attacked South Korea on 25 June 1950, the *Valley Forge,* the only American carrier in those waters, was in Hong Kong. Eight days later, her planes joined with aircraft from a British carrier to attack the North Korean capital of Pyongyang.

The Korean War shifted the focus of American naval power from the Mediterranean, where Sherman thought it should be, back to the Pacific. But it also permitted the carriers, with their planes striking from both sides of the Korean peninsula, to demonstrate once again the value of sea-based air power. Within months of the outbreak of war, Congress and the Truman administration approved the construction of the U.S.S. *Forrestal,* the first of a new class of modern, angled-deck carriers designed to handle the new jets coming into service.

The debate over the value of carriers has continued, especially when difficult budget decisions have to be made. But every postwar president from Truman to Bush has called on the carrier force to back up his policies, most often in a modern version of the old "gunboat diplomacy." One study in the 1970s found that, of 215 incidents in which the U.S. used military power for political purposes between the end of World War II and 1975, almost half involved the movement of carriers.

The longest and most frustrating war for naval aviators was Vietnam. Carriers were first stationed off Indochina in the 1950s but, despite a plea from the French, did not send planes to aid the French troops surrounded at Dien Bien Phu, which fell to Vietnamese forces on 7 May 1954. Later in the 1950s and early 1960s, carrier-based planes flew frequent intelligence-gathering flights over Vietnam. The American carriers became involved in direct combat operations in mid-1964 and continued until the American withdrawal from Vietnam, in 1972.

Perhaps the most shocking lesson of the Vietnam War to those aboard the carriers was the realization that their planes were not equipped to fight the war in which they were involved.

Political control from Washington resulted in the most rigid rules under which any Americans had ever fought. Pilots were ordered not to fire on enemy planes until they had made visual identification. And yet the navy had designed its planes for an entirely different kind of war in which the enemy would be picked up on radar and, if everything went right, killed by a missile before he ever came in sight. The navy's first-line fighter, the F-4 Phantom, in fact, did not carry a gun until the plane was hastily redesigned to conform to the realities of this new kind of warfare.

It was also during this period that the officers who, in the next few years, would be in a position to shape the navy's future, confronted the problems of decks jammed with different types of aircraft, and the excruciating lack of reliability of many of their planes, electronic gear, and weapons. As American involvement in the war drew to a close, they returned to Washington prepared to make some changes.

CHAPTER THREE

"Holy Moly! We Are in Trouble!"

Thomas V. ("Tom") Jones had a dream. Looking out from the hushed grandeur of Jones's wood-paneled, nineteenth-floor office suite in the new Century City section of Los Angeles in the early 1970s, other equally ambitious men might have dreamed of building skyscrapers, making movies, or seeking high political office. But Jones had a singular dream: he wanted to be the one to supply the world's vast market for new fighter planes.

Nearly everywhere he looked among America's friends, old planes were reaching the end of their useful life, if they had not already become dangerously obsolete. In Jones's dream, his company, the Northrop Corp., would design and build a new fighter and then sell a thousand or more.

For Jones, it was not an idle dream. Once before, Northrop had produced a fighter plane so good—and so cheap to buy and operate—that it had become the standard in more than two dozen countries throughout the free world. Why not do it again on an even vaster scale?

To be sure, other aerospace chieftains saw the same market. But they had a cautious, conventional approach to capturing their share. First, they would sell a new plane to the U.S. Air Force or Navy and then, with the backing of the U.S. government, they would sell it to American allies throughout the world. Jones took a more daring approach. He proposed to design, build, and sell a new fighter as a straight commercial venture. He would take the risks, but he would also garner the rewards.

A similar system had worked well with the F-5 Freedom Fighter. Developed in the mid-1950s by Northrop, the F-5 was adopted by the defense department as the plane to be provided to smaller nations under heavily subsidized terms, as part of the U.S. military assistance program. When production of the F-5 and the T-38 trainer version finally ended in mid-

1989, Northrop had sold more than 3,800 planes over a thirty-year period.

There was, of course, no guarantee that the new fighter Jones had in mind would receive a similar assist from the government, so there was considerable risk involved. That such a bold approach would have its birth in the anything-goes atmosphere of southern California is not surprising. What is somewhat surprising is that executives of General Electric's fighter engine plant in the staid New England community of Lynn, Massachusetts, agreed to join with Jones and commit their company's money to this ambitious and risky venture. But the two companies had long worked together and each had faith in the technical competence of the other. And GE had shared in the phenomenal sales Jones had racked up for the Freedom Fighter. Jones was the world's greatest fighter plane salesman, and GE counted on him to deliver the market for the new plane.

Jones was also intimately involved in the design of the plane. Described by one aide as "the last of the breed of designer-CEO's"—Jones preferred to go to the aircraft division rather than have his engineers come to corporate headquarters several miles away. He worked closely with the late Lee Begin, who was responsible for many of the innovative features of Northrop planes. Begin, an intuitive designer with little formal education, used to tell associates, "If it looks right, it will fly right."

Work began in the mid-1960s and by the early 1970s, after 4,000 hours of wind tunnel tests, the new plane was beginning to look like a sure winner. Viewed from the front, with the cockpit looming over the nose, it resembled a cobra, and that quickly became its name. Designing such a plane involved a sizeable investment. But it would cost some $100 million more to build a couple of prototypes, test them, and prepare for production. Jones came up with a novel scheme: He proposed to a number of the smaller NATO allies of the U.S. that they agree to buy the Cobra and, in return, share in the production. The new plane would truly be an international fighter.

Negotiations with the European countries were going well, and Jones's dream was coming true. But in January 1972, the U.S. Air Force turned everything topsy turvy when it announced a competition to design a light-weight fighter. Four companies submitted bids and two were selected to build two prototypes each. Northrop received $39 million and General Dynamics received $38 million for work on its YF-16. There was no promise that either plane would ever go into production. Instead, the companies were challenged to try out new ideas in fighter design. But the air force also insisted that the plane be cheap as well as lightweight:

no more than $3 million apiece in 1970 dollars, based on an order of 300 planes. At the time, the cost of the navy F-14 and the air force F-15 were soaring toward the $20 million mark.

For Northrop, the air force contract was both a great opportunity and a formidable challenge. Here, suddenly, was the money to build two prototypes so potential customers could see and even fly a real airplane. But the Cobra had been designed as a strike-fighter, not just a lightweight dogfighter. It was bigger than the General Dynamics plane, had two engines rather than one, and carried more weapons. "We had to change all our briefings overnight," recalls one Northrop executive. "We had the right plane in the wrong competition."

The first Northrop prototype, now called the YF-17, was rolled out in April 1974 and was being prepared for its first flight in June, when the Pentagon suddenly announced a winner-take-all fly-off between the General Dynamics YF-16 and the YF-17. The prize would be a contract to build hundreds, perhaps thousands, of fighters for the air force and then for American allies overseas. What had been a relatively low-keyed technology demonstration program was converted overnight into the fighter plane deal of the century.

It was while preparations were underway for this competition that Congress ordered the navy to adopt the air force competition winner for carrier use, adding even more to the stakes on the table.

Theoretically, the navy was deeply involved in the testing and selection process. Practically, the navy representatives felt like barely tolerated aliens when they came to meetings with the air force.

Robert H. Thompson, who worked for Houser in OP 05 (the office of the deputy chief of naval operations for air warfare), vividly recalls one meeting he attended:

> We were told to get together on requirements with the air force. As usual, they took three navy guys and twenty-five air force guys and that's balance, and put us in a room. They said, "You guys get together and see how you can merge requirements." There was a navy admiral and an air force general, and the air force general walked in, looked at all the light-blue suiters and said, "Now, guys," he says, "if you guys change one number of our requirements, you're going to Adak." And he left. So we had two weeks to come up with requirements. What are we going to do for two weeks, guys? They thought that was a good way to work a joint exercise.

Suddenly, things were moving much faster than the navy had expected—and moving in the wrong direction. There were two immediate concerns.

First was the fact that neither Northrop nor General Dynamics had experience building carrier aircraft. Second was the explicit congressional order that, if followed literally, would force the navy to buy a plane that would, at best, be barely suitable for carrier operation.

The solution to the first problem was a decision to require General Dynamics and Northrop each to team up with an experienced builder of navy planes.

General Dynamics looked first to McDonnell Douglas and this seemed to offer the prospect of a peaceful, if far from ideal, working relationship. Both companies were St. Louis based and had a similar stolid midwestern style of doing business. Their relationship was so close, in fact, that David Lewis, head of General Dynamics, had, until a short time before, been president of McDonnell Douglas. The McDonnell Douglas firm was the result of a merger in 1967 of the McDonnell and Douglas aircraft companies and both had had a long history of building carrier aircraft. Douglas turned out a series of torpedo planes and bombers during and after World War II, and McDonnell was responsible for the navy's first carrier-based jet, as well as the F-4 Phantom, the first-line fighter for both the air force and navy for many years. At the time of the merger, however, Douglas had shifted its interest to commercial airliners while McDonnell built fighter planes. That division continues to this day, with the company's commercial operations largely located in southern California and its military business in the former McDonnell plant in St. Louis.

Northrop first approached LTV, the Texas builder of the A-7 Corsair attack plane used by both the navy and air force. One of its predecessor companies, Chance Vought, had built the famous gull-winged F-4U Corsair during World War II.

The talks between McDonnell Douglas and General Dynamics soon collapsed because of General Dynamics' insistence on the dominant role in the partnership, and both General Dynamics and Northrop focused their attention on LTV.

For normally astute executives, some of the officials involved in these negotiations made some remarkably bad business judgments.

At Dallas-based LTV, officials studied the competing planes and then made two assumptions. The first was that the air force would choose the General Dynamics plane on its merits. The other was that, given the climate in Congress and the Pentagon, the navy would be forced to take the same plane chosen by the air force.

LTV decided on 27 September to team with General Dynamics, even though Northrop had offered extremely favorable terms. The next day, Paul Thayer, chairman of the board of LTV, called Tom Jones and told him of the company's decision.

The arrangement LTV made with General Dynamics was a heavily lopsided deal. If both the air force and navy picked the YF-16, General Dynamics would be prime contractor for the air force and LTV would be prime for the navy. If the air force rejected the YF-16 but the navy chose it, General Dynamics would be the prime contractor and LTV the subcontractor. But if the air force chose the YF-16 and the navy didn't, LTV would have no part in the deal. LTV at the time was building the A-7 attack plane—a derivative of the navy's F-8 fighter—for both the navy and the air force. But once production of the A-7 stopped, the company would be out of the combat aircraft business.

Northrop turned to McDonnell Douglas and the two worked out a more even-handed arrangement. If the team won the air force competition, Northrop would be the lead contractor and do the majority of the work. If they won the navy contract, McDonnell Douglas would be the lead and do the majority of the work. It never occurred to the people at Northrop that their plane could lose the air force fly-off and that they might end up as a junior partner to McDonnell Douglas.

Flight tests of the competing planes would normally have taken a couple of years. But the air force, eager to get into production, condensed the fly-off into about three months at the end of 1974. Results came to the air force's Aero Systems Command at Wright-Patterson Air Force Base near Dayton, Ohio. Reports from the pilots were ecstatic.

Both planes were close to being a fighter pilot's dream, although the YF-16 probably came a little closer. The General Dynamics plane, with its single engine, was smaller than the YF-17 and thus a little bit harder to see. It had an innovative control system in which electronic pulses from the cockpit moved the controls. The pilot's seat was cocked back at an angle to permit him to experience as much as nine times the force of gravity (nine Gs)—and remain conscious.

With its twin engines, the Northrop plane was bigger than its competition, but many pilots like the security that two engines give them. Where the YF-17 stood out was in its ability to fly very slowly—as slow as thirty-seven miles an hour—with its nose pointing almost straight upward without falling off into a spin. In a dogfight, planes slow dramatically as they burn off energy in tight turns. The pilot who can continue to control his plane at very slow speeds is likely to win. Northrop engineers had worked very hard to make this a virtually stall-proof plane, hoping finally to eliminate the deadly threat of a spin, which had killed so many pilots over the years. One pilot likened two YF-17s, circling each other in that way, to two cobras waiting for the chance to strike.

The navy was, theoretically, involved in evaluating the two planes. Practically, it was an all-air force show.

Kent Lee represented the navy on the board making the choice between the two contenders, and he went to Wright-Patterson on the day the decision was to be made.

"I thought the board picked the wrong airplane," Lee says. "I really didn't have a vote. They had their minds made up."

Even though the navy was far from ready to make a decision on its plane, the secretary of defense gave the air force permission to go ahead with its announcement. On 13 January 1975, it chose the General Dynamics YF-16.

The reaction in Tom Jones's office in Century City and at the Northrop plant in nearby Hawthorne was one of anger and incredulity. Jones's dream had turned into a nightmare.

Particularly galling to the Northrop people was the speed with which the air force and General Dynamics exploited the work Northrop had already put into courting the smaller NATO nations. As soon as it had picked the YF-16, the air force moved immediately to work out a deal in which Norway, Denmark, the Netherlands, and Belgium would share in production of the F-16s, and buy 650 of them for their air forces at a cost of $2.1 billion. Northrop had thought the Europeans would have a vote, but the choice they made was between a French plane and the YF-16, not between the two American planes. Northrop not only lost the air force contract, but it also lost the customers it had so zealously courted.

There was also the feeling that there was something suspicious about air force motives in picking the YF-16. One theory was that the engine in the YF-16 had tipped the scales. The General Dynamics plane was powered by the same engine already in use in the air force's F-15. Choosing a new plane with the same engine would increase the number of engines to be purchased and thus hold down the cost. It would also simplify maintenance and reduce the number of spare parts in the inventory. But there may have been something more sinister involved. The engine in the F-15, made by Pratt & Whitney, was running into severe technical and cost problems. Buying more of those engines would make more money available to help solve those problems. "They wanted us to use the Pratt & Whitney engine," says one top Northrop official. "They wanted to solve their engine problem by magnifying it."

Years later, after the emotions of the moment had faded away, however, Thomas Burger, who was involved in the YF-17 program and later became Northrop's program manager for the F/A-18, said: "I don't think there was anything peculiar about the decision. The F-16 clearly won that competition, in fair retrospect. The F-16 was a good airplane. We had trouble admitting it, but it really was. It was a hot rod. It had better acceleration, better turning. It was a pretty clear-cut winner."

If the F-16 was a winner for the air force, however, it was not at all what the navy needed or wanted. While the admirals were sharply divided on what kind of plane they did need, they had no trouble agreeing on what they didn't need. None of them wanted a little, lightweight fighter, and they didn't want to have to try to make a plane designed for the air force suitable for carrier operations. And yet there was that order from Congress to adapt the air force choice for carrier use, and there was heavy pressure from the air force and Pentagon officials for the navy to make its decision and "get with the program."

The navy pulled together a team to evaluate both planes in terms of their suitability for carrier operations. The source selection evaluation board was made up of six civilians and seventeen captains. Reviewing their work was an advisory council, headed by Lee, made up of seven admirals, a marine general and two civilians. Both boards were backed up by more than 500 experts, representing the distilled wisdom of the navy's half-century of experience operating aircraft on carriers at sea.

G. W. ("Corky") Lenox, then a captain, was on the engineering staff at NAVAIR and was assigned to help out in the technical evaluation of the planes. Later, Lenox was to be the program manager guiding the F/A-18 through the critical development phase. Lenox recalls the instructions the team got from Lee:

He told us: "You let me worry about the politics. You guys are the evaluation board. You do the best job you can to get a thorough evaluation of the designs submitted and you pick what's best for the navy. Don't worry about politics. But you damn well better be able to defend to the ultimate degree your analysis and your recommendations because whichever way it goes there's going to be controversy and Monday morning quarterbacking."

After a quick look at the two airplanes, the team gave Lee a negative assessment: neither one looked very good as a navy plane. Representatives of both contractor teams were brought in for separate day-long sessions within a week of the air force announcement and told what they would have to do to make their planes suitable for carrier operations.

The navy naturally looked to LTV and McDonnell Douglas, the two companies with long experience in building carrier planes, to take the lead. General Dynamics, with the big air force contract in its pocket, was content to let LTV adapt its plane for carrier use. But the sudden reversal of roles in which Northrop was reduced to playing the part of the junior partner to McDonnell Douglas made for some difficult days.

"We had a hard time getting started," recalls R. D. ("Bob") Dighton, chief operations analyst for McDonnell Douglas. "Northrop was saying, 'What happened?' There were hard feelings. Northrop had an entirely different culture. They are entrepreneurial, take gambles. They have a lean, mean staff. They don't have time to do all the detail our tradition has been. We didn't know anybody in their company."

Of course Sanford N. ("Sandy") McDonnell, the board chairman, knew Tom Jones. But, says Dighton, "it's hard to work engineering at that level."

To make things more difficult, McDonnell and Jones are quite different kinds of men. Those in the navy who dealt with them often sensed that they didn't like or trust each other very much.

McDonnell, a nephew of James Smith McDonnell, the aviation pioneer who founded McDonnell Aircraft Corp. in 1939, appeared to navy men to be a typically staid, moral midwesterner. His speeches often focused on work with boys and the importance of instilling the moral virtues in the nation's youth. Unlike other aerospace giants, McDonnell Douglas, under McDonnell's guidance, largely avoided playing politics, either within the navy or in Washington, D.C.

Jones, on the other hand, was the quintessential Washington insider, working the halls of the Pentagon and Capitol Hill and, especially, the White House, to further the interests of his company. In May 1974, Northrop and Jones, who was then the company president, pleaded guilty to a misdemeanor charge of making an illegal contribution of $150,000 to President Nixon's re-election campaign. Both Jones and the company were fined the maximum of $5,000. During the Watergate investigation, it was revealed that the company had set up a political slush fund years before, in 1961. As much as $1.2 million was sent overseas to be "laundered." Then at least $472,000 was funneled back to Jones and a company vice president to be used for political contributions.

An insight into the way Jones operated came in court testimony by Herbert Kalmbach, Nixon's personal lawyer, in November 1974. He told how he had gone to Jones in August 1972, and how Jones had handed him a package of $100 bills—$75,000 worth—to pay for the silence of the men accused in the burglary of the Democratic headquarters at the Watergate complex in Washington—the event that set off the scandal culminating in Nixon's resignation. Kalmbach said he misled Jones into believing the money was for the re-election fund and tearfully described Jones as "a fine man."

Jones personally repaid Northrop $172,000 of the amount he had improperly distributed to politicians and resigned his post as president. But the company board retained him as chairman and chief executive officer, a tribute to his value to the company. Several years later, when the Democrats were in the White House, an internal Pentagon memo to the secretary of defense warned: "As you are probably aware, Northrop seems to have a lot of political clout, particularly in the VP's office."

One admiral who worked closely with both men summed up his impressions of Jones and McDonnell: "Jones was an operator, a promoter, a salesman, probably the best promoter, operator, salesman in the aerospace industry. Sandy McDonnell was something of a Boy Scout, a little naive. Jones . . . you didn't want to let him out of your sight. He could run circles around Sandy, in and out of the White House, the Pentagon."

Northrop had, to this point, put almost all its effort into designing and selling a land-based fighter. But the engineers at McDonnell Douglas had given a good deal of thought to developing a dual-role strike-fighter suitable for use on a carrier. What they had in mind didn't look at all like the YF-17. But everyone knew that there would be enough trouble getting congressional approval for a plane that looked like one of the competitors in the air force fly-off, let alone something that looked like a brand new plane.

As one navy official described the situation: "I think Sandy McDonnell called in his engineers, gave them a picture of the YF-17 and said, 'I want you to design a carrier-based strike-fighter and I want it to look exactly like this.' "

Donald Snyder, a McDonnell Douglas engineer who was involved in design of the plane, says: "The F/A-18 looks like the YF-17, but it is a brand new plane, aerodynamically, structurally, in all ways. It's a brand new airplane from the ground up and I don't think that was sufficiently recognized, certainly not by the customer and the Congress and perhaps not by us as well.''

It was obvious that the effort to make either the YF-16 or the YF-17 suitable for taking off from and landing on a carrier would have to begin with a substantial beefing up of the plane's structure. When a fighter lands on a carrier, it is dropping at the rate of twenty-four feet a second or more, or about fifteen miles an hour. A fighter landing on a runway touches down at less than half that velocity. When a fighter hits the carrier deck, a heavy cable snags its tailhook and jerks it to a stop within 300 feet. To absorb the stress of this kind of controlled crash, the landing gear and the body of the plane have to be much heavier and stronger. The tailhook itself requires special attention. It must work perfectly every time. If it breaks, there is no way to bring the plane aboard a carrier.

Further strengthening would be needed to deal with the stresses involved in a catapult launch. On shore, a fighter plane may make a 5,000-foot takeoff run. On a carrier, a plane must absorb a stress equal to four times its weight as it is jerked from a standing start to its 125-knot flying speed in 250 feet. The forward landing gear would need special attention because it is pulled in one direction on takeoff and slammed back in the other direction on landing.

In the air force fly-off, both planes were equipped with small, lightweight radar sets of minimum capability. A substantially more powerful radar would be needed to enable the plane to do all the navy wanted it to do.

Much more attention would have to be given in the design of the navy plane to resistance to ocean spray, to prevent it from being eaten alive by salty sea air.

Many of the changes that would be needed to navalize a plane designed for air force use were fairly obvious. But engineers and managers from both competing teams spent a good deal of time trying to find out what the navy wanted, and that was complicated by the dispute within the navy over the kind of plane that was needed.

John Capellupo, who later managed the F/A-18 program for McDonnell Douglas, recalls flying to Washington for a couple of days every week or two. "The difficult question," he says, "was, 'who's the navy?' " Although there was doubt then about who in the navy the companies had to satisfy, it seems now that McDonnell Douglas, which believed it could build a dual-role strike-fighter, correctly understood that the choice was being made by people who worked for Lee, who strongly favored such a plane, and that was the "navy" that had to be pleased.

Gradually, the designs and proposals coming in from St. Louis, as the McDonnell Douglas engineers worked over the YF-17, began to ease navy doubts. One Hill staffer who watched the whole process unfold was impressed by the masterful job McDonnell Douglas had done in understanding what each of the experts assembled to evaluate the designs wanted to see in an airplane, and in satisfying each of them in its proposal.

But the navalized versions of the YF-16 offered up by LTV remained troublesome. A number of naval officers had the impression that LTV, apparently assuming the navy would be forced to adapt their plane for carrier use, wasn't trying very hard.

LTV's engineers designed three different versions of a modified YF-16 in an attempt to satisfy the navy, so it is really not fair to say that they didn't try. At least part of their problems may simply have been bad luck of the kind that struck the day the final drawings were due. All of the paperwork was loaded onto a company plane at Dallas and then, on takeoff, the plane slid into a duck pond, thoroughly drenching the drawings. The crew and passengers, including the company president, emerged unscathed but had to wade ashore, muddy and dripping. The joke around NAVAIR was, "Well, that bird won't fly."

As the source selection board compared the proposals from the competing teams, the most striking change from the prototypes involved in the air force fly-off was the significant growth in weight. The original YF-16 weighed 13,559 pounds without fuel or weapons. The three designs offered by LTV weighed from twenty-four to fifty-two percent more. The McDonnell Douglas–Northrop entry grew from 16,940 pounds to 20,583 pounds, nearly twenty-two percent. Neither, it was clear, would be a true lightweight fighter after it had been navalized.

It was also clear that none of the three navalized versions of the YF-16 measured up. A major concern was that the LTV planes would have difficulty landing safely aboard a carrier. A special device had been installed to keep the plane from banging its tail on the deck, but that made the plane more difficult to maneuver in the moments before touchdown.

Another worry was the so-called "fly by wire" electronic control system used in all the designs. The navy had two fears: One was that electronic emissions, especially in the shadow of a carrier's giant radars, would damage or confuse the control systems. The other was that combat damage might make a plane uncontrollable. The study of the designs showed that, in the LTV proposals, the multiple sets of wires carrying electronic messages to the control surfaces merged in five distinct "single-shot kill points." A hit at any one of those points would send the plane out of control. While the experts were still nervous about a similar arrangement in the derivative of the YF-17, they were comforted by the presence of a separate mechanical control system that would at least enable the pilot of a crippled plane to get back near the carrier before he punched out and parachuted into the sea.

When the board had finished adding up the score, all three LTV proposals were rated unacceptable or marginal in almost all categories. The McDonnell Douglas–Northrop proposal was found acceptable in almost all categories. Its separate mechanical control system saved it from an unsatisfactory rating on survivability, and it was considered marginal in carrier suitability because of a high approach speed, as well as in avionics, reliability, and maintainability. Although great stress was to be placed on reliability and maintainability of the new plane, and Northrop was to be a leader in that effort, that had not been a major consideration in building the YF-17 prototypes. They were expected to last only about a thousand hours, enough to test the design.

Were the two planes really that far apart? Probably not. Yet the selection board clearly found the YF-17 version superior. And then it almost certainly went on to make its assessment in such a way as to dramatize the difference between the winner and the loser.

On 2 May 1975, the navy announced the winner: McDonnell Douglas received $4.4 million to continue with work on the plane until a final contract was signed, and General Electric got $2 million for work on the engine. Northrop signed on as subcontractor to McDonnell Douglas. And Jones, characteristically, set out to sell a land-based version of the F/A-18 in the international market. Perhaps his dream could be made to come true after all.

William Clements, the deputy defense secretary, huddled with the secretary of the navy to look over a list of suggested names. He picked the name "Hornet." He had no particular reason for his decision, but the name did endow the plane with an honorable pedigree. The navy's first Hornet was a sloop chartered in 1775. Since then there have been seven more ships named Hornet, including two World War II carriers, one of which launched General Jimmy Doolittle's raid against Tokyo in 1942. Clements also decided to give the plane a new number in an attempt to divorce the navy plane from the air force competition. The fighter version would be the F-18, and the attack version the A-18. But a simple change in the designation wasn't enough to prevent a firestorm of protest.

For a number of companies in the aerospace industry, the outcome of the debate over the navy's new plane was almost literally a matter of life or death. If the navy's decision stood, Grumman, LTV, Lockheed, Fairchild, and Boeing were in danger of being locked out of the fighter plane business if they were not already excluded.

The one company that stood the best chance of a successful challenge of the navy's choice was LTV. On 9 May, just a week after the decision was announced, LTV filed a formal protest with the General Accounting Office, a semi-autonomous agency that acts as a watchdog over the executive branch of government for Congress.

Kent Lee had seen such a protest coming as soon as he read the congressional language ordering the navy to use the same plane chosen by the air force. In fact, he considered the whole process "odd, unusual . . . unfair in many ways." So he put together a small team at the Naval Air Systems Command to work out a strategy to get around the seemingly obvious language of the congressional directive ordering the navy to adapt the winner of the air force competition for carrier use.

Masterminding the effort were Harvey Wilcox, general counsel of NAVAIR, and Charles J. ("Chuck") McManus, counsel for the F/A-18 program. Backing them up was John Shephard, who had retired as a captain after a career as a naval aviator and then had gone back to school in his fifties to earn a law degree. When Shephard came by Wilcox's office looking for a job, Wilcox hired him on the spot and made him his link with the aviators and engineers so everything the lawyers did would be technically accurate. By the time they finished, Wilcox, under Shephard's tutelage, knew more about how to build an airplane suitable for carrier operations than many aeronautical engineers.

Looking at the issue as a lawyer, Wilcox probably understood the full implications of the situation better than anyone else in NAVAIR. His reaction when he read the congressional orders was: "Holy moly! We are in trouble!" Almost immediately, he began stockpiling the legal ammunition he knew would be needed.

This is the way Wilcox analyzed the situation: "We've got excellent directives and procedures for doing methodical, rational, sensible, yet flexible decision-making when we start a new weapon. The problem is that only in the smaller programs do we actually use them. The bigger programs refuse to live by the rules. There are powers at work that no number of mortals seem to be able, with the best of intentions, to overcome.''

That was true, in spades, of the new fighter plane program. And yet Wilcox reasoned that, if it appeared that the navy had not followed the rules, the new plane was almost certainly doomed. He and McManus set about trying to shove the program back on the tracks—or at least to make it appear to be on the tracks—every time it veered off. The two men were also convinced that the program was vulnerable to so many threats that, when it came to an almost certain protest, they couldn't afford a partial victory. They began to talk, like fighter pilots, of the need for a "clean kill."

Their first step was to draft identical letters to the chairmen of the two appropriations committees, John L. McClellan (D-Ark.) in the Senate and George H. Mahon (D-Tex.) in the House. The letters informed them the navy intended to use $12.5 million of the $20 million provided by Congress for development of a navy plane and evaluation of the designs. The letters were artfully written. They carefully left out any reference to the most troublesome sentence in the congressional directive, the one that said: "Adaptation of the selected Air Force Air Combat Fighter to be capable of carrier operations is the prerequisite for use of the funds provided."

Once the letters were written, they were then lobbied up through the bureaucracy of NAVAIR, then to Houser, up to the chief of naval operations and the secretary of the Navy, and finally to Clements, the deputy defense secretary who served as a kind of procurement tsar during those days. Clements signed the letters on 4 November 1974, and both chairmen wrote back approving the navy's plans—and neither used those dreaded words requiring adaptation of the air force choice.

Clements also played a key role in another way. On 16 October 1974, he called representatives of the two competing teams to his office at the Pentagon and outlined the rules for the competition for the navy plane. A summary based on notes taken during the meeting by his executive assistant tells how he moved away from the language of the congressional directive: "At no time did Secretary Clements state or imply that the NACF [Naval Air Combat Fighter] must be a derivative of the selected Air Force ACF, that performance was of lesser importance than commonality and cost, or that the evaluation criteria were other than those clearly set forth in the solicitation [sent to the contractors on 12 October]."

Clements himself was not nearly as concerned by the congressional language as those in the navy who were closer to the situation. With many more issues to worry about, he dismissed the troubling congressional language as "absurd."

"We sure as hell didn't do that and I never would have had any intention of doing that. The airplane picked to be the air force fighter, hell, it wouldn't work as a carrier plane. No way it could work. That's nonsense," Clements says. While the navy worried, Clements put the peculiar congressional instructions out of his mind.

But his cooperation in the navy's campaign to save its airplane paid off. When the expected protest came, the folks at NAVAIR were as ready as they could be. There was even some comfort to be taken from the fact that Fried, Frank, Harris, Shriver, & Kampelman, the powerhouse New York–London–Washington law firm retained by LTV, appealed to the GAO rather than going directly to federal court. A federal judge would probably have issued a routine order delaying the aircraft program until he had a chance to look at the facts. The resulting headline—"Judge Blocks New Navy Fighter"—might have been the curse of death, given the program's uncertain backing on Capitol Hill. On the other hand, the GAO would have access to the navy's internal evaluation documents— something that would have been much more difficult for LTV to obtain if it had gone into federal court.

Unlike a trial in court, the GAO handles an appeal entirely on paper. The two sides never meet face to face to argue their cases. Normally, LTV would have filed its appeal, the navy would have responded, there might have been one more round of arguments, and then the agency would render its decision. But in this case, because of its importance, Ronald Berger, who served as GAO's judge, permitted Fried, Frank to raise a number of new issues after its initial filing.

"It was a good fifteen-rounder for big stakes," Wilcox said later. "The referee had shown in the first round that he wasn't going to penalize a little butting and gouging. So we both just stood toe to toe and slugged it out."

Both sides pulled out all the stops. The navy tried to entice Berger into making a visit to a carrier. When the GAO decided that wasn't a good idea, the navy sent him a training film showing what happens in a bad carrier landing, including several crashes. It was a less-than-subtle reminder of the navy's concern about the difficulty in bringing the F-16 aboard the carrier safely. LTV's lawyers objected indignantly.

For their part, Fried, Frank managed to inundate Wilcox and his small staff with carefully researched legal arguments, each of which demanded study and a precise response. The paperwork became so voluminous that once, when Admiral Lee visited the lawyers' office, the only place he could find to sit was on a cardboard box. Not only were the hours long, but Wilcox found his life disrupted in another way. His wife, Leslie, worked for GAO in an office next door to Berger's. She didn't handle any navy matters, but to avoid any possible conflict, she was sent to Capitol Hill for the summer to work with the Senate Public Works Committee on Tennessee Valley Authority matters.

On 1 October 1975, the GAO submitted its thirty-eight-page verdict, summed up in one final sentence: "We have concluded that the navy's actions were not illegal or improper and that therefore the protest must be denied." It was the "clean kill" for which Wilcox and McManus had worked so hard. And, as they had realized from the beginning, the issue was not the qualities of the two competing airplanes, but the question of whether the navy had followed the rules. The artfully drafted letters to the powerful chairmen on Capitol Hill had played a major role in convincing the GAO that the rules were followed.

The clear-cut decision by the GAO did not, however, end opposition to the new plane. Most importantly, it did not end opposition by factions within the navy itself and by manufacturers who felt they had been badly treated.

Because of the unusual process forced on the navy by Congress, several of the country's major aircraft companies had simply been excluded from the competition. This was especially troublesome in the case of Grumman Aerospace Corp., which, of all the companies, had always had the best of relations with the navy. Many veteran naval aviators felt, with a good deal of justification, that they owed their lives to the Grumman planes, such as the Wildcats and Hellcats of World War II, that had brought them home time after time.

Whenever there was a gathering of naval aviators, like the annual Tailhook Association meeting, Grumman representatives were much in evidence, setting up drinks at the bar, organizing the golf match, and handing out golf balls. And now, with the biggest navy aircraft contract in history, Grumman was left out entirely.

Grumman did not protest formally. But Joseph Gavin, chairman and chief executive officer of the company, testified against the F/A-18 at a hearing of a Senate Armed Services Subcommittee on 17 September 1975.

"Grumman finds itself in an extremely sensitive position to be setting forth viewpoints on future weapons systems which appear to differ from those of our major customer, the U.S. Navy. . . ." Gavin said. "Our decision to speak out about the F-18 is not taken lightly. I hope it will do nothing to disturb the productive relationship which has long existed between the navy and our company."

The F-18, he argued, would not only be "an inferior product" compared with the F-14 built by his company ("Today there are two kinds of fighters, the F-14 and all the rest"), but also more expensive.

Even more compelling testimony against the F-18, as the plane was then known, came from George Spangenberg, who had, until his retirement in 1973, been the Naval Air Systems Command's almost legendary airplane designer. He had been deeply involved in the navy's struggle against McNamara's TFX or F-111. The F-14, which took its place on the carrier decks, had, to a large extent, been his inspiration. He had not budged from his conviction that the Tomcat was the fighter the Navy needed. The whole idea of trying to get a usable airplane for the navy from the air force competition, he told the senators, was "foolish."

As a consultant to Lee's source selection advisory council, Spangenberg had had a good chance to evaluate the plane. Asked his opinion of the F-18, he said: "It is clear that the F-18 is neither effective, nor cost effective, in either fighter or attack roles. It is vastly inferior in capability to the F-14 at about the same total cost, somewhere [sic] less capable and considerably more expensive than the F-4 and is inadequate in range and more costly than the A-7. There is no justification for continuing the program."

Spangenberg also spoke for many in the navy who didn't like the way things were going. He told the committee: "I think, overall, I have been the spokesman of naval aviation, for the man in uniform that couldn't talk up when I could. I have been in many situations where I could talk and a younger officer in blue could not talk. And I was shoved forward and said, 'go tell him, George.' I think, in general, I speak for most of the naval aviation in the statement I made here. I think that there are, obviously, some people that disagree with me. I don't take issue with their sincerity. I believe that they are wrong."

Houser, who had long been the most outspoken advocate of an all-F-14 carrier navy, came to accept the F/A-18 as a useful complement to the Tomcat. Certainly it was far better than if the navy had been forced to accept a lightweight dogfighter that could do nothing else. In congressional testimony, Houser dutifully supported the navy's choice of the F/A-18.

Lee, who was in the opposite corner from Houser during the long fight leading up to the choice of the F/A-18, says: "To Houser's credit, I must say he swallowed his pride and testified as necessary. It was tough for him. In fairness to Houser, I never ran across his going around the corner to bad-mouth the F/A-18. I think he took it like a man."

Throughout this period, Houser was in a peculiar position. His office was in the Pentagon, whereas Lee was a few miles away in Crystal City. Because of this accident of geography, Clements saw Houser two or three times a week, much more often than he saw Lee. He came to like and respect Houser—"a super guy," he calls him—and to rely on his advice and judgment. This would seem to have placed Houser in a position to put the F/A-18 in a bad light with Clements, but he didn't.

Clements, who considered himself a general manager dealing with broad issues rather than details such as whether the new plane should be a fighter or an attack plane, or both, tended to discount whatever bias Houser may have showed for the F-14. He saw that as part of the navy culture:

"They are a culture that believes that everything they have got in hand is the best in the world and cannot be improved upon. Anytime you're getting ready to change that culture, whether it be in a destroyer or in radar detection or in an airplane, there is immediate resistance. First of all, it wasn't invented here, and second, we don't need it. We like what we've got."

If Houser himself was careful to play the honest broker in his relations with Clements, the bureaucracy over which he presided as deputy chief of naval operations for air warfare (OP 05) was, and continued to be long after his retirement, a center of opposition to the F/A-18. After Corky Lenox became program manager for the plane in 1976, he quickly learned to be cautious about what he told anyone in that office.

"I was very fearful . . ." Lenox says. "I really felt there were not very many one could trust with sensitive information related to procurement strategy or problems. I found many times, things I would say in discussions, in briefings, in dialogue on what's going on would very quickly find its way to [Grumman headquarters at] Bethpage. I felt there were no secrets in OP 05. . . . It was a period of the most intense opposition. It was very, very difficult. I always felt the other side had my game plan, had my play book, so to speak."

Much of the opposition to the F/A-18 within the navy was emotional and to many aviators, especially the more experienced ones, the new plane was seen as a threat. "It was a challenge to a whole lot of different rice bowls," says Admiral Michaelis.

Although the F/A-18 would come in a two-seat version for training purposes and later, for under-the-weather attack missions, it was basically a single-seat plane. The navy's two first-line fighters, the F-14 and the F-4, both carried a two-man crew. With a single-seat, dual-mission plane coming into service, there would be far fewer planes with a back seat for a radar intercept officer, known as a RIO, or bombardier-navigator, known as a BN. This not only threatened the job security of the man in the second cockpit, but even those who continued to fly would suffer a loss of prestige.

There was as much or more opposition to the F/A-18 from crew members of the heavy A-6 day-night, all-weather bomber as there was from the crews of the F-4s, which would be replaced by the F/A-18. To the A-6 crews, the navy seemed to be saying that one man in an F/A-18 could do almost as well what it took two men to do in an A-6, and they resented it. They also feared that they would often be called upon to provide fuel for the Hornets—acting as flying fuel trucks rather than doing their real job of ground attack.

From 1975 until 1978, Paul Hollandsworth, the former skipper of an A-6 squadron, sat in a small office at the Pentagon as the representative there of the A-6 community in the fleet. Alongside him sat other pilots representing the F-14 and A-7 crews.

Hollandsworth, who was later to play a key role in one of the most controversial episodes in the F/A-18's history, felt all along that the navy should rely on the F-14 as a fighter and develop a replacement for the A-6 attack plane rather than spend money on a dual-purpose strike-fighter. But in those early days, he recalls, feelings toward the F/A-18 leaned more toward apathy than outright hostility: "Nobody really expected it to fly because we couldn't see a mission for it. The F-14 seemed to us to meet all the requirements. It didn't seem like the F/A-18 was going anyplace. In our office, it didn't get a great deal of attention."

But as the F/A-18 moved along, it attracted more attention—and more hostility.

An important source of opposition was the pilots of the single-seat A-7 attack planes who would have to learn to fly the Hornet. Many of them honestly doubted that one man could be both a first-rate fighter pilot and a first-rate attack pilot. Others had a sneaking suspicion that the new plane really would make that possible and that made some of them fearful.

Senior aviators, even squadron and wing commanders, were faced with the possibility that all the effort they had put into learning to bomb accurately would be washed away when raw "nuggets" just out of flight school showed they could hit their targets just as accurately with the new plane. This generational difference continued even after the plane had gone into service. When a senior aviator took the microphone at one Tailhook gathering and began to bad-mouth the F/A-18, the younger pilots hooted him off the stand.

The fact that the A-6 and F-14 were made by Grumman, and the A-7 by LTV, meant that the two factions in the navy that felt most threatened by the F/A-18 flew planes made by the two companies that also felt most threatened. Together, they formed a network that funneled information to opponents of the F/A-18 on Capitol Hill and fueled a steady stream of critical information to the press.

Politicians on Capitol Hill divided fairly predictably on the navy's choice. The entire delegation from Texas, where both the F-16 and A-7 were built, lined up against the F-18. Even though his favor had been carefully courted in the letters signed by Clements, George Mahon, a Texan and powerful chairman of the House Appropriations Committee, was still incensed to learn the navy was not going to use the air force plane. Why, he asked Pentagon officials, did you "lead us down the primrose path of commonality and then come up here and tell us it is not possible, you cannot achieve it, and so forth?" Congressmen from California (Northrop), Ohio and Massachusetts (General Electric), and Missouri (McDonnell Douglas) lined up solidly in favor of the plane. And many other congressmen were pointedly reminded that General Electric had 222 plants in thirty-four states.

Mahon complained that he had never seen such fierce lobbying. A Senate staffer told the *Wall Street Journal:* "The F-18 is the biggest candy in our store. There is an amazing matrix of interests who want to eat it." A House defense expert was quoted in a similar vein: "The employment issue is very strong. Some Congressmen will see the F-18 as spreading joy and happiness, arguing that it is better than food stamps. And that is an argument that people listen to these days."

The opponents of the F/A-18 found their most sympathetic ears in the House Defense Appropriations Subcommittee. The chairman was the late Joseph P. Addabbo (D-N.Y.), many of whose constituents worked at the Grumman plant on Long Island. Much of the contact with the committee by navy people unhappy with the F/A-18 came through two men who, in their earlier years, had also been naval aviators. They were the late Rep. William V. Chappell, Jr. (D-Fla.), whose district included a Grumman plant in St. Augustine, and Burton R. ("Bud") Otto, an aide to Chappell who had once been the congressman's squadron commander.

Chappell took to the House floor on 1 October 1975 to condemn the F/A-18 program as "a wild goose chase" and attempt to cut all the funding for the new plane—although money would be available for continued engine development. After a marathon debate that consumed thirty pages of the *Congressional Record* when it was printed the next day, Chappell lost by a vote of 243 to 173.

In mid-November, Sen. Barry Goldwater (R-Ariz.), a general in the air force reserve and one of the Senate's experts on military aviation, made a similar effort in the Senate. "What happened here," Goldwater told his colleagues, "is that the navy took what it liked out of the F-17, which is a very good airplane, and they took it over to McDonnell Douglas and said, 'Hey, make this into a navy fighter.' I want to see them acquire this aircraft through competition, not through merely picking what is best from one airplane, going to a superb aircraft manufacturer, and saying, 'This is the airplane we want.' "

Goldwater's summary was right on the mark. That is exactly what the navy had done. But he lost, sixty-four to nineteen, to an unusual coalition of conservatives who tended to favor defense spending and liberals who often opposed defense spending but who, in effect, voted for jobs in their districts.

While much of the continuing opposition to the F/A-18 was based on emotion or politics or self-interest, the plane, as it emerged from the competition between the two prototypes, had one very serious deficiency: it simply couldn't carry enough fuel.

The navy has long had a fairly simple rule of thumb to determine how much fuel a plane must carry to operate effectively from a carrier. The weight of the fuel in a fully loaded plane—the "fuel fraction"—should, according to this rule, be about one-third the total weight. But in the F/A-18, the fuel fraction is only about twenty-three percent. This means it must carry external tanks, which pilots dislike, or be refueled often, or remain in the air a shorter time than normal, or be flown in a manner different from other planes.

How did it happen that the chosen plane could meet all the requirements laid down when the navy asked the manufacturers for proposals on a strike-fighter, and yet not carry enough fuel?

Lee offers this explanation: "Those specifications were deficient in two areas. We should have specified internal fuel for certain missions and endurance for a two-hour flight. That, we didn't do. Why? I don't know. It didn't dawn on me that we didn't have it in in that fashion until the competition was over."

But if the specifications had called for sufficient internal fuel, that would have caused problems, too. If the navy had required several thousand pounds more internal fuel, it is likely that the designers would have found it very difficult, and perhaps impossible, to turn out a plane that looked like the YF-17—a plausible derivative based on the air force competition. It would have been bigger, with a somewhat different shape, and it would have required extensive new design studies and wind tunnel tests.

Ever since the plane was chosen, thought has been given to ways to increase the amount of fuel it can carry and none of them has proved feasible. A major reason is that, after a certain point, adding more internal fuel becomes self-defeating. Each additional pound of fuel at takeoff requires adding four more pounds to the plane's weight, quickly making it too heavy to be an agile fighter.

The relatively limited range of the F/A-18 was for a number of years a legitimate complaint of critics, and, for the fleet, operating the Hornet effectively despite its limited fuel capacity is a continuing challenge.

With the LTV protest settled in the navy's favor, and the failure of critics on Capitol Hill to block the program, the F/A-18 seemed, by the fall of 1975, to have fairly clear sailing. But there was still cause for serious concern. The navy planned to buy about 800 planes. While that was a sizeable number, all of the research and development costs would have to be absorbed by those 800 planes. That guaranteed that the cost of each plane would be far above the $3 million per plane that had once seemed a realistic goal. The F/A-18 was no longer a lightweight fighter and it would certainly not be cheap.

And then the U.S. Marines came to the rescue.

At least since Guadalcanal, when the carriers sailed off and left them, the marines have insisted on owning and controlling the planes that provide close air support for their men on the ground. With a complete wing of aircraft for each of their three divisions, the marine air force is larger than those of most nations, including Britain's Royal Air Force. With some of their squadrons operating from carriers, the marines add to the punch of naval aviation. But money to buy the marine planes comes from the naval aviation budget—"blue money, not green money," as one admiral puts it—and this is a source of some resentment within the navy.

In the early 1970s, as the cost of the F-14 seemed about to price the plane out of the budget, the marines succumbed to navy pressure and reluctantly agreed to buy at least eighty Tomcats. But many marines considered the F-14 too sophisticated and too expensive for marine use. And, even worse, it was not equipped to drop bombs. In July 1975, Gen. Louis Wilson became marine commandant and, as one of his first acts, decided to buy F/A-18s rather than F-14s. The Tomcats on order for the marines would be assigned to the navy, and the marines would get along with their aging F-4 Phantoms until the Hornets came along. This added more than 260 planes and, by increasing the production run by one-third, helped greatly to hold down the price per plane.

As 1975 neared its end, Lee was under growing pressure to move ahead with contracts for full-scale development of the new plane. But Admiral Michaelis, who had recently become chief of naval materiel, and thus Lee's boss, put the contracts on hold.

Michaelis had come under the influence of Willis ("Will") Willoughby. A soft-spoken South Carolinian, Willoughby had been responsible during the Apollo program for making sure that NASA's spaceships worked perfectly all the way to the moon and back. Early in 1975, Adm. Isaac Kidd, Michaelis's predecessor, arranged to have a reluctant Willoughby transferred to the navy to help improve the reliability and maintainability of navy equipment across the board.

Willoughby was appalled by what he found when he and the score of people he brought along from NASA moved into their new Crystal City offices.

Reports from the fleet showed that planes required repairs after only half to three-quarters of an hour in the air. When everything was working, the planes were superb. But too often they didn't work long enough to get the job done. It was the same thing that had bothered Kent Lee during his carrier days.

Willoughby was given a civilian ranking corresponding to that of a three-star admiral (which caused a good deal of resentment among many of the admirals, who considered civilians an alien breed, not to be trusted), and he demanded a written charter that gave him extraordinary power, up to the point where he could, single-handedly, close down a production line if the manufacturer wasn't measuring up to his standards.

The first major program coming down the pike after Willoughby arrived was the F/A-18.

"They said they were getting ready to buy an airplane. I said, 'Lord a mercy, we can't buy it that way! If we do, we won't have anything but another low-reliability plane out there,' " Willoughby says.

Willoughby set to work to make the new plane a model of what he likes to call "big R, small m." By this, he means that reliability built into a plane or ship or weapon automatically results in reduced problems with maintenance.

Willoughby insisted that the contracts for the F/A-18 contain specifications spelling out reliability. Up till that time, contracts contained specifications for performance but only goals for reliability. Manufacturers tended to pay a good deal more attention to specifications, which could determine how much money they made, than they did to mere goals.

"I give great credit to this guy Willoughby," Michaelis says. "He never let up on me. I asked him not to let up on me. I had long talks with Willoughby. God, those were terrible days. The contractors all told us, 'Okay, if you want to double the cost of the airplane, put all those requirements on us.' "

When the contracts were signed, they spelled out for the first time what the contractors agreed to provide in terms of reliability and maintainability as well as performance.

Willoughby was not the only one concerned about building planes so they would be reliable and easy to maintain. That was, of course, one of Lee's major goals. But Willoughby came to personify the navy's interest in this issue as he descended on the contractors with all the zeal of a tent show revivalist. At McDonnell Douglas, employees who make significant contributions to the quality of naval planes compete for the "W. J. Willoughby Salty Dog Award." Winners receive a figurine of a sailor—the Salty Dog—and $1,500.

It was not until the end of January 1976 that contracts for full-scale development and the production of the first eleven planes were issued.

Even as the program moved into high gear, plans called for three distinct versions of the plane. There would be an F-18 fighter and an A-18 attack plane for the navy, and something close to today's F/A-18 strike-fighter for the Marine Corps. Theoretically, it would be possible to convert back and forth between fighter and attack versions of the plane, but it would be a somewhat cumbersome and time-consuming process. The disaster that befell Admiral Nagumo as he was changing the bomb load on his planes at Midway was not forgotten. And there were still many in the navy who just didn't think one man, flying alone, could learn to do two jobs traditionally done by four men in two different planes.

Admiral Thomas Hayward, a former test pilot who was later to become chief of naval operations, summed up the doubts harbored by many in the fleet as the navy prepared to move into full-scale development and then production of this new plane:

A number of people like myself, who had seen a number of claimed achievements by the technical people fail again and again in the 1950s and 1960s, were not very enamored of the thought we were going to have all kinds of new things none of us had seen before: Heads-up displays, computers that could be used for air-to-air as well as air-to-ground at a time our air-to-air radars were still having lots of trouble, and our air-to-air fire controls were still not all that good. Our air-to-ground computer system was certainly open to plenty of doubts. How, then, were we to believe the technical people could possibly be right in their claim that we were going to see one airplane do both roles very well?

CHAPTER FOUR——————————
One Plane, One Man

When full-scale development of the F/A-18 began in 1976, almost every-one involved assumed that the fighter and attack versions of the plane would each require a separate set of black boxes to control the radar and other electronic operations. It would be possible to change the boxes and convert an A-18 into an F-18 and vice versa, but it would be a difficult, time-consuming process.

One of the few who were convinced it would be possible to do something far better was Kent Lee. He reasoned that most of the technology needed to produce a true strike-fighter was already flying and performing well. The A-7E, the latest version of the LTV attack plane, had a good computer, a good radar and a good inertial navigation system. Together, these made the plane an extremely accurate bomber.

All that was needed, Lee concluded, was a single radar that could be used for both bombing and air-to-air combat. He described it as a "pro-grammable radar." This meant that, instead of being wired to do just one job, the radar would be controlled by software—electronic instructions—that would permit it to be changed back and forth between the two missions with the flip of a switch.

To say that this was "all that was needed" was not literally true. A true one-man plane would also require breakthroughs in cockpit design and computerized controls. But it was true that, without a programmable radar, development of an effective strike-fighter would be difficult at best and probably impossible.

To many in the navy, the odds against success seemed so high that they discounted this as just another of Lee's pipe dreams. No one had ever built such a radar. No one was quite sure whether such a radar could be designed. And there were many who doubted that it could be produced even if it could be designed.

It might seem that combining the two jobs in one radar set would be fairly simple, just a matter of which direction the radar beam is pointed. In practice, however, the solution is far from simple. The demands placed on the radar when it is used for air-to-air combat are almost the opposite of those involved when it is used to drop bombs. When the radar sweeps the sky in search of hostile planes, it covers a large area that is virtually empty. It must be able to find the few moving targets very rapidly. When the radar is used for ground attack, it must sort out vast amounts of confusing information reflected back from the ground, but speed is not nearly as important as it is in air-to-air combat.

McDonnell Douglas took the problem to the nation's two most experienced radar manufacturers, Westinghouse and Hughes Aircraft. Westinghouse was, like McDonnell Douglas itself, a stolid, conservative organization, content to build carefully on technology that had already been proved in practice. Hughes, like its southern California neighbor Northrop, was more innovative, more inclined to take a chance on new technology that might promise a breakthrough.

Westinghouse adapted a radar it was already working on for the air force's F-16 fighter and, as might have been expected, came in with a hard-wired radar system with different black boxes for the attack and fighter modes. The more daring Hughes engineers gave life to Lee's pipe dream. They proposed a programmable radar controlled by changeable software. Hughes, under prodding by McDonnell Douglas, then went on to sign a contract that was almost as daring as the radar. The company agreed to a fixed price for full-scale development and options on the first three years of production—before a single circuit board or component of the radar had been built.

"It was a courageous contract," says John L. Conklin, manager of the advanced programs staff in Hughes's F/A-18 program division. The company's bid was reviewed by its top officials and they knew it was risky. There were two reasons why they took the risk. One was the likelihood that, if their bid was not extremely competitive, they would lose the business. The other was their confidence in their large, competent team of software engineers, and a history, as Conklin puts it, "of records of firsts in almost everything of importance in airborne radar."

The company had developed its first airborne radar for the air force a quarter of a century before. In 1949, equipped with that radar, the F-94A

became the first plane to shoot down a target drone without the pilot seeing the target. Hughes went on to develop the radar for the high-flying
YF-12 Blackbird spy plane, as well as radars for the navy's F-14 Tomcat and the air force F-15 Eagle.

But nothing prepared the Hughes engineers for the challenges they faced
when they attempted to put a dual-purpose radar in the F/A-18.

The very first problem was size. Under ideal circumstances, a plane is
designed around its radar. In a rough way, it can be said that the performance of an airplane's radar set depends on the size of its radar antenna:
the bigger in diameter the antenna, the farther the radar can see and the
smaller the target it can discern. This all translates into a big airplane.
The ultimates in antenna sizes are seen on the air force AWACS and the
navy E-2C. Each has a huge radome sprouting at the top of a pylon above
the fuselage like some giant growth. With such large antennae, these
planes serve as airborne battle-management stations, capable of keeping
track of everything flying in an area of thousands of square miles.

If the goal is a fighter-interceptor like the F-14, whose radar can see
tiny targets more than 100 miles away, keep track of twenty-four of them,
and shoot at six targets at the same time, then a big antenna is needed—
in the F-14, thirty-six inches in diameter. This means a large fuselage, a
big wing and tail, and large tanks to carry enough fuel for long endurance.

But the shape of the new navy plane had already been determined.
There was no way Hughes or anyone else was going to put a big radar
antenna in the nose of that plane. The original YF-17 had been designed
with enough room for an antenna twenty-three inches in diameter, just
big enough for a simple little radar set suitable for rudimentary air combat
operations. The radar in the F/A-18 would have to be far more capable
than that. Not only would it have to be powerful enough for close-quarter
dogfighting with guns and the Sidewinder missile, but it would also have
to support the medium-range Sparrow missile and an even longer-range
missile then on the drawing boards. And, of course, it would also have
to do the quite different job of helping the pilot drop his bombs with
precise accuracy.

The aircraft engineers managed to expand the diameter of the nose by
eleven inches, to thirty-four inches, but that still meant the size of the
antenna would be severely limited. Hughes focused on the other three
parts of the radar set. In addition to the antenna, the radar consists of a
transmitter, a receiver, and a signal processor.

The transmitter sends out bursts of energy that bounce off the target and return to their source. They are captured by the receiver and then run through the processor, which analyzes the signals and determines such things as the location and distance of the target and, if it is another plane, the speed and direction it is flying. If the size of the antenna is limited, as it was in the F/A-18, the performance of the radar can be carried to its ultimate by increasing the size and power of the transmitter so it can hurl its bits of energy farther away, by making the receiver more sensitive so it will be able to capture even faint echoes, and by making the processor more sophisticated so it will be able to analyze these faint signals. That is what the Hughes engineers set out to do. But they soon realized that the two obvious solutions to their problem—increasing the size of the radar and the electrical energy fed into it—were out of the question. The radar would have to be smaller, not larger, than anything they had ever built before, and it would have to use less, not more, power.

When they designed the radar for the F-14, they were pleased to compress it into sixteen major components. With the F-15, a few years later, they got it down to nine smaller components. But they would never be able to cram that amount of equipment into the tiny nose of the F/A-18. McDonnell Douglas helped a little by moving the cockpit wall back about three inches, increasing the space available for the radar by half a cubic foot, but a lot of squeezing would still have to be done to accommodate it.

Increasing the electrical power supplied to the radar seemed, on the surface, to be an easy solution. With its two high-performance jet engines, the F/A-18 has an abundance of electrical power. Unfortunately, electrical energy causes heat, and heat is the deadly enemy of electronic circuits.

In the past, radar designers had reached for the best possible performance even at the risk of a buildup of heat. But the radars they produced were notorious for malfunctions. A number of F-4 Phantom pilots were able to brag, in a perverse way, that they had gone through an entire career without ever having a radar that wasn't malfunctioning in one way or another.

McDonnell Douglas, which was beginning to catch Willoughby's "reliability and maintainability" religion, adopted a new slogan: "We operate them cooler to last longer." They borrowed a page from NASA's space flight book and reduced the current, power, and voltage flowing through the radar. The result was to cut the temperature in the transistors, which switch messages in the electronic system, from an average of more than 100 degrees centigrade to seventy degrees, thus dramatically increasing the lifetime of the components in the radar. The standards were made even more strict than those for space flight when it was realized that the thermal shock suffered by a radar set when a plane zooms from the desert floor into the stratosphere and back again is greater than that suffered by the equipment in a spaceship.

The designers saved a little room by replacing the heavy hydraulic system used to move the antenna in older planes with a lightweight, virtually fool-proof electrical drive system. This gave them enough room for a special liquid cooling system for the transmitter, the heaviest user of heat-producing electrical energy. Lightweight corrugated and honeycomb panels were developed to separate parts of the radar and help keep the heat from building up.

This still left the radar too big and too hot. Denied more space and more electrical power, the Hughes designers focused on constructing their radar with the solid-state components that were becoming available in the mid-1970s. This would not only squeeze more performance into a smaller package, but it would also mean fewer moving parts and less buildup of heat.

Up to that time, scientists had found ways to make little computer units, known as circuit boards, in which as many as eight layers of circuits were stacked one on top of the other. If they could produce boards with fourteen layers of circuits, the Hughes designers calculated, they could save a cubic foot or more of space—room for greater power and more cooling capacity.

While Hughes focused on the problem of squeezing the radar into the plane's nose, McDonnell Douglas and the navy were at work on another problem that would vastly complicate the job of the radar designers.

In the early days of the development of the plane, the navy went through one of its perennial arguments over whether the Hornet should carry a gun. One admiral, since retired, who worked on the early designs says he put the gun in, and the top brass removed it three times before he finally made it stick. The argument in favor of leaving the gun off was a powerful one. With missiles of increasing accuracy, there were those who insisted that the gun would never be needed—despite the experience in Vietnam. An even more persuasive argument was that the gun and ammunition and the fuel required to carry it around added about 5,000 pounds to the weight of the plane. That was a lot of weight for a weapon that might not be needed.

The fliers who had learned the hard way in Vietnam, when they went into combat with missiles but no gun, prevailed. The F/A-18 would have a gun. But where should it be placed? It might be hung on a pod under the plane. That would be fine for strafing, but it would be a sure loser in a dogfight. Similarly, if it were placed in the wing, it would suffer in accuracy and would degrade the performance of the plane.

The only really suitable place for the gun was right on the center line, directly in front of the pilot. Hughes was given the bad news: their radar would essentially be in the same compartment as the gun. The gun mechanism would be between the pilot and the radar, and the barrels of the gun would extend out through the nose, only an inch and a half from the top of the radar.

Because a pilot in a dogfight may have his opponent in his sights for only a few seconds at a time, the gun must be capable of putting out as many bullets as possible in those brief moments. In World War II, many fighters carried six machine guns in their wings, with the guns aimed so the bullets would converge a short distance in front of the plane. During the Vietnam War, when serious attention was once again focused on the gun, the experts searched for a way to pump as many bullets as possible from a single gun aligned with the centerline of the plane. That way, it would not be necessary to worry about focusing the converging lines of bullets from a number of guns. It proved impossible, however, to fire enough bullets through the single barrel of a conventional machine gun without quickly burning out the barrel.

Radar-Gun Configuration in Hornet Nose

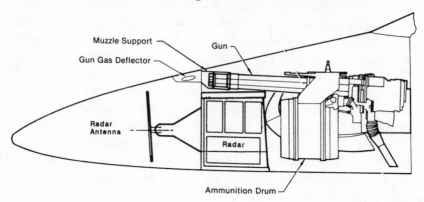

The gun, with its six barrels capable of firing 100 rounds a second, nestles on top of the delicate radar set.

The search for a solution took the scientists to the Army Ordnance Museum at Aberdeen Proving Ground, north of Baltimore. There, they examined a Gatling gun of the type developed by Richard Gatling in 1862, during the Civil War. A predecessor of the machine gun, the Gatling gun consisted of a cluster of barrels around a central axis. As a soldier turned a crank, each barrel rotated into position in turn, and a bullet was fired through it.

The guns carried by modern fighter planes employ the same principle. A motor turns a cradle holding the six barrels, and the gun spews out big 20-mm bullets at the rate of 6,000 rounds a minute, although it holds only enough bullets for about six seconds of sustained fire.

When the gun goes off, it sets up a tremendous noise and vibration, heats the surrounding air to 700 or 800 degrees Fahrenheit, and belches out clouds of noxious gases. A more unlikely marriage than that between the delicate radar and the loud, smelly gun is hard to imagine.

The problem faced by the Hughes designers was to insulate the radar against the heat of the gun, seal out the smoke and gas of the burning powder, and cushion the radar so it would not be damaged or thrown out of alignment by the mechanical and acoustical vibration of the gun.

The cooling system already in place was beefed up to solve the heat problem, and the entire radar system was tightly sealed to keep out the gases. Instead of surrounding the radar with access doors, the entire set was mounted on rails. When a mechanic wants to work on the set, he opens one door—the hinged nose of the plane—and the set slides forward on its rails. When he is done, he slides the radar back in place and closes the nose, sealing the radar away from the outside world in its own little cocoon. The most difficult problem was to deal with the vibration. The solution was to identify the frequencies of all the vibrations coming from the gun, create baffles to dampen them, and then tie all the parts of the radar together into one package and balance it delicately so that it acted as a single vibration isolation system.

By the time the Hughes designers finished their work they were confident they had solved the problem of shielding their radar from its noisy, smelly neighbor, but they still waited with crossed fingers for the first tests in actual flight. They could also boast that they had cut the components in the radar from nine in the F-15 to five, and reduced the number of individual parts by 8,000 from the radar in the older F-4. The radar, not including the antenna, took up less than four and a half cubic feet and weighed only 338 pounds.

It was a magnificent breakthrough—in the design laboratory. But it didn't travel well. In the short trip to the factory floor, something went very badly wrong. Even the highly skilled production workers, laboring in a spotless, dust-free area that was more like a scientific laboratory than a factory, were unable to conform the circuit boards to the extremely demanding tolerances required. They even had trouble attaching one layer of the circuit board to the next. More than half of the boards went directly from the production line into the garbage. And, what's worse, Hughes learned the penalties of being a pioneer. There was no one else they could turn to who knew how to make such circuit boards any better than they did.

Looking back on the experience, it was clear to people in the navy that they should have paid far more attention in the early design of the plane to the problem of producing it efficiently and economically. For Hughes, especially, this proved to be far more difficult than anyone had imagined.

It took Hughes several years to work out the problems of building the components of the radar efficiently, and in the meantime, under its fixed-price contract, the company lost a good deal of money. Just how large the loss was is not known because the company was, at that time, a private firm, not required to publish financial data. Eventually, the company turned the situation around, and the F/A-18 radar became one of its most profitable operations. The solutions involved moving the design lab onto the same "campus" as the factory, just south of Los Angeles International Airport, creating a "producibility lab" where the designers and those who would assemble a new product worked together, and designing an automatic machine capable of making circuit boards with as many as eighteen layers.

Hughes was well along toward solving its production problems when, in the summer of 1980, Mike Tkach, a McDonnell Douglas test pilot, strapped himself into an F/A-18 at Patuxent River Naval Air Station and took off to find an answer to that nagging question of what would happen to the radar—and the plane's other electronic equipment—when the gun was fired in flight.

While the engineers worried about the radar's performance, Tkach had two very personal concerns. One was that the firing of the gun might disrupt the operations of the flight control computers, making it difficult or impossible for him to control the plane. This problem had already occurred in tests of the F-16. His other concern was that he might shoot himself down.

"I had to shoot the gun at all parts of the envelope, from as slow as the plane would go to as fast as it would go,'' Tkach says. ''I remember the stories I had heard as a young boy about an F-100 or 101 shooting itself down. I had this fear.''

Before the flight, in which he was to shoot the gun while flying straight and level at 40,000 feet and 1.5 Mach—faster than a bullet—he asked the engineers about his fear. This is what worried Tkach: During design of the plane, there had been a sharp argument between the fighter and attack pilots. The fighter pilots wanted the gun cocked up at a two-degree angle so they could get an enemy in the sights without turning or pulling up quite so sharply. The attack pilots wanted the gun aimed down about one and a half degrees, so they wouldn't have to fly quite so steeply while strafing. The fighter pilots won the argument and the gun was cocked upward. Tkach could imagine the bullets arcing upward and then falling back down on him as he sped under them. The engineers told him there was no problem; the bullets would fall below his flight path before he got there.

''They had it all figured out. You can study all the physics and they tell you, 'Don't worry about it, kid.' But when you're out there, you want to be sure. I was pretty nervous. It was sweaty-palms time,'' Tkach says.

Before he took off, another plane flew out over the Atlantic off the Virginia coast near Wallops Island and checked to make sure there were no ships in the test zone. That assured Tkach of a 100-square-mile area in which to do his testing. He leveled off at 40,000 feet, pushed the throttles forward and felt the familiar kick in the backside as the plane surged up to one-and-a-half times the speed of sound. Then he took a deep breath and pressed the gun trigger on his control stick for a full second. He heard the whirrrr of the gun firing and saw the muzzle gases whip back past his canopy as a hundred bullets sped out into the space in front of his plane.

And then . . . nothing. The bullets didn't hit the plane. And the radar and flight control computers continued to operate flawlessly.

In a later test, he put the plane into a turn and fired an entire drum of 600 bullets in a six-second burst. No pilot would be expected to do that in combat, but the test proved that it could be done without melting the gun barrels or causing parts of the plane to burn. He also strafed ground targets and found that the fact that the gun was cocked upward to satisfy the fighter pilots caused no problems. When he was finished, he concluded that, despite all the early worries, the gun tests had been ''benign.''

The engineers back on the ground, who had been anxiously monitoring data automatically transmitted by the sensors on the plane, were ecstatic. Their fears about the performance of the radar had been groundless. It had operated as though the gun weren't there.

Well before the radar passed that final examination, Kent Lee, worn out by years of bureaucratic battling, decided to retire to a farm near Charlottesville, Virginia. A few months before he left in the fall of 1976, he called in Captain H. L. ("Hank") Halleland, the project officer during the gestation period of the plane, and told the captain he was going to be replaced.

"We decided we needed a different man to run the program," Lee says.

> What we needed was a man who was a better manager, who was technically qualified to take the program at that point and run it through the research and development phase. The toughest thing I had to do when I was at NAVAIR was to tell Halleland he would be replaced. Halleland was a good man. He had worked long and hard at this. I know he felt very let down, indeed. He had put his heart and soul into it, but we decided he just wasn't the man to pick up the project at this point and drive it through. We needed someone with more technical experience, who would be a tougher manager.

The choice was Corky Lenox, who took over early in 1976. He was also promoted from captain to rear admiral, giving him the added clout that comes with rank. A 1952 graduate of Annapolis, Lenox had spent most of his career as a fighter pilot, but he had also flown attack planes and, during the Vietnam War, had commanded an air wing with both attack planes and fighters. He had also picked up degrees in aeronautical engineering from Princeton and the Naval Postgraduate School.

During two tours of duty in NAVAIR, he worked on the F-14 and later headed the carrier branch, overseeing development and production of all carrier aircraft. When he became program manager for the F/A-18, he felt he had a better understanding than most officers of the development and production part of naval aviation. He also had the advantage of being one of the relatively few naval aviators who shared Lee's belief that a true strike-fighter was feasible.

The appointment of Lenox was part of the navy's response to a problem that Will Willoughby had quickly discerned when he came to work for the navy in the mid-1970s. He found the program management offices filled with very bright officers who "had never been in a design room, never been on a manufacturing floor." And as soon as they learned, through on-the-job training, he complained, they were sent off to another assignment.

Lenox, who had become familiar with the F/A-18 while serving in NAVAIR and on the source selection board for the plane, was to remain as program manager through the entire development process.

A few months after Lenox took over the program, Lee retired and was replaced by Vice Adm. Forrest S. Petersen. The assignment of Lenox and Petersen to their new jobs fortuitously brought together two men almost ideally suited to manage a project as difficult, both technically and politically, as the F/A-18.

Petersen graduated from the Naval Academy in 1944, in time to spend the last months of the war on a destroyer in the Pacific. After the war, he completed flight training, served in three fighter squadrons, and then became a test pilot. In 1958, he was chosen as the navy test pilot on the X-15, a plane designed to fly at several thousand miles an hour and soar into the edges of space.

In three and a half years at NASA's high-speed flight station at Edwards Air Force Base in California, Petersen took the X-15 aloft on five flights, up to more than five times the speed of sound and an altitude of 102,000 feet. Unlike the early astronauts, who were strapped into their little Mercury capsules like the monkeys that had preceded them, Petersen was a true test pilot, fully responsible for his plane as it hurtled through the last few molecules of air at the limits of the atmosphere. To younger navy pilots, Petersen was an almost legendary figure.

Later in his career, Petersen commanded the U.S.S. *Enterprise* in the late 1960s. Lenox was air wing commander aboard the *Enterprise* on one of her tours in the South China Sea, and he and Petersen became close friends. The result, when Petersen headed NAVAIR and Lenox was responsible for the F/A-18, was that Petersen trusted Lenox enough to give him a great deal of latitude in running his program. He was given the freedom to be a real program manager.

" 'Pete' Petersen was a tough taskmaster, a tough boss," Lenox says. "But if he had confidence, he would give you a lot of rope. He trusted me. I was able to do things most rear admirals would be hesitant to do, making decisions, taking positions. I felt we made a good team."

Although the programmable radar had seemed to Kent Lee to be the key to building a true strike-fighter, many navy pilots were still deeply skeptical when Petersen and Lenox took over. The nagging question remained as to how one man would be able to master all the skills involved in both air-to-ground and air-to-air combat and be able to use all the information made available to him by his radar and other electronic equipment.

The first planes had few, if any, instruments. The pilot, sitting out in the open, could feel the wind in his face and see the ground clearly as it passed below him. It was almost literally true that he flew by the seat of his pants, sensing the movement of the plane in relation to the air through which it flew. Sometimes a scrap of yarn was tied to a strut to indicate whether the plane was side-slipping, but for the most part, the only "instruments" a pilot relied on were those built into his own body. Gradually, more and more help was built into the plane: a compass; fuel, temperature, and oil pressure gauges; an altimeter; a turn-and-bank indicator; finally, a radio, a radar set, and computers. Military planes required even more gauges and switches to monitor and control the weapons they carried.

By the time the F-4 Phantom came along in the late 1950s, the pilot found himself surrounded by a bewildering array of instruments and switches. They not only spread across the front wall of the cockpit but filled the spaces on either side of his seat. To reach some switches, in fact, he had to grope back over his shoulder, hoping to find the right knob. Pilots complained about having to look down at the control panel, beside the seat, in order to change radio channels—a particularly hazardous exercise while flying in formation through clouds.

And this, of course, was the challenge facing the pilot of a two-man plane, who had a radar intercept officer in the back seat with his own massive set of dials and control knobs. In the one-man F-15 fighter, first flown in the early 1970s, the number of controls and switches surrounding the pilot had soared to 300. How were all these instruments to be crammed into the single cockpit of an F/A-18 and even leave room for the pilot, let alone permit him to function effectively?

To understand the problem facing the cockpit designers, it is useful to try to imagine what it is like for a pilot going into combat for the first time, to bomb an enemy target.

He is flying at high speed—500 or 600 miles an hour—at very low altitude—perhaps little more than a hundred feet off the ground. He is frightened and uncomfortable, buffeted by the rough air close to the ground, and driven down into his seat by gravity as he jinks the plane to avoid antiaircraft fire. As he comes within range of air-to-air missiles, warning lights flash, and he hears a buzzing sound in his earphones. His head swivels constantly as he checks the skies for enemy fighters.

Suddenly, he is close to the target. At his low altitude and high speed, he may have as few as twenty seconds from the time the target comes in view to identify it, lock on his radar, steer toward the target, release his weapons, and escape. Add to this the fact that other members of his squadron will be flashing across the target within seconds, in maneuvers as precisely timed as any performed by the Blue Angels. If he is a moment too early, he risks a mid-air collision. If he is a few seconds too late, the fragments of a "friendly" bomb may blow him out of the sky just as surely as an enemy missile. If he becomes confused and fails to drop his bombs, he will have to come back to try again. The people on the ground will be waiting for him this time and they will be very unhappy.

When he comes off the target, he may well find enemy fighters ready to pounce. Flying close to their own base, they will probably be lighter and more maneuverable and under precise control from the ground. If he wants to get home, the pilot who was, a moment before, flying a bomber, will have to become a superior fighter pilot. And he will urgently need a whole new array of information quite different from that he needed a few moments before when he was on his bomb run.

At the McDonnell Douglas plant in St. Louis, a visionary named Eugene C. Adam had long been worried that the cockpits in combat planes were becoming so cluttered that, while all the instruments gave the pilot vital information, the message they sent was so confusing as to be almost useless. And even if the pilot understood what needed to be done, he often had trouble finding the right combination of switches to do it. Adam proposed what he called a "glass cockpit," a revolutionary new kind of cockpit in which all those gauges would be replaced by a few cathode ray tubes, similar to little television or computer screens. Everything the pilot needed to know would be flashed on one of those screens right before his eyes. And all the switches would be replaced by a few controls on the throttle and control stick and a panel at eye level in front of the pilot.

"The trick is to do a lot of things automatically for the pilot but never, ever, to leave him in the dark as to what's happening," says Adam, who began his career with four years as a navy combat aircrewman before earning his engineering degree and going to work for McDonnell Douglas in 1956.

The technology for the kind of cockpit Adam envisioned was beginning to become available in the late 1960s. When McDonnell Douglas won the contract to build the F-15, it urged the air force to use the new type of cockpit. But the air force turned the proposal down. Precise military specifications spelled out the kinds of round "steam gauge" dials that belonged in a fighter plane cockpit and even dictated where they would be. The air force agreed to a few innovations, but essentially the early models of the F-15 retained the familiar cockpit layout.

There were several reasons for the air force decision. One was concern whether the new system would work. Another was the danger of pilot confusion due to an entirely new cockpit design. Perhaps the most important reason was that the need for a new cockpit did not seem urgent. The F-15 was being designed as a single-purpose, air-to-air fighter, rather than a strike-fighter like the F/A-18, and it had a cockpit big enough to hold all the familiar instruments and switches. There was so much room, in fact, that Adam worried that the pilot's workload in the F-15 would be increased because his instruments were spread over such a large area.

By the time the navy came along with its F/A-18 only a few years later, the situation was dramatically different. Computer technology had advanced to the point where Adam's proposal seemed much more feasible. McDonnell Douglas had done a great deal of preliminary work and was able to take visitors to a big domed simulator and show them what the new cockpit would look like and how it would function. But the biggest change was that there simply wasn't enough room in the F/A-18 cockpit to cram in all the displays and switches needed for both dogfighting and bombing.

The F/A-18 cockpit, having already surrendered half a cubic foot to the gun and radar compartment, was a full forty percent smaller than the cockpit of the single-purpose A-7 attack plane. There were only 350 square inches of space on the F/A-18 instrument panel, compared with 450 square inches in the F-15 and a mammoth 2,700 square inches in the two cockpits of the F-4.

To Adam, the tiny cockpit was a challenge, but also a great blessing because it virtually forced the navy to give him a chance to try out his new design. It was one of those cases where it paid to bring in the best experts available, almost regardless of cost.

Adam puts his philosophy this way: "We are an engineer-run company. If it is easy, we go by price. But if it is more art than science, we do an evaluation of risk. I've chosen the highest bidder out of eight. I know I will have trouble with the guy who bids $8 million on an $11 million job."

One of the first in the Pentagon to clearly see the need for a dramatically new cockpit was Robert Thompson, who worked for Admiral Houser and was largely responsible for drawing up the operational requirements for the cockpit in the F/A-18. With some trepidation, he sent his recommendations down the river to Lee's shop at Crystal City, to be turned into specifications for the plane.

"We pushed hard for a really advanced cockpit, but we never thought NAVAIR would go along," Thompson recalls. "They came back and fully embraced the whole concept. That really surprised me. That was the item that has made the F/A-18 a useful airplane."

With NAVAIR and OP 05 in agreement, Adam was given permission to set aside the almost-sacred military specifications for the cockpit and to start with a clean slate.

When word of this decision reached the fleet, however, there was an anguished cry of protest. Despite the daring things they often do in the air, military pilots tend, in other matters, to be rock-ribbed conservatives. They had all grown up with round "steam gauges," and they loudly complained that changing over to this new cockpit would be not only wrong but dangerous.

It is not difficult to understand why pilots in the fleet who had not had a chance to visit the simulator and who had heard about the new cockpit only by word of mouth reacted with so much hostility.

Since the early 1930s, before most of them were born, the most important flight instruments had been clustered right at the pilot's eye level. In the center were the two instruments that, if everything else went wrong, would permit a pilot to turn himself right side up and assure him he was not headed toward the ground. Those were the attitude director indicator and, right below it, the horizontal situation indicator. Grouped nearby were the altitude, angle of attack and air speed indicators, and the compass— all embedded in the consciousness of generations of pilots.

Adam began by discarding almost all those dials. In his method, information generated by the plane's computers is reflected on a glass screen at the top of the cockpit. This is called the Heads Up Display and of course it has an acronym—the HUD. As the pilot looks through the HUD toward the sky or the earth or the sea below, he sees symbols telling him everything he needs to know to fly his plane safely. And, because all the symbols are projected at infinity, he doesn't have to change the focus of his eyes constantly from distance to the close-up view of his instrument panel.

The F/A-18 was not the first plane to have a HUD. What was different was that, in the Hornet, the HUD became the principal flight instrument, replacing the cluster of vital dials that pilots had always relied on. As a concession to habit, Adam tucked a few of the old familiar dials down in the lower right-hand corner of the cockpit, as a kind of high-tech security blanket. He reasoned that they didn't cost much, the space they occupied was not very useful and, in the unlikely event that all electrical power failed, they would help get the pilot home. In practice, many pilots routinely use the backup instruments, cross-checking the information supplied by the HUD.

Once Adam had decided on his principal flight instrument, he then turned to the question of what kinds of displays and controls the pilot needed and where they should be placed. Among pilots, there is a running controversy over whether bombing or dogfighting is the more demanding skill. But for the cockpit designer, ground-attack poses the most difficult challenge. Adam started with the problems faced by the green pilot making his first foray into enemy territory in a bombing attack. If he could help that pilot hit his target on the first pass and get home safely, everything else would fall into place.

The first requirement was to help the pilot find his way to and from the target. Adam put the first cathode ray tube, with its television-like screen, at the bottom of the panel, between the pilot's legs. Then he arranged for five million square miles of jet pilot charts to be reproduced on a sixty-five-foot-long strip of 35-mm film that could be projected on the screen. This gave the pilot instant access to the maps that he would otherwise have to balance on his knees. The map was also cued into the plane's computers, so that symbols showing navigation check points and even the location and lethal radius of antiaircraft missiles were displayed on the map.

While he was at it, Adam also put into the system 200 color pictures that can be projected onto the screen that normally displays the map. If the pilot sees a ship, he can flip through pictures until he identifies it. If he suffers a malfunction, he can call up a diagram of the system to find the trouble. Pilots consider this a good idea, but they never use it because emergency procedures in the system are not kept up to date.

Adam then added two more screens. The one on the upper right is used primarily for radar contacts and attacks. The one on the left is used primarily for other kinds of sensors, such as infrared; for selecting weapons; and for caution signals.

Each of the screens is surrounded by twenty buttons, which can be used to manipulate the symbols on the screen. By pushing one button, the pilot can see a "menu" of the choices available. Then, by pushing additional buttons, he can, for example, see a diagram of the weapons he is carrying, designate which weapons he wants to use, and select how they are to be delivered. Except for the larger number of buttons and variety of choices, the whole thing works much like an automatic teller machine.

The three displays are identical, so if one malfunctions, the pilot can use either of the others. And the information shown on the cockpit screens can also be flashed onto the HUD so the pilot does not have to focus his eyes on the instrument panel even for a moment.

At the center of the panel is a cluster of buttons that permit the pilot to change radio frequencies—which he may do as often as thirty or forty times an hour. These are the controls that used to be deep down in the cockpit or even behind the pilot. With a little training, most pilots can hit the right button without looking. As soon as he touches a button, a symbol indicating his choice appears on the screen, so if he has made a mistake, he can correct it instantly.

In a dogfight or while diving on a target, the pilot may be pulling so many Gs that lifting a finger to the control panel is difficult, even impossible. Therefore, the controls that a pilot needs to manipulate during those kinds of stressful maneuvers are all placed on either the stick, which the pilot holds with his right hand, or on the throttles, which he holds with his left. This system also has an acronym. It is called HOTAS, which stands for Hands On Throttle And Stick.

In his left hand, he holds the throttles for the two engines. He can move them together or separately. If he wants to go into afterburner, he pushes one or both throttles full forward. Under the index finger of his left hand, there is a pressure-sensitive button that operates like the "mouse" attached to a home computer. With it, the pilot can move a pointer on his radar screen to indicate which target he wants to attack.

In his right hand, the pilot holds the control stick, which is in the conventional position between his knees. The designers of the F-16 replaced the stick with a control lever on the right side of the cockpit. But the McDonnell Douglas designers decided the pilot would be freer to swivel his head and body in a dogfight if the flight control was in the center of the cockpit. Under the pilot's right thumb on the control stick is a three-position switch that permits him to choose to use his gun or Sidewinder or Sparrow missile. If the plane is flying cross-country or attacking a surface target, and the pilot is threatened by a fighter, moving this control in any direction switches the plane from air-to-ground to air-to-air.

While the ground-attack mission provided the biggest design challenge,

HOTAS Weapon System Control

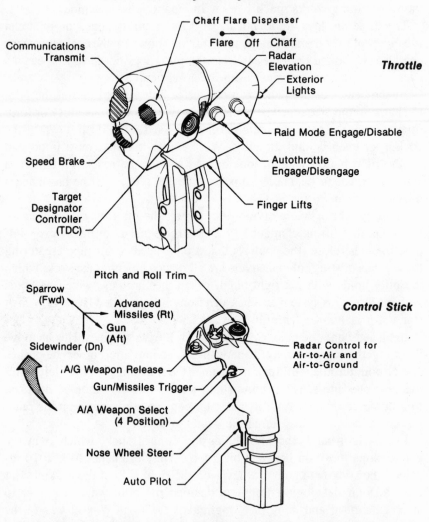

Almost all the controls a pilot must manipulate to fly and fight his Hornet are clustered together on his control stick and throttles. The system is called HOTAS, for Hands On Throttle And Stick.

Adam knew that a pilot's survival could depend on how fast he can prepare to defend himself from attack by a hostile fighter.

"If you're in navigation or air-to-ground mode, if someone jumps you, you move that switch in any direction and the whole plane reverts to air-to-air," Adam explains. "The computer says, 'This guy wants air-to-air NOW!' In less than half a second, you have it. By the time you pull your head up and start to maneuver the plane, you'll be in full air-to-air."

In the past, a pilot in a dogfight had to estimate the distance to his target and then use his gun sight to calculate how far in front of the other plane to aim so the bullets would arrive at the right moment.

In the F/A-18, the plane's radar measures the distance to the other plane, and the computers do all the calculations with much more precision than the pilot could do in his own mind. The computers even take into account the speed at which a bullet travels, how long it will take to reach the target, and how far the other plane will fly in that time. When the radar is locked on to the other plane and it is within range of the weapon, whether it be the gun or one of the missiles, a strobe light on the HUD flashes *SHOOT . . . SHOOT . . . SHOOT*. If the pilot presses the trigger on the stick, he can't miss.

As the pilot looks through his HUD, all the information he needs will be right before his eyes while he concentrates on keeping track of the other plane. This is an example of what he might see on his HUD: His target is at 28,000 feet, traveling at .6 Mach. A Sidewinder missile fired at the other plane is ten seconds from a hit. The F/A-18 is at 21,000 feet at 548 knots on a heading of fifteen degrees. The pilot has twenty-four seconds until his first opportunity to shoot at his next priority target.

In addition to the HUD and HOTAS and the other parts of the glass cockpit, the F/A-18 has one more innovative feature that Adam calls the most important development in more than forty years.

In the past, the instruments told a pilot where the nose of his plane was pointing, but it was difficult for him to calculate where he was actually going. If he attacks a target on the ground and then pulls up, for example, his nose will be pointing upward, but the force of gravity may still be pulling him earthward.

In the F/A-18, sensors in the plane feed information to a computer and it calculates where the plane is actually going, not just which direction the nose is pointed. The computer then generates a little blip of light on the HUD (called the "velocity vector"), and it shows the pilot where he is headed.

"If you are coming in for a landing and the velocity vector is off on the grass, I don't care where you think you're going, the airplane is going to hit the grass," Adam says. But it doesn't just warn when something is going wrong. It also helps the pilot fly more accurately. He adds: "It makes it so easy for the pilot to do something. He puts the velocity vector on the part of the outside world where he wants to be, and he will go there."

To veteran pilots, all these changes made the cockpit of the F/A-18 a very strange and even threatening environment. Would pilots have to learn to fly all over again?

To help in the design work, and also to help sell this whole new way of doing things to the fleet, the navy set up an Aircrew Systems Advisory Panel, made up of seven pilots representing the East and West Coast navies and both fighter and attack units. The pilots came to St. Louis two or three times a year for seven to ten days to try out the new cockpit arrangement in a simulator.

On one visit, they would concentrate, for example, on navigation problems and leave Adam with a list of suggestions for changes. On the next visit, they would use the improved navigation system on a simulated mission, concentrating this time on attacking a surface target.

"It was heartening to see pilots step out of cockpits built in the 1950s with all round dials, step into that simulator with no round dials, and consistently fly better," Adam says. When those pilots said, "this is the way to go," a great deal of the opposition to the new cockpit faded away.

Since then, the F/A-18's glass cockpit has become the standard for combat aircraft in the Western world. Similar cockpits have been installed in late models of the Air Force F-15 and F-16, the Israeli Lavi, the European Fighter Aircraft, and the Swedish Grippen. The Soviet MiG-29 Fulcrum, a plane similar to the F/A-18, has a HUD and radar display, but the rest of the instrument panel continues to be filled with the old round dials— a throwback to the technology of the 1960s.

The new cockpit would of course be impossible without the compact high-speed computers that were just becoming available when the F/A-18 was designed. In effect, the two mission computers and the sensors built into the plane to monitor its performance take the place of the eyes and ears and fingers of a second crew member.

The two Control Data Corporation mission computers weigh forty-two pounds each, and together they take up about one and a quarter cubic feet of space. Although they are physically identical, the two computers have different software. One is programmed to handle navigation and other tasks involved in flying the plane. The other is dedicated to aiming and shooting the gun, firing missiles, and dropping bombs. Each, however, has a small portion of its memory devoted to the tasks assigned to the other. If one computer goes out, the pilot will still have enough computer power left to fly and fight.

In addition to the two mission computers, there are a dozen other computers connected to sensors, and they constantly feed information into the mission computers. The air data computer, for example, measures the outside air pressure and temperature and helps calculate the plane's altitude, airspeed, and Mach number.

While much of the work of the computers is involved in gathering information and delivering it to the pilot in a useful way, the mission computers fulfill an equally important function by transmitting the pilot's instructions to the airplane.

In early planes, and for many years afterward, the pilot guided the plane by moving his control stick and rudder pedals. As he did so, cables running through the fuselage and out through the wings moved the control surfaces. By the time of World War II, that system had been refined so that the control cables activated little electrical motors or hydraulic systems that did the actual work of moving the ailerons and the tail surfaces.

With the fighter planes designed in the late 1960s and early 1970s, a new concept was introduced. Instead of cables, these planes have electrical wires. In this new "fly by wire" system, the movement of the controls by the pilot sends messages through these wires to the wings and tail.

In the F/A-18, the designers took this concept one step further. Instead of sending his instructions directly to the control surfaces, the electrical signals generated when the pilot moves his controls go to the flight control computers. The computers then decide what needs to be done. It is like having two very smart genies with a flock of helper genies responding instantly to the pilot's every wish.

The effect of this system is visible from the deck of a carrier as an F/A-18 comes in to land. The approach to a carrier is always rocky because the movement of the ship creates a burble of turbulent air in its wake. Even though the pilot of an F/A-18 is making only slight corrections with his controls, the plane is constantly adjusting itself to carry out his instructions. Adm. "Mike" Michaelis recalls the early carrier landing tests on the U.S.S. *America:*

"I went out to watch the very first landings. The first thing I noticed was how neatly the plane flew through the burble. All those controls are working. The plane is working like hell. The control surfaces do a St. Vitus's dance. It made me wish I was a kid again.''

The computers are smart enough, in fact, that they can control the takeoff and landing without help from the pilot. When an F/A-18 is launched by the catapult, it is routine for the pilot to keep his hands and feet off the controls. Everything happens so fast that it is safer to let the computers do all the work until the plane is safely airborne. The F/A-18 also has an automatic landing system that will bring the plane right down onto the deck with the pilot riding along as a passenger. When the system was demonstrated for a skeptical navy in January 1983, Hornets made sixty-three perfect landings aboard the U.S.S. *Eisenhower*. Even when the burble was most severe, the planes strayed from the correct glide path by less than a foot.

Almost everyone was nervous, when the F/A-18 was being designed, about putting so much trust in the plane's computers. Even one little error in the software might send a plane tumbling out of control. To avoid such errors, McDonnell Douglas set up an elaborate system for testing and proving all the software, including lengthy tests in which simulators ran through every possible flight maneuver to make sure that nothing went wrong. The testing was so intensive, in fact, that it consumed half of the entire time devoted to developing the software. And every time the software is changed, similar tests are run to make sure that no new bugs have found their way into the system.

Although the designers were comfortable with the reliability of their control system, the navy insisted that the plane also needed a backup mechanical control so that, if everything else failed, the pilot could at least return close to the carrier. The backup system helps pilots to feel a little more secure when they are flying out over the ocean hundreds of miles from any landing spot. But the designers are still not sure it is worth the cost. In a technical report to a meeting of avionics experts in 1984, three McDonnell Douglas engineers reported that there had been only two minor software errors detected in flight in five and a half years of flying and added:

"The F/A-18 experience shows that even the simplest backup modes impose major penalties in terms of complexity, weight and cost. . . . If we in the aircraft industry do our job properly, there should be minimal requirement for backup control system modes, which generally increase cost and complicate the flight control system design.''

With all the testing they did in the simulator, the engineers could not have foreseen the kind of severe test their computerized flight control system would receive in actual service. That test came in the skies over Florida on 10 November 1988.

Lt. Tom Chapin and a squadron mate from VFA-132 took off from Cecil Field for a bombing attack at the nearby Pine Castle range. Following close behind the other pilot, Chapin came in low, popped up to 3,000 feet, rolled over and down, dropped his bomb, and made a hard turn—a jink—to avoid antiaircraft fire.

He was less than 500 feet off the ground, going about 500 knots. He was turning hard, pulling five and a half Gs with his wings nearly perpendicular to the ground. Suddenly, the plane rolled violently to the left. ''I thought I was in somebody's jet wash,'' Chapin says. ''There was a loss of lift on one wing, as though it had gone through low pressure air. I rolled upside down for an instant. I tried to counter the roll, not knowing why it had happened.'' Chapin rolled the plane right side up and then did another jink, pulling about four Gs. But something didn't feel right. In the F/A-18, the pilot sits high up in his bubble canopy, close to the nose of the plane. To see his wings or tail, he has to swivel around as much as he can in his seat and look back over his shoulder. Chapin craned for a look back at his plane and was startled to see a gap on the left wing where a big chunk of his leading edge flap—later estimated to be twelve to fifteen inches wide and nine feet long—had torn off.

Chapin kept up his speed as he climbed to 10,000 feet—high enough to permit him to eject safely if the plane fell off into a spin. Then he gradually eased back to about 300 knots and began to worry about landing. At Cecil, the traffic controllers cleared the area and sent crash trucks out to the runway. The natural inclination when something goes wrong is to slow down. But, with so much of his wing missing, Chapin wasn't sure how the plane would handle as he cut back on air speed. He decided to come in hot, landing at 160 knots—185 miles an hour, or about sixty-five miles an hour faster than a normal landing. Despite the high speed and damage to the plane, the landing was uneventful.

When Chapin climbed down from the cockpit and examined his plane, he found that it had not only lost a big chunk of its leading edge flap, but the pieces of metal had battered the vertical and horizontal tails and the fuselage as they tore off.

What caused the damage to the plane was under investigation as this was written. But it was clear to Chapin and other members of his squadron that if he had been in any other type of plane he would have died that day at Pine Castle. They agreed that it was the plane's computers that had brought him home. When he told the computers he wanted to roll right side up, they instantly compensated for the damage to the plane and used other control surfaces to carry out his commands. And when he came in for a landing the computers got him down safely.

"The damage was similar to what you might get from AAA [Anti-Aircraft Artillery] in actual combat," Chapin says. "If you can keep the engines running, keep the airspeed on, it will fly."

Eugene Ely, a civilian pilot flying a Curtiss biplane, makes the first landing on a ship, the U.S.S. *Pennsylvania*, anchored in San Francisco Bay, on 18 January 1911. (*Smithsonian Institution.*)

Ely takes off from *Pennsylvania* and flies ashore, duplicating his first takeoff from a ship two months earlier. (*Curtiss Wright Co. photo from Smithsonian Institution.*)

Royal Flying Corps aircraft similar to the Morane-Saulnier Roland Garros fitted with a machine gun that could shoot through the propeller. (*Smithsonian Institution.*)

A plane prepares for takeoff from a sea-based aircraft carrier to rendezvous with the airborne carrier *Los Angeles*. (*U.S. Navy photo from Smithsonian Institution.*)

A biplane "lands" on a retrieval mechanism extending below the hangar bay of the airship *Los Angeles* at Lakehurst, New Jersey, in 1931. Note the metal guard extending out over the propeller. (*U.S. Navy photo from Smithsonian Institution.*)

In this painting by artist R. G. Smith, Douglas SBD Dauntless dive-bombers are shown attacking Japanese carriers at the Battle of Midway on 3 June 1942. (*McDonnell Douglas Co.*)

Hellcats preparing for takeoff jam the decks of a carrier late in World War II. (*Smithsonian Institution.*)

A Grumman F-6F-5N Hellcat of VMF-511 gets the signal for takeoff near Okinawa in May 1945. Note the radar antenna protruding from the right wing. Installed late in the war, radar permitted the Hellcat to operate as a night fighter. (*Smithsonian Institution.*)

The famed gull-winged F-4U Corsair, at first considered too hot for carrier operations, became one of the workhorses of both World War II and the Korean War. (*Sciences Services Inc. photo from Smithsonian Institution.*)

A landing signals officer, or LSO, uses colored paddles to guide a Corsair to a carrier landing. (*Smithsonian Institution.*)

Here, in the first official photo of the plane in its new role as a fighter bomber, a Corsair is shown on 11 September 1944 carrying a thousand-pound bomb. (*Chance Vought Aircraft Division of United Aircraft.*)

Photographic proof of the existence of a new Soviet bomber, the Tu-26 Backfire, sent a shock wave through the U.S. Navy's hierarchy in 1970. The four-man plane is seen here with its wings fully extended. For supersonic flight, they are swept back close to the fuselage. (*Smithsonian Institution.*)

Jack Krings, chief McDonnell Douglas test pilot, takes the new F/A-18 Hornet into the air for the first time on 11 November 1978. (*McDonnell Douglas Co.*)

The Northrop YF-17 prototype, left, and the F/A-18, right, look almost like twins. But beneath the surface similarity, the Hornet is almost entirely different— bigger, heavier, and no longer a cheap lightweight fighter. (*McDonnell Douglas Co.*)

The U.S.S. *Coral Sea* is shown here with an F/A-18 ready for takeoff. During the raid on Libya on 14 April 1986, the *Coral Sea* was ready to respond with Hornets if Libyan fighters had taken to the air. (*U.S. Navy photo.*)

Artist's rendering of L.T.V. and General Dynamics' navy F-16s flying from the U.S.S. *Enterprise*. The McDonnell Douglas-Northrop team won the competition with their F/A-18, and the F-16 never joined the fleet except for use in air combat training. (*L.T.V. Aerospace.*)

The main landing gear of the Hornet dangles awkwardly below the plane, seeming to grope for the deck, as a pilot comes in for a carrier landing. (*McDonnell Douglas Co.*)

The main landing gear of a Hornet abruptly changes its appearance as the plane settles onto a carrier deck. The gear bends at the ''knees'' and seems to crouch beneath the plane. (*McDonnell Douglas Co.*)

As one Hornet banks away to the left, it provides a clear view of the leading edge extension—the LEX—that extends forward from the wing to the area beneath the cockpit. Each plane carries two Sidewinder missiles on the wingtips and a 330-gallon external fuel tank on the centerline. (*McDonnell Douglas Co.*)

Air sweeping over the LEX moves so rapidly that it forms a visible gray fog. This vortex gives the tall vertical tails a bite on the air, but also causes buffeting so severe that it damages the tail structure. (*McDonnell Douglas Co.*)

A smoke generator mounted near the nose of this test plane operated by the National Aeronautics and Space Administration gives a clear view of the vortex aiming toward the tail like a powerful fist. (*National Aeronautics and Space Administration.*)

The navy and McDonnell Douglas rushed to get the Hornet back in the air by attaching cleats at the base of the tail to give added strength and prevent cracking of the beams that support the tails. The three strengthening cleats can be seen at the base of the left vertical tail. (*McDonnell Douglas Co.*)

These two planes of Strike-Fighter Squadron 192 have been equipped with the new "LEX fence," the small piece of metal protruding from the upper surface of the wing just behind the "USS Midway" lettering. (*U.S. Navy Photo by Lt. Comdr. T. B. Surbridge.*)

The General Electric F-404 engine has proved one of the stellar features of the F/A-18. It is designed for ease of maintenance and can be removed and replaced in a few minutes. (*General Electric Co.*)

The new "glass cockpit" pioneered in the F/A-18. The pilot's principal flight instrument is the Heads-Up Display—the HUD—that projects information on a transparent screen at the top of the cockpit. Three television-like screens help him control his radar, keep track of his location and monitor the performance of his plane. Note the round dials in the lower right corner—the only vestige of the traditional cockpit design. (*McDonnell Douglas Co.*)

Canada was the first foreign country to obtain the F/A-18. Note the distinctive outline of a cockpit painted on the bottom of the plane by the Canadian air force to confuse hostile pilots during aerial combat. (*McDonnell Douglas Co.*)

The Hornet carries a formidable array of air-to-air and air-to-ground weapons. Each of these planes carries Sidewinder heat-seeking missiles on its wingtips, a Harpoon antishipping missile under the right wing, a Harm antiradar missile under the left wing, two Sparrow radar-guided missiles on each side of the fuselage, and a 20-mm cannon in the nose. (*McDonnell Douglas Co.*)

Carrier pilots vie with each other for the chance to intercept potentially hostile planes. Here, a Hornet pulls up alongside a long-range Soviet Bear reconnaissance plane. (*U.S. Navy Photo.*)

CHAPTER FIVE

"Excess Energy" to Fly and Fight

Development of a new jet engine can take a decade or more, longer by far than the airplane itself or most of the other components of which it is made. By its very nature, the jet engine business forces otherwise staid, conservative businessmen to become high-rolling gamblers.

The first F/A-18 didn't fly until November 1978, but General Electric began spending money on the engines that took it into the air at least thirteen years earlier, in the mid-1960s—when hardly anyone in the navy was giving much thought to the need for a new plane, and certainly before anyone knew what such a plane might look like.

Predicting the time when a new plane will be needed does not take much skill—just looking at the calendar. Combat planes have a first-line lifetime of thirteen to fifteen years. They may continue in service for many years beyond that time but not at the cutting edge of technology and combat power. As the General Electric executives looked at the calendar, it was obvious that the F-4 Phantom, powered by GE engines, would have to be replaced sometime in the latter half of the 1970s, or certainly in the early 1980s. If GE was to stay in the fighter plane engine business, it would have to gamble a good deal of money in its effort to have the right engine ready to go at the right time.

William ("Bill") Rodenbaugh, the unofficial historian of the GE engine plant in Lynn, Massachusetts, describes the dilemma this way: "If you don't get ahead of the power curve, by the time you wake up to the fact there is a competition for a new engine, you're going to lose. You have to anticipate the systems. You have to know what they want. You have to know what the technology's going to be. You have to know how to translate that into a piece of equipment, and you have to go out and sell the bejesus out of it. You do all of that stuff before it ever happens."

General Electric had learned that lesson the hard way. The company had gained a huge head start in the jet engine business when it was asked, in 1941, to build America's first jet engine in its turbine factory at Lynn. It then went on to provide engines for the P-80 Shooting Star, the B-47 bomber, the F-86 Sabre jet, the B-58 bomber, the F-104 Starfighter, and the F-4 Phantom. But, despite its dominance of the market for military jet engines, GE didn't have a winning engine available in the late 1950s, when the airlines switched from propeller-driven planes to jets. For a full decade, the company was entirely out of the commercial-aircraft engine market and did not fight its way back in until the late 1960s.

It was with that unhappy experience in mind that GE began in the mid-1960s to position itself to capture its share—or, preferably, more than its share—of the future market for military jet engines. This was not a matter of trying to design a specific engine to be ready at a specific time in the early 1970s. In this business, the future is too unpredictable for that. Instead, GE tries to keep a family of about fifteen engines in various stages of development and production and to keep pushing technology so that the company will be ready no matter what happens.

The lineage of the F-404 engine eventually chosen to power the F/A-18 can be clearly identified in engines under development in the mid-1960s, and its ancestry can be traced clear back to the first jet engine more than two decades earlier. If the line is followed forward, it is obvious that the F/A-18's engine is a sibling of GE power plants in the B-1 bomber, the F-16, the F-14, the F-117 stealth fighter, and the B-2 stealth bomber—and a cousin of engines in commercial aircraft, helicopters, ships, and electric generators.

As the people at Lynn looked toward the future and tried to adapt one of their big "family" of engines to use in a new fighter plane, one need was increasingly obvious. The fighter planes then in use by the U.S. military were too big and relatively underpowered. They were, as Rodenbaugh puts it, "refined trucks . . . that couldn't get out of their own way."

The air force, for example, was using the F-4 Phantom, originally developed by the navy as an air superiority fighter, as both a fighter and bomber. Designed to be a nimble dogfighter at 35,000 pounds, the Phantom was being sent into combat at 54,000 pounds, carrying a bigger bomb load than a World War II B-17 bomber.

The conventional wisdom was that America's fighters did not have to be nimble if their radar could pick up an enemy before he came in sight of the human eye, and if they carried a missile that could hit the other guy before he even knew he had been spotted. The trick, it was argued, was to put the agility in a small, powerful missile, so you wouldn't have to put it in the big, relatively awkward, airplane. This was the same thinking that sent the early Phantoms into combat without a gun.

By the mid-1960s, a small group of air force officers and civilians, working out of an office in the basement of the Pentagon, were preaching a new doctrine. They were the evangelists of the lightweight, "wrap around" fighter concept that was to capture the fancy of important members of Congress a few years later. They argued that there would unavoidably be many times when pilots would find themselves in close-in dogfights where the ability of the plane would make the crucial difference. In those situations, they argued, the thing that counted was "excess energy"— the power to climb faster and turn sharper than the enemy or, if need be, to bug out and go home.

They quietly conducted some tests in which first-line fighters were put up against the F-5, the little Northrop fighter being sold to America's allies who wanted something smaller and cheaper than the big planes in the U.S. inventory. In the tests, the little F-5 blew the big brutes out of the sky. The proponents of the new doctrine were quick to note that the features that made the F-5 a winner—its small size and its agility—were exactly the features of the MiG fighters in service in the Soviet Union and in the air forces of many of its allies.

The test results were confirmed when the big American fighters, despite all their advanced technology, barely held their own against the little North Vietnamese MiGs in the early days of the war in Vietnam.

As word of this new thinking filtered back to Lynn, it was obvious that the engines for the new generation of fighters would have to be designed to provide that "excess energy" needed to win a dogfight. Working with Northrop, GE began trying to build that kind of performance into the engines for the Cobra.

The first chance GE had to design and sell an engine based on the demands of the new doctrine came in 1969, when the air force staged a competition for the engine for its F-15. The F-15 was by no means a lightweight fighter. But, as far as the engine makers were concerned, the demand was the same. The F-15 was to be so powerful that it would be able to accelerate straight up, and it would have enough "excess energy" to make it a winner in a dogfight.

In the competition for the F-15's engine, GE came head-to-head with

Pratt & Whitney, then threatening to move into a commanding position in the military jet engine business—and lost. Was this to be a repeat of the experience of the 1950s, when GE had been driven out of the commercial jet business?

That might have been the case if the air force had not come along with its lightweight fighter competition, pitting the General Dynamics YF-16 against the Northrop YF-17. For GE, it was a new lease on life, but there was no question it would be an uphill fight. The YF-16 would be powered by the same Pratt & Whitney engine the air force had chosen for the F-15. It was in production and flying and had had thousands of hours of tests. GE, on the other hand, had little more than a paper engine and only three years to refine the design, produce five prototypes, and conduct about a thousand hours of tests—only a third of the test time normally devoted to a new engine.

GE set up a small, very competent team of engineers—what is known in the aircraft business as a "skunk works"—that operated seven days a week, around the clock. The air force let them alone, doing without the layers of reports and reviews that encumber most development projects. Work moved very rapidly.

When the YF-17 took to the air, pilots were dazzled by the performance of its new GE engines. Glowing reports on the engines continued to pour in as the YF-17 was put through its paces in competition with the YF-16. They continued to pour in right up to the point where the air force chose the YF-16, with its Pratt & Whitney engine, as its new lightweight fighter.

GE had had two chances to break Pratt & Whitney's growing dominance of the fighter plane business and had lost both times.

Life seldom offers a second chance, practically never a third. In this case, GE got that third chance when the navy chose to develop the YF-17 as a strike-fighter.

This was a great opportunity but, in many ways, a daunting challenge. To understand that challenge, it helps to understand how a jet engine works.

As Bill Rodenbaugh likes to explain to visitors, a jet engine is nothing more than a device that takes cold air and turns it into hot air.

But what a device!

In one-thirtieth of a second, the air entering the engine of an F/A-18 is raised from fifty degrees Fahrenheit to 2,500 degrees—hot enough to melt the metal of which the engine is made, if it weren't for a thin layer of cooler air blowing across the metal.

In one-fiftieth of a second, the air is squeezed from the normal at-mospheric pressure of 14.7 pounds per square inch to 370 pounds, enough pressure to rupture any boiler made by man.

The engine's turbine, spinning at nearly 300 revolutions each second, sucks energy out of the hot air. Each of the sixty-four two-inch-long blades ringing the turbine produces horsepower equal to that delivered by the engine in a large truck.

A moment after the air begins its wild ride, it whistles through a nozzle at the back of the engine at 1,650 miles an hour. It has given up energy and more than a thousand degrees of temperature, but it is still a sizzling 1,400 degrees.

The difference in the pressure at the front of the engine and that at the rear—a distance of only a little over thirteen feet—is what sends a fighter plane streaking through the air.

When a mechanic removes the engine from an F/A-18 and takes it apart, this is what he sees:

At the very front is a large fan, taking up most of the thirty-nine-inch diameter of the engine. If it were not encased in the engine housing, it would look much like the propeller of a conventional engine, although with more blades. The fan divides the air into two streams. One stream flows between the outer casing and the engine itself. The larger stream is squeezed slightly and goes into a compressor where the big squeeze takes place.

From the compressor, the air goes into a combustion chamber—a round tube like a big oil drum. Fuel is injected into the compressed air and burned, raising its temperature.

The hot, dense air then goes through two turbines, causing them to spin. A shaft connected to the first turbine turns the compressor. The second turbine turns the fan up front.

The air, having given up some of its energy, spews out through a nozzle at the back of the engine. On the F/A-18 and other jet fighters, there is one more big chamber at the back end called the afterburner. When the pilot kicks in his afterburner, more fuel is injected into the hot air coming from the engine, and it is burned once more, increasing the speed of the air from 1,650 to 2,600 miles an hour. Pilots use the afterburner sparingly because it burns prodigious amounts of fuel and is grossly inefficient. But it gives a sudden jolt of speed that could be the difference between life and death.

When the designers were working on the engine for the lightweight fighter competition, the problem was fairly straightforward: to provide the plane with as much "excess energy" as possible so it would be a superior dogfighter. They thought first of making the engine without a fan up front. That would be a turbojet. They finally settled on a turbofan engine, but with a fan so small that, while it provided some thrust by pushing a small amount of air around the engine, it sent most of the air through the compressor and turbines. So little air went around the engine, in fact, that some called the engine a "leaky turbojet."

This was a deliberate compromise between fuel efficiency and excess energy. The more air that is forced through the engine, the less efficient it is at subsonic speeds. The ratio of the percentage of air that goes around the engine compared to the amount that goes through it is called the "by-pass ratio." In a commercial transport engine, where the goal is fuel economy, most of the air bypasses the engine, and the bypass ratio is about six—six parts of air going around the engine to every one that goes through. In the B-1 bomber, which may need sudden bursts of power on takeoff and in the target area, but also needs to fly long distances, the bypass ratio is two. In the YF-17, the bypass ratio was about .25: almost all the air was forced through the compressor and turbines.

But that wouldn't do for a strike-fighter, which not only needed high performance but also required relatively long range. A compromise was reached in which the size of the fan on the original engine was increased, raising the bypass ratio to about .4. In the process, the thrust—or power—of the engine was increased by thirteen percent.

Finding just the right balance between the magic excess energy and the fuel economy needed to reach distant targets was a daunting challenge, but it was not the only one. The navy told GE it wanted something quite different in this engine than it had ever demanded before.

The navy had traditionally ranked the characteristics of an engine in this order of importance: (1) performance; (2) weight; (3) cost; (4) reliability and maintainability; and (5) operability.

In this case, the navy turned the requirements upside down and put them in this order: (1) operability; (2) reliability and maintainability; (3) cost; (4) performance; and (5) weight.

In one sense, this was a psychological trick played on the engineers. As Corky Lenox, who was then program manager, put it: "If you ride herd on the designer for cost and reliability, you don't have to worry about performance. That's in his blood."

As Lenox and Will Willoughby analyzed the situation, the navy's past emphasis on performance had often been a costly mistake. The result of pushing too hard for performance had been high costs, weight growth, poor reliability and, too often, poor performance.

Willoughby noticed this problem in connection with jet engines almost as soon as he arrived at his new job with the navy.

"When I looked at aircraft on carriers, I immediately came to the conclusion the engines were over-stressed," Willoughby says. "What tears an engine up is stress. Stress is moving the throttle back and forth, like bending a coat hanger."

Willoughby tried to convince the navy to put a plug or stop on the throttles of the planes in the fleet to keep the pilots from going to the very edges of the engine's limits. He calculated that would double, perhaps even triple, the lifetime of the engines. But the fliers in the fleet wouldn't listen to such a restriction on performance.

Willoughby focused on making the next engine so the pilot would not be able to press the engine to its limits. This meant looking at the way the engine would be used in the fleet, and then designing it so it would provide the desired performance without being over-stressed. But when Willoughby took a good look at the "throttle profiles"—the statistics that supposedly told how the pilots manipulated their throttles—he found they bore little relationship to what actually took place in the air.

"The throttle profiles were all fouled up," Willoughby says. "Holy cow, what a screw up!"

When realistic tests were run, it was found that a pilot in a dogfight works his throttle back and forth faster and much more often than anyone had imagined.

"The first time I saw one of those throttle plots it blew my mind," recalls Frank E. Pickering, general manager of the GE aircraft engine engineering division, who was involved in the early development of the F/A-18's engine.

General Electric later used these realistic profiles to test its new engine. To their surprise, they found the throttle movements were so fast and frequent that a human operator couldn't duplicate them. They had to program a computer to mimic the throttle movements of a pilot in combat.

Designing an engine so the pilot could move his throttle freely without putting undo stress on the engine and causing it to require many hours of maintenance for each hour in the air was one part of the goal labeled "operability." But the engine also had to be designed so it would operate flawlessly no matter what the pilot did with the plane.

To understand the problem faced by the designers, imagine the wildly distorted air flowing into the engine in the thirty to sixty seconds that a dogfight might last. The pilot would certainly turn his afterburners on and off several times; bank as tightly as possible, one way and then the other, pulling seven and a half Gs; fly straight down and straight up; fly supersonic at one moment and then fly less than a hundred miles an hour with his nose pointing skyward. Finally, he might well want to kick in his afterburners, accelerate as rapidly as possible and head for home, probably trying to outrun a missile as he goes. For all this he needs an engine that will go from idle to full power in three seconds.

If the air coming into the engine becomes too turbulent, a number of things may happen—all of them unpleasant from the pilot's point of view. His compressor may stall, interrupting the flow of high-pressure air to the combustor and turbines. The engine stops. Or the afterburner may belch, sending a sheet of flame into the rear of the engine, again causing it to stall. Air bypassing the engine may become so turbulent that the engine loses power or a fan blade breaks, destroying the engine.

Such problems were not uncommon. In fact they were a way of life in every combat aircraft. Pilots were warned that, if they performed certain maneuvers, they would suffer an engine failure. Such failures are so common and so predictable that one of the tactics used by a skilled pilot in a dogfight is to force his adversary into maneuvers that will cause an engine stall or loss of power.

George Rapp, who has since retired but was involved in the development of the F-404 from the time it was just a paper engine until it powered the navy's new strike-fighter, knew from the beginning that GE's new engine would have to be designed to avoid the stalls and failures common to other jet engines. One of the reasons GE lost to Pratt & Whitney in the competition for the engine for the F-15, he believes, is that they were unable to convince the air force they had done as good a job as they had in designing a fool-proof engine. As it turned out, the Pratt & Whitney engine chosen by the air force was plagued for years by the problem of compressor stalls.

Even before the navy made operability its number one priority, GE had put a small team of some of its best engineers to work on that very problem. Other designers had focused their efforts on the inlet through which air comes into the engine, hoping to avoid turbulence that way. The GE engineers did their best on the inlet design, but they concentrated most of their attention on the design of the fan, the first moving part the air encounters as it enters the engine. They succeeded in designing a fan that, in a fraction of a second, smooths out the air before it goes into the compressor.

"The fan takes junk in and attenuates it before it goes into the high-pressure compressor," Rapp says. This made the F-404 the first fighter plane engine in which there are no restrictions on how the pilot flies the plane or moves his throttle. "Under the worst conditions, if the pilot makes the worst possible throttle movements, the engine will not stall."

Well before the navy came along with its new priorities in engine design, General Electric had begun to concentrate, on its own, on two of the things that turned out to be among the most important to the navy: reliability and maintainability, plus cost.

"GE was the first company to really adopt internally the commitment to do the right kind of job in the design," Lenox says. "Northrop was next, then McDonnell Douglas. Hughes finally came around under pressure from the navy and McDonnell."

In his evangelizing tours of the plants that built planes and their components for the navy, Will Willoughby was at first met by stiff opposition. To build in reliability, they argued, would cost far too much. But he won over many in the industry by convincing them that a well-designed airplane, engine, or radar would mean greater efficiency—and thus greater profits—for the companies involved.

General Electric was, on its own, one of the first to recognize the value of worrying, early in the design phase, about the cost of building and maintaining an engine. Although this seems a commonsense approach, it runs contrary to the natural inclinations of most engineers. One McDonnell Douglas manager summed up the problem this way: "From years of training, all engineers possess inordinate amounts of 'technical greed,' the desire to do a perfect job, to wring the last bit of performance out of a design whether or not it is required or cost effective." Officials at General Electric also noted that engineers like to start from scratch and create their own new design when, from a business sense, it is much better to adapt a design already in production to new uses.

Frederick A. Larson, who was put in charge of the cost-cutting effort in the early 1970s, had to counter both these natural tendencies of engineers. Larson and his boss, Paul Setts, the general manager for combat aircraft, set two goals: The new engine would be much smaller than the engines then being made for the F-4 Phantom, but provide at least as much thrust. And two engines would cost about the same as the air force was spending for one engine for the F-16.

Once the general structure of the engine had been determined, the drawings were turned over to the company's design organizations. One group of engineers worked on the turbine, another on the compressor, a third on the overall structure of the engine, a fourth on lubrication systems, and so on for each part of the engine. Their drawings were then turned over to manufacturing engineers who thought through the problems of producing each component.

A value engineer or an advanced manufacturing engineer would determine, for example, how long it would take to drill each hole and calculate the cost. This forced the designers to consider whether they could reduce the number of bolts in a major component such as the compressor if the bolts were made slightly larger.

In some cases, the designers even let the weight creep upward—something they instinctively fight against—because they could save money by eliminating some of the expensive machining required to cut away excess metal.

Through this whole process, the designers faced the challenge to reduce the cost of each component of the engine by fifteen percent. If they fell short, they had to give their reasons in writing, including a list of the alternatives they had considered.

One result of this meticulous attention to detail in the early design of the engine can be seen by comparing it to the J-79 engine, which was developed by GE in the 1950s to power the F-4 Phantom. The J-79, a highly successful engine, was the yardstick against which GE measured its design for the F-404. The new engine is a little over thirteen feet long, slightly less than three feet in diameter, weighs 2,180 pounds, and produces 16,000 pounds of thrust. The older engine produces about the same power, but it is four feet longer and five inches wider in diameter, weighs 1,165 pounds more, and has half again as many parts.

When the engine moved from development into production, GE had none of the kinds of problems that Hughes faced when it began to produce its new radar. The design-to-cost effort had forced the GE engineers to think ahead to the question of how to produce the engine most efficiently.

The early emphasis on holding down costs also had a spin-off in greater ease of maintenance when the engine reached the fleet. In the past, many of the bolts in an aircraft engine were wired in place to prevent them from vibrating loose and causing damage inside the engine. Wiring all the bolts ran up the cost of production, and it was a constant nuisance and frustration for maintenance mechanics. Every time they repaired an engine, they had to remove the wires and then, when they were finished, put new wires back in place. Bloody fingers were a normal hazard of the trade. In the F-404 engine, the wires have been eliminated from all of the bolts mechanics normally have to remove. Each bolt is locked in place and held there—even if it should happen to vibrate loose—by a little pin.

The maintenance men were also kept in mind in other aspects of the engine's design. The directions for maintenance of engines in some earlier planes read like a bad joke. The first step involved in replacing the engine in an A-4 Skyhawk, for example, is to remove the plane's tail. The engine in the F/A-18 is attached at only three points. One engine can be lowered through a hatch on the bottom of the fuselage and another inserted in a matter of minutes. The navy set two goals: it wanted to be able to change the engine "within the shadow of the airplane," and it wanted to change an engine in twenty-one minutes. Mechanics have been able to do it in less than seventeen minutes.

In previous engines, many of the controls were built into the plane. This meant that mechanics had to spend hours tuning a new engine. On the F-404 engine, the controls come with the engine, so no tuning is required. Once the engine is installed and checked for leaks, it is ready to fly.

Unlike earlier jet engines, the F-404 is not routinely taken out of service for an overhaul after a certain number of hours in use. The designers decided this was wasteful because the wear on an engine can vary dramatically depending on how it is used. The engines in a plane used routinely for aerial combat take much more of a beating than those in a plane that spends much of its time in straight and level cross-country flight. For example, at Lemoore Naval Air Station in California's Central Valley, pilots fly across the Sierra Nevada mountains to ranges in Nevada or Arizona for most of their training. But pilots at Fallon, Nevada, or Canadian fliers at Cold Lake reach their bombing and air combat ranges soon after takeoff. Instead of being packed off for a scheduled overhaul, each F-404 engine is individually monitored and pulled out for maintenance only when work is needed.

The life of the engine is monitored in two ways. Each engine has thirteen borescope ports through which mechanics can peek inside to see if there is any sign of damage. It also has an automatic system that constantly monitors the condition of the engine. If something serious happens, a voice in the pilot's earphones intones: "Engine left" or "Engine right." He immediately cuts power to that engine. Earlier warning systems told the pilot when something was wrong with an engine—but left him to figure out which engine was acting up.

Information about performance of the engine—and many other parts of the plane—is also recorded automatically on a device in the nose wheel bay. A quick look tells the mechanic where to search for signs of trouble. The system also keeps a record of the performance of the engine over its lifetime.

The engine monitoring system uses thirteen sensors that check temperatures, air velocity, and vibration and speed of the moving parts. All but one of the sensors is needed to help control the engine, so the system adds little to the weight or cost of the plane. The measurements from inside the engine are flashed to the mission computer ten times each second and compared with numbers for normal performance in the computer's memory.

The system has one feature that seems almost magical. Whenever anything goes wrong, a record is preserved showing the engine's performance, beginning five seconds before the malfunction and continuing thirty-five seconds afterward. This makes it possible to turn the clock back and, in effect, watch the problem occur. This feat of legerdemain is accomplished by having the computer constantly erase data from the sensors—but waiting forty seconds before beginning to erase. If anything goes wrong, the tape is not erased, so it preserves the record of the engine's operations just before and after the malfunction.

The value of the engine monitoring system was demonstrated early in the flight tests of the F/A-18 when an engine destroyed itself in flight. Normally, it might take months or even years of tests to try to duplicate such a failure, determine what had gone wrong, and find a way to fix it. In this case, the system quickly pinpointed a tiny sensor about the size of a person's index finger as the source of the trouble. The sensor, consisting of a platinum wire in a metal case, is attached at the front of the engine. As the temperature of the air coming into the engine changes, the electrical resistance of the platinum wire changes. This tells the engine the temperature of the air, so it can adjust the speed of the fan and the angle of the vanes that both guide the air into the engine and control the tail pipe temperature. All of this is critical to the proper running of the engine.

Tests showed that the platinum wire had come in contact with the metal casing and shorted out. This sent a signal to the engine that it was receiving air that was very, very cold. As the engine adjusted to this false information, it ran out of control, came apart and destroyed itself. With the clues provided by the monitoring system, it was possible to understand the problem, work out a modification of the faulty device, and install new sensors in the fleet, all within six months.

The investigation of the engine failure was aided immeasurably, of course, by the fact that the other engine continued to operate, and the pilot was therefore able to bring the plane back to be examined. In a plane with only one engine, such a failure would have forced the investigators to begin their work with a pile of scrap metal.

In the course of their investigation, the engineers found that a similar failure had occurred once before. In that case, the pilot recalled hearing a "pop," but the engine continued to operate and he completed his mission. Later, when mechanics looked inside the engine with a borescope, they found that a turbine blade had broken loose and careened through the rear of the engine without causing further harm.

This was one of the early bits of evidence demonstrating that the F-404 is often capable of shrugging off damage that would destroy another engine. Mechanics report a number of occasions when engines continued to operate even after suffering major damage.

Master Chief Don Leap, a mechanic with VFA-125, the training squadron at Lemoore, speaks with awe of the damaged engines he has seen: "They'll eat damn near anything and keep running. On one plane, the motor ate a forty-pound piece of copper and kept running with a hole in the side. One ate a landing gear pin. You find a pilot flying with a motor that's all torn up, and not know about it."

In these cases, the monitoring system may not even alert the pilot because the temperatures, rotation speeds, and vibrations it checks ten times every second all remain within normal limits, despite severe damage. The ability of the engine to keep operating, despite these peacetime accidents, is an encouraging sign that the plane would be able to withstand severe battle damage and continue to fly.

Throughout the development of the F/A-18 and its F-404 engine, both McDonnell Douglas and General Electric often found themselves in an awkward political position.

McDonnell Douglas had a vital business interest in sales of the F/A-18, not only to the U.S. Navy, but to other countries as well. But it also had a very special relationship with the U.S. Air Force. It produced the F-15 Eagle for the air force, and it was important to maintain cordial relations with this major customer. On the other hand, McDonnell Douglas, as manufacturer of the F/A-18, produced the chief rival to the air force F-16 fighter in international sales. While the companies involved with the F/A-18 pooled their resources and met for strategy sessions to coordinate their lobbying on Capitol Hill, Lenox and other navy officers noted that McDonnell Douglas was more reticent than the others—especially if there was a danger of stepping on air force toes.

McDonnell Douglas also had a complex relationship with the nation's two major jet engine makers. It dealt with Pratt & Whitney for engines for its F-15 and with GE for F/A-18 engines. The aircraft manufacturer had to be careful not to openly favor either of the two engine makers. But there is no question that the McDonnell Douglas engineers and managers were at that time much more comfortable in their dealings with GE than they were with Pratt & Whitney. As one McDonnell Douglas official put it:

"Pratt & Whitney was 'king of the hill.' It was not responsive to problems. The Pratt & Whitney practice was to confuse the situation until the problem was so severe that the government put a lot of money into solving it. GE was second to Pratt & Whitney, and their management knew they had to be better to be number one. They worked the engineering on the F-404 very hard. They worked their problems, and they solved their problems. When you worked with the GE guys, you planned on working late. When you worked with the PW guys, when it came time to go home, they went home."

The problem, it seemed to the people at McDonnell Douglas, was that Pratt & Whitney, in those days, was part of a conglomerate run by lawyers and accountants, while GE was run by its engineers.

Pratt & Whitney suffered two stunning reversals. In one case, Japan Airlines, a longtime customer, dropped Pratt and Whitney and switched to GE engines. In the other instance, the air force awarded GE a contract to provide a new engine, based on the design of the engine in the F/A-18, for use in its F-16 and F-15 fighters. It was not until these incidents that Pratt & Whitney brought a new emphasis on quality production and service to its customers. "Pratt & Whitney has come a long way since then," a McDonnell Douglas official says.

For General Electric, the fact that its engines were used in a variety of planes, some of which were direct rivals, caused some awkward moments.

"We consciously and religiously do not favor one aircraft company over another," says Burton A. Riemer, who was general manager for the engine chosen to power the F/A-18. "Our job is to sell engines. If we're not in an airplane, we don't sell engines."

The company's policy of not favoring one company over another was put to the test in the late 1970s when Grumman officials, who were continuing to lead the opposition to the F/A-18, came up with a novel idea. They quietly enlisted GE's cooperation in designing a new model of the A-7 attack plane made by LTV—the big loser in the earlier competition for the new navy strike-fighter. Instead of a single engine, the new A-7 would be powered by two of the new engines GE designed for the F/A-18.

The beauty of this plan was that it would allow for the death of the F/A-18 but still provide for continued production of the new jet engines at Lynn. And this, Grumman hoped, would deprive the F/A-18 of two of its most powerful backers on Capitol Hill: House Speaker Thomas ("Tip") O'Neill, Jr., whose district was next door to that in which the Lynn plant is located, and Senator Edward Kennedy, the Massachusetts Democrat. The assumption was that the two legislators cared more about engines—and jobs—than they did about the F/A-18.

A top Grumman official hand-carried the proposal to the Pentagon to the office of Russell Murray II, a key aide to Defense Secretary Harold Brown. Murray, who began as a strong critic of the F/A-18 program but later became one of its most influential supporters, says: "It was a most wonderfully ingenious proposal. It was pure political engineering. I've never seen one as ingenious as that."

The twin-engined A-7 didn't fly, either politically or in the air. But LTV and, even more, Grumman, continued nipping at the F/A-18 at every opportunity. At one point, Grumman hired a public relations firm to visit news offices to spread bad news about the F/A-18. Both Lenox and his boss, Forrest Petersen, felt compelled on several occasions to call officials of the two companies and tell them to lay off.

Petersen considered the opposition to the plane unjustified and wrong. He told company officials in scathing language that it was not their responsibility to their stockholders to criticize a major navy program that was approved and underway; they should not try to sell their product by killing someone else's product. The open sniping stopped, but Petersen was never convinced the behind-the-scenes attack had ended.

Despite its aid in helping design the twin-engined A-7, GE was never caught up in this controversy. One reason is that the company strongly supported the F/A-18, reminding members of Congress from districts where GE plants were located of the importance of this program to the company.

The F/A-18, powered by GE engines, made its first flight on 18 November 1978, and, by the fall of 1980, all reports from the test site at Patuxent River Naval Air Station indicated that GE had a real winner on its hands. The test pilots were most impressed by the fact that there were no restrictions on their use of the engine, no matter what kind of maneuver they attempted.

The afterburner lighted instantly, and it did so without the puff of smoke that signals a plane's presence or tells a hostile pilot the afterburner has been ignited. When the Blue Angels adopted the F/A-18 for their spectacular demonstration flights, they were especially impressed with the performance of the afterburner. In one maneuver, five planes dive in front of the audience in very tight formation, then ignite their afterburners and accelerate straight up. One plane could veer into another if all ten afterburners don't light at exactly the same moment; but they always do.

In two respects, the engine fell slightly short of the goals set by the navy: It burns a little more fuel while cruising than the navy would have liked, and it is a little slower accelerating than specified. In both cases, it would have been possible to bring the engine up to the mark. But improving the fuel consumption would have involved tampering with the air inlets to the engine, increasing the likelihood of an engine stall. And acceleration could have been improved by making the engine operate at a higher temperature. In tests, the plane accelerated from .8 Mach to 1.6 Mach in 143 seconds, rather than the 110 seconds set as a goal. But "turning up the wick" on the engine would have made it less reliable and reduced its service life. In both cases the navy decided the cure was worse than the problem.

The F/A-18 was also knowingly made slightly slower in its top speed than planes such as the F-4 Phantom, built a generation before. The Hornet can fly almost twice the speed of sound. To push its speed up above that mark to match the top speed of the Phantom and the F-14 Tomcat would have required a more complex variable inlet on the engine. Again, it was decided to stick with the simpler fixed inlet and forgo the additional speed.

By the time the F/A-18 was far enough along in its tests for everyone to begin to feel comfortable about the engine, Burt Riemer had been living in a pressure cooker for eight years and felt he had earned a vacation. He chose a bed-and-breakfast hostelry in the peaceful countryside in England's Cotswold district. No television. Nothing louder than the songs of the meadowlarks and the baaing of the sheep. He didn't even read the newspapers.

Then one morning at breakfast, another guest casually mentioned the crash of some new type of military aircraft with two engines. With a sudden knot in the pit of his stomach, Riemer called Lynn to learn that the F/A-18 dedicated to testing of the engine had crashed a couple of days earlier, on 8 September 1980, only a few miles from where he was staying. Thus began the most frustrating, traumatic few days of his life. The folks back in Lynn said there was no sense going to the crash site and no sense hurrying home because there was nothing to be done until parts of the engines had been recovered. Riemer stayed in the Cotswolds for a few more days and worried.

The crash occurred shortly after Jack Krings, chief McDonnell Douglas test pilot and the first man to fly the F/A-18, and marine Lt. Gary Post had taken off to fly to Spain after demonstrating the plane for the first time to an international audience at the Farnborough Air Show.

Suddenly, there was a loud explosion, followed by a rapid rise in temperature in the right engine. Krings pushed the other engine to full power and headed for the nearby Royal Air Force Test Center at Boscombe Down. But both the flight controls and the controls for the left engine had apparently been damaged in the explosion. He fought the controls for about five minutes and was within five or six miles of his goal when the plane began bucking like a bronco. With the plane down to 4,000 feet, Krings and Post ejected while flying at about 400 knots. Krings suffered a broken shoulder and sprained neck. Post broke his leg.

As soon as Krings reported in, it was obvious that the loss of the plane had been caused by engine failure and that GE had a very serious problem on its hands. The first job was to find the offending part. The company offered rewards and spent thousands of dollars hiring Boy and Girl Scout troops and church groups to scour the landscape. They found two-thirds of the turbine disk that had failed—but not the portion that had come apart and caused the crash. Riemer assumes that, someday, a farmer will hear a "clunk" as his plow hits a piece of metal and will come up with the missing piece. But that will be years too late.

Using deductive reasoning, the GE engineers decided that the failure was the result of a new manufacturing process in which a metal alloy is reduced to a fine powder and then pressed together to form the turbine wheel. They immediately switched back to a type of material that had been used earlier. And since then, an improved material has been developed.

Even though the plane lost in England was the one dedicated to engine testing, the crash and subsequent effort to find the cause and make sure it didn't happen again caused only a relatively small disruption of the F/A-18 test program. Riemer, looking back on the incident, called it a "burble that we got over quickly." Everyone at GE was pleased that, if they had to have a problem, it occurred when only a few engines had been delivered, rather than later with hundreds or thousands of engines in service. That would cause far more than a mere "burble."

The early engine failure did, however, serve to introduce a new and very important player to the drama of the F/A-18. Two months after the Cotswolds crash, Ronald Reagan became president; and early in 1981 a forceful young man named John F. Lehman, Jr., managed, by pulling as many strings as he could find, to have himself named secretary of the navy when he was only thirty-eight years old.

Lehman, who had served as an aide to Henry Kissinger when he was President Nixon's national security adviser, was firmly anchored in the conservative wing of the Republican party. He also held a naval reserve commission as a bombardier navigator in an A-6 and had served five brief tours of duty in Vietnam, including one mission over the north, while working at the White House. Although he had inherited a love of the sea from his father, who commanded an amphibious assault ship in the Pacific in World War II, Lehman loved airplanes even more than ships.

Lehman was a supremely self-assured and ambitious man, and he had ambitious plans for a major buildup of American naval strength. While Reagan's new secretaries of the army and air force were quietly learning how to find the men's rooms, Lehman quickly set out to create a 600-ship navy, reinvigorate the navy as a fighting force, and reform the way it procured weapons. To do this, he needed both to establish his credibility on Capitol Hill as manager of an often unwieldy bureaucracy and to let the major defense contractors with whom the navy dealt know who was boss. The loss of the plane following the Farnborough show was just the opportunity he needed.

Almost as soon as he settled into his office on the Pentagon's fourth floor, he sent word to McDonnell Douglas that, since the plane was on loan to the company for the airshow, he expected McDonnell Douglas to provide the navy with a new plane—free.

For company officials, this was a rude shock. To provide a replacement for the lost plane this early in the production run would cost an estimated $38 million dollars. When the officials objected to paying for the plane,

Lehman accused them, in a speech, of trying to "rip off" the navy. Their lawyers told them they could make a good case that the navy should bear the cost, even though McDonnell Douglas had borrowed the plane to show it off at Farnborough, because there was a military pilot aboard.

Harvey Wilcox, who was general counsel for NAVAIR, agreed that the company had a strong argument and might win if the issue went to court. But in this, Lehman's first showdown with a major contractor, it was McDonnell Douglas that blinked. J. C. Waldner, who was then general manager of the company's F/A-18 program, says: "We didn't agree that was the way it should be done, but the other choice was a debate that would have antagonized both sides. That is not the way you treat one of your best customers."

Lehman's victory identified him, very early in his time in office, as a tough cookie, a force to be reckoned with by the companies, by Congress— and by the navy. In a book he wrote after leaving office, Lehman included a picture of the replacement Hornet, gleefully labeling it "the only navy aircraft that was never paid for."

Even though it was the engine that had caused the loss of the plane, Lehman quickly became a big fan of the F-404 engine. As a flier, he was familiar with the many problems the navy had experienced with the engines in other planes, especially what he termed "just a terrible engine" in the F-14. His enthusiasm for the engine in the F/A-18 was universally shared by pilots and mechanics as the number of Hornets in service increased.

For GE, the F-404 engine held promise of a huge commercial success. Not only did it power the Hornet, but the same basic engine was being adapted for use in other American bombers and fighters and in combat planes in France, Sweden, India, and Singapore.

Then came two bad shocks.

On 20 September 1984, Lehman sent a memo to the chief of naval operations, instructing him to set up Pratt & Whitney as a second source for production of GE's F-404 engine.

Such an action was virtually unprecedented. At least since World War II, there had been an understanding between the Pentagon and the major defense contractors that, once a company won the competition to build a weapon or an important component such as an engine, it would have a monopoly on production of that item. In this case, GE had spent years and as much as a billion dollars to develop a winning engine, and it looked forward to revenues of more than $6 billion from sales of that engine in the next decade. Now, it was suddenly being ordered not only to hand over its blueprints to its deadly rival, but actually help its competitor set up shop, as Lehman put it, "in minimum time, at minimum cost to the navy, and with minimum risk."

Vice Adm. Robert F. ("Dutch") Schoultz, who was just finishing up a tour of duty as deputy chief of naval operations for air warfare—Houser's old post—sat in on some of the meetings with angry GE officials.

"There was some real arm waving and name calling. It was really a bloodbath. But by God, he pulled it off," Schoultz recalls.

Lehman's most convincing argument was that the navy owned the blueprints, and he would simply give them to Pratt & Whitney if GE refused to cooperate. In fact he did order a new engine trucked from GE to the Pratt plant so engineers could study it.

General Electric was in a somewhat awkward position to resist Lehman's decision to create a second source. Only a few months earlier, the air force had awarded GE a contract to provide engines for its F-15 and F-16 fighter planes, which had been a Pratt & Whitney monopoly. There was a vital difference between the two actions, however. The engine the air force bought from GE was a new design, based on the powerplant for the F/A-18, so it wasn't a matter of taking Pratt & Whitney secrets and giving them to GE. In the case of the navy decision, GE was expected to help Pratt & Whitney produce an engine identical to those coming off the production line at Lynn. Since the two companies were direct competitors for both military and civilian contracts, GE had good cause to worry that it might lose some of its competitive edge.

Lehman had two reasons for his decision. One was to make sure Pratt remained in the military jet engine business so its plants would be available in the event of war. The company, a division of United Technologies, was still a major player in the jet engine business. But it had lost the dominant position it had once enjoyed as a result of faulty business decisions by its corporate masters, failure to keep up quality and service on its engines, and GE's aggressive marketing strategy. The idea that Pratt might drop out of the military jet engine business seemed farfetched, especially to angry GE executives, but that possibility did exist.

Lehman's other reason was to keep a lid on the cost of engines by forcing two manufacturers, both capable of making the same engine, to compete for production contracts each year. He was worried that, if there was only one source, "they'd take you to the cleaners on price," as Schoultz put it.

Whether the decision to create a second source for the F-404 engine was a wise one is debatable. Certainly officials of GE do not think so. They argue that, even without the F-404 contract, Pratt remains very much a major force in the manufacture of military jet engines. And, they say, the navy not only had to pay to set up Pratt's production line but had to pay to support two production lines, with their associated overhead costs, rather than one more efficient line. Whether GE would have taken advantage of its monopoly to jack up the price of the engine remains a matter of speculation. But company officials say that, until the contract was split, the price of engines was going down—to about $1.5 million apiece. But since then, the price has grown to about $2 million.

In 1989, GE edged out Pratt when it won a contract to provide all of the F-404 engines to be purchased in 1990, as well as the option to provide all the engines for the F/A-18 for the six-year period beginning in 1991. Company officials said the contract was potentially worth more than $2 billion.

General Electric had barely recovered from the shock of losing a portion of its engine business when it suffered another severe jolt.

In 1987, reports began coming in from the fleet of a few scattered engine failures.

One of the early ones occurred on 4 June 1987. About 1:30 that afternoon, four marine pilots took off from Beaufort Marine Corps Air Station, South Carolina, and headed for the Townsend Target Complex in a forested area about forty miles southwest of Savannah, Georgia. All four planes carried twelve practice bombs.

On the second bombing run, Captain S. T. ("Perk") Perkins had just dropped his bomb and leveled off at 2,500 feet when he was startled by a loud explosion that seemed to be behind and below his plane. Perkins heard a somber recorded voice intone: "Engine right!" A red fire-warning light flashed on. Moments later, he heard "Engine left!" Another warning light came on.

The engines in an F/A-18 are located in a compartment behind and below the pilot, so Perkins couldn't see anything wrong. But about five seconds after the explosion, Perkins's wingman radioed he could see flames streaming from the back of the plane. Three seconds later, he reported the fire was out. Then, a moment later, he again saw flames. Perkins, struggling to understand the problem and get the plane under control, told the other pilots to shut up. Watching from a tower nearby, the range controllers saw Perkins's plane roll uncontrollably and nose up almost vertically. Then they saw the bright flames of the rocket propelling the ejection seat away from the plane.

Perkins floated to earth with only minor injuries. The plane crashed into a wooded area and then burned for sixteen hours.

When General Electric investigators arrived, they were unable to determine how much damage had been caused by the fire in flight and how much by the intense fire on the ground. But every part of every engine is stamped with a number so that even widely scattered parts can be reassembled. The investigators were able to determine that four blades of the compressor in the right engine had broken loose, severely damaged the engine, and caused a fire burning at a temperature of 3,100 degrees F. It was that intense heat that had set off the fire alarm in the undamaged left engine.

Safety investigators concluded that Perkins might have been able to save the plane if he had pulled the left engine back to idle, watched to see the fire warning light go out, and then increased power again. In a similar incident in Nevada, the pilot had been high enough so he had time to determine that, despite the warning lights, only one engine was on fire, and he was able to land safely. But Perkins didn't have the altitude or the time for that kind of experiment. The investigators agreed he was right to get out when he did.

Were the loss of the plane in Georgia and a few other reports of engine problems just isolated events? GE didn't treat them that way.

Fred Larson tells of his reaction when the engine failures were reported: "If you have a problem and someone says, 'that's an isolated event,' you say: 'Oh, no. There's going to be another one. There is no such thing as an isolated event.' Gerhard Newman [a legendary engine designer and manager at Lynn] used to say: 'The engine is talking to you. Listen to it. Don't say, "say it again." ' "

This was clearly not a burble like the engine failure that had cost a plane in 1980. By the time these problems turned up, the engine had racked up more than a million flying hours and there were some 1,700 engines in service. If there was a basic problem, it would cost a great deal of money to fix it.

As General Electric began to analyze the reports of engine failures, it soon became apparent that it didn't have one problem. It had three problems.

The first problem, and the cause of the fire in Perkins's plane, was high-frequency vibrations inside the engine that caused the compressor blades to crack and eventually break loose. Such a failure is especially troublesome because the compressor is located up front, right behind the fan. When a blade breaks off, it may go rattling down the full length of the engine, tearing off pieces as it goes through the combustor and the two turbines and out the afterburner. The problem was serious enough to require a redesigned compressor with thicker blades.

The second problem was a real surprise. The engine is designed with a tough titanium casing so that, if a part breaks off inside the engine, it will not tear through the side of the engine and cause other damage to the plane. The investigators found that the heat of an engine fire is so intense that it could ignite the titanium itself, so the casing, far from controlling the damage, actually contributed to it. This forced the design of a new type of liner.

Compared to these two problems, the third one seemed relatively minor. In some cases, it was found, the pressure and heat in the afterburner were so severe that they caused the afterburner liner to collapse and the engine to lose power. The solution was a stronger liner.

"Warranties aside, GE considered it its responsibility to put the engine in good shape," Larson says. "At no cost to the customer, we provided improved components and sent maintenance teams out at very, very great expense. We were saying, 'you can rely on GE.' "

The three problems with the engine, serious as they were, turned out to be manageable and far less severe than problems that had plagued earlier jet engines. It now appears that the F-404 engine, in various modified forms, will be flying successfully well into the next century.

And, serious as the problems were, they were confined to the engine. They did not involve the airplane itself. If worst had come to worst, it would have been possible to adapt another engine to keep the F/A-18 flying.

Adm. Wesley L. ("Wes") McDonald, who was DCNO for air warfare at the time of the crash in England in 1980, says he was at first concerned about the viability of the whole program, but he was relieved to learn the problem was confined to the engine. "The engine," he says, "is not as critical as something that is weird in the airplane itself."

As the F/A-18 completed its testing and went into service, the navy and the contractors were to learn just how weird and troublesome problems in the airplane itself could be.

CHAPTER SIX
When Weird Things Happen

Commercial airline pilots are not noted for giving up their places in line so other planes can take off first.

But, at Lambert Field, the St. Louis International Airport, they happily wait while F/A-18 Hornets, fresh off the assembly line, take to the air for the first time, putting on a free air show for the airline pilots and the passengers lucky enough to get a glimpse of the action.

Usually flying in pairs, the test pilots wheel out onto the field, run up their engines, release their brakes, and hurtle down the runway. For a few seconds, they hug the earth to be sure both engines are delivering full power. Then they pull back on their control sticks and zoom almost straight up in what is known as a "Viking Departure."

Moments later, they level off at 10,000 feet, clearing the airport traffic pattern and permitting the airliners to resume their orderly operations.

As the new Hornets take to the air for the first time, they are dazzling creatures—sleek, powerful, agile—a seeming triumph of the science of aeronautics. But the design of these aircraft owes almost as much to the art of politics as it does to skillful engineering. Therein lie the secrets of the strengths of the Hornet and most of its weaknesses.

As the Hornet has moved through testing and into the fleet, it has encountered a series of problems—with its landing gear, its tail, its wings, its fuselage, its range, and its price—and all can be traced back to the series of compromises, involving both engineering and politics, made during its development.

It is at the sprawling McDonnell Douglas plant bordering the airport that all the components for the Hornet come together to form an airplane. Many of the parts of the plane have been slowly moving through the

117

supply line for months, even years, because it is a forty-four-month process from the time a plane is ordered until it is delivered. McDonnell Douglas waits twenty-two to twenty-seven months for a landing gear, twenty-seven to twenty-nine months for the radar, and twenty-six months for an engine.

The biggest component, shipped to St. Louis in special railway cars, is the rear portion of the plane—from the back of the cockpit to the tail—which is assembled by Northrop in its plant at Hawthorne, California. That comprises roughly forty percent of the plane. It consists of the center and aft portions of the fuselage and the two vertical tails. It contains few of the high-technology parts of the plane that are relatively light and easy to assemble—and which are more profitable.

In its plant at St. Louis, McDonnell Douglas assembles the front end of the plane with the cockpit, the radar, the computers, and the avionics. This is the high-technology end of the plane and it is more profitable. If one is going to build half a plane, this is the half to build. McDonnell Douglas also makes and attaches the landing gear, the horizontal portion of the tail, known as the stabilator, and the landing hook, even though they fit on the Northrop part of the plane.

By the time a Hornet reaches the end of the assembly line in St. Louis, the two halves have been joined; the engines, computers, and other equipment have been installed; radios have been set to the proper frequencies, and everything has been checked to make sure that the test pilot will be able to make his Viking Departure without undue concern.

As the new Hornets scream almost vertically into the sky, their gray paint quickly merging with the atmospheric haze, they seem almost perfect examples of the airplane designer's art. It is only when one looks closely at the plane, inspecting each of the parts that makes the whole, that one begins to see the results of the long series of aeronautical and political compromises of which this airplane was made.

First, go out to the end of the runway or, better yet, stand with the landing signals officers near the stern of an aircraft carrier, with the wind whipping over the deck at thirty knots, as a Hornet comes in for a landing. The two main landing gear, splayed out at an angle, dangle below the plane like the scrawny legs of some huge bird, groping for the deck. Surely those thin stalks will collapse when the weight of the plane crunches down on them. But as the plane touches the deck in its barely controlled crash landing, the gear folds at its "knees" and seems to crouch beneath the plane, cushioning the shock of its descent.

The gear was designed by the engineers at McDonnell Douglas as part of the process of navalizing the YF-17 that Northrop had built as a lightweight air force fighter. The gear does not look at all the way it would look if they had started with a clean sheet of paper. By the time they began their design work, decisions made by others had vastly complicated their lives.

Normally, the landing gear of a navy plane would be attached farther back than that of an air force plane, to help absorb the crushing impact of a carrier landing and prevent the tail from banging on the deck. But moving the entire gear would have forced a redesign of other parts of the plane. The decision was made to keep the gear where it was but to put in that "knee" that moves the wheels themselves further back.

The second compromise involved making room for two Sparrow missiles to be carried on the "shoulders" of the plane near the points where the gear is attached. Both the missiles and the landing gear were in competition for the same small piece of real estate on the bottom of the plane.

One solution that had a good deal of logic behind it was simply to leave off the Sparrows. The Sparrow was a relatively new missile designed to be guided to its target by radar. It filled the gap between the long-range Phoenix carried by the F-14 and the short-range, heat-seeking Sidewinder. The Sparrow had two advantages. It could hit a target beyond visual range, and it could hit a target head-on. The Sidewinders then in use had to be launched from behind the enemy in order to home in on the heat of his engines. The great disadvantage of the Sparrow was that it simply didn't work very well. But a group of experts in the Pentagon thought the issue through, concluded that the new plane should carry the Sparrow, and prevailed with an unusual argument.

Robert Thompson, who had gone through the Navy Fighter Weapons School, the Top Gun air combat course at Miramar, as a civilian, made the case for arming the plane with a radar missile: "Whether it was good or not, the Sparrow was a threat. It is like you going after a drunk armed with a gun. Whether or not he can hit you, it alters your tactics. I felt, it alters the other guy's tactics knowing you have a head-on weapon."

The designers were told they had to find a way to get the landing gear in and out of its compartment in the bottom of the plane without banging into the Sparrows. It was a challenge Rube Goldberg would have relished.

When a Hornet is launched from a carrier, it crouches on the deck with its "knees" bent. The heavy main portion of the gear—the equivalent, in a human, of the leg between the knee and the ankle—is parallel to the deck. As soon as the plane is airborne, the gear once again dangles awkwardly below the fuselage before it begins the strange minuet in which the knee bends and rotates, the wheel twists, and the whole assemblage tucks itself up into the bottom of the plane.

As might be expected of a mechanism so complex, things could go wrong—and did.

One of the most tragic incidents occurred on 3 December 1985, at the Miramar Naval Air Station.

Early that morning, Capt. Henry M. Kleemann took off from the Point Mugu Naval Air Station, on the coast north of Los Angeles, for the short flight to Miramar, which is in the northern suburbs of San Diego. Kleemann was one of the navy's most experienced fighter pilots, with nearly 4,000 hours in the air. In August 1981, he was flying one of two F-14s over the Gulf of Sidra, when they were attacked by two Libyan planes, one of which fired a missile at Kleemann. Within seconds, the two U.S. planes shot down the Libyans with Sidewinder missiles. It was the first time the Tomcat had been involved in combat. Only a short time before the 3 December flight, Kleemann had been given one of the navy's most prestigious posts as commander of VX-4, a special squadron based at Mugu,

F/A-18 Main Landing Gear

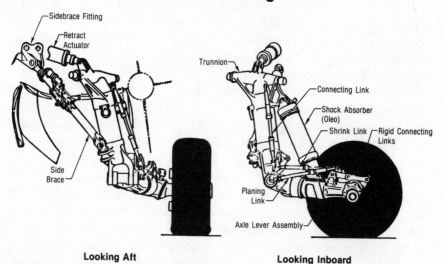

Looking Aft   **Looking Inboard**

This shows the complexity of the Hornet's main landing gear, which has been responsible for a number of accidents.

and assigned to do the operational testing of new fighter airplanes and weapons.

Although Kleemann had flown thousands of hours in navy fighters, he had less than forty-three hours in the F/A-18, and he had hurried in five days through the four-week training normally required before an experienced pilot is considered qualified in the Hornet.

Piloting a nearly new plane, with only 327 flying hours, Kleemann, accompanied by another pilot in an F/A-18, took off at 8:30 A.M.

When the two pilots reached Miramar, they were held in the landing pattern for a few minutes and then the other plane was cleared to land first. Two minutes later, Kleemann made a relatively hot landing, touching down near the end of the 12,000-foot runway at about 140 knots (160 miles an hour). There had been half an inch of rain during the night. But, despite scattered puddles of water remaining on the concrete, he rolled normally down the runway for about twenty-six seconds. Then, while he was still traveling more than eighty miles an hour, the plane suddenly swerved to the left, then veered sharply to the right, ran off into the soggy grass, turned almost completely around, and flipped upside down.

The crash crew reached the scene within a minute. The canopy was broken off and Kleemann's head was pushed down into the mud. The rescuers dug frantically with their hands to pull the mud from his face, but water, mixed with fuel and hydraulic fluid, ran into the hole as fast as they dug. They also groped unsuccessfully in the cockpit for the throttle controls to shut down the right engine, which continued to run. With the engine still turning over and the leaking fuel, the wreckage could have broken into flames at any moment. The danger to Kleemann and the rescuers was compounded by the possibility that he had tried unsuccessfully to eject. If the plane was moved, the rocket under the ejection seat might go off, driving the pilot down into the soggy ground and igniting the leaking fuel.

It took almost an hour to secure the ejection seat, raise the plane, remove the pilot and fly him to a nearby shock trauma unit. But Kleemann was dead. Members of the rescue team agonized over the possibility that he might have survived if they had been able to extricate him from the wreckage more quickly. But autopsy surgeons later confirmed that he had died almost immediately after the crash from a severed spinal cord.

What went wrong to cause a highly skilled pilot to lose control of his plane during a routine landing?

Accident investigators pinpointed the trouble in a short piece of metal called a "planing link." The purpose of the link is to guide the landing gear's intricate maneuvers during retraction in the few moments after takeoff. The best guess is that, when Kleemann took off at Mugu and retracted his landing gear, the wheel was still spinning rapidly as it moved up into the fuselage. When brakes were applied automatically, the spinning stopped suddenly, with a jerk that bent the planing link.

When Kleemann landed, according to this theory, the bent link pushed the right wheel slightly out of line. And then, as the plane slowed down and its weight settled onto the wheels, the plane veered so sharply that Kleemann was powerless to keep it under control.

Although they were not able to prove it, the accident investigators concluded that Kleemann may have received a warning that his landing gear was not properly aligned but that, because he was not as familiar with the plane as he should have been, he didn't understand the danger. He may also have been in a hurry to land because he was already late for a meeting—on the subject of safety.

Ironically, Kleemann probably would have survived if he had experienced the same problem while landing on a carrier, even though that is normally more hazardous than putting down on a long runway. The cables on the ship's deck would have stopped him before the cockeyed wheel had thrown the plane out of control. If he did receive a warning, he should have gone around again and called for a "trap," in which cables at the end of the runway at Miramar would have been raised to catch the plane, just as though he had landed on a carrier.

The landing gear failure that cost Kleemann his life is one in a series of such problems that has plagued the plane since early in its test program. Not only was there the planing link problem, but there had also been cracks in the heavy section of the landing gear between the "knee" and the "ankle," near the point where the main shock absorber is attached.

Bent planing links have been blamed for dozens of accidents, most of them much less serious than the one that took Kleemann's life. A major reason there have been so many accidents is that the delicate link can be damaged on a single takeoff, as seems to have happened in the case of Kleemann's plane, so there is no opportunity to detect the problem by inspection.

Cracks in the heavy portion of the gear, on the other hand, can be seen on routine inspection, before damage has progressed to the point where an accident occurs. However, the cracks were of deep concern to the designers because of the possibility of a basic flaw in the design of the gear.

As each weakness in the gear has been identified, the mechanism has been modified. On several occasions, where cracks pinpointed areas of weakness, more metal was added. Kleemann's plane had come off the assembly line only ten months before his crash, and its gear had all the latest modifications. It also had a warning system that, while it wouldn't detect a bent planing link, should have told him that his right wheel was not properly aligned for a landing.

The navy and McDonnell Douglas are continuing to keep a very careful eye on the plane's landing gear. Pilots are also being given special training so they will be aware if there is a problem and know what to do about it.

Unfortunately, the stresses that cause cracks tend to "migrate" from the newly strengthened area to the next weaker section. Landing gear problems may still crop up in the future as Hornets build up flight time—and number of landings—in the fleet.

Such problems, expensive and dangerous as they may be, can be understood and fixed. But some of the other weird things that went wrong with the Hornet during its testing, and even after its introduction into the fleet, proved much more difficult to understand and more difficult to fix.

Marine Lt. Col. Peter B. ("Pete") Field, military program manager for the test program at Patuxent, found one of those difficult problems in the worst possible way. It was a day on which he earned his pay as a test pilot, and then some.

The procedure for testing a new airplane is carefully designed to explore first the areas in which the plane is not expected to encounter any serious problems. Gradually, the test pilots move cautiously further and further out toward the corners of what they call the "flight envelope," into the areas where there is more uncertainty and greater danger. The first flights are flown below the speed of sound at relatively high altitudes, so there will be room to recover or eject if something goes wrong. As the test program progresses, the pilots go very fast, very slow, very high, and very low, and they experiment with maneuvers that put more and more stress on the plane.

This prudent practice of tip-toeing up to the toughest maneuvers is one reason the biggest surprises tend to come late in a test program.

The F/A-18 had been put through many of its paces and was performing well on the day that Field set out to see how the plane reacted as he went through a tricky high-speed, low-altitude maneuver. Testing at the potentially dangerous low altitude was essential because the plane's performance might be different in the dense air close to the ground than it was at a safer high altitude. The test was especially crucial because it duplicated a tactic used routinely in bombing attacks, in which the pilot comes in very low and fast and zooms up sharply. Then he rolls upside down, pulls the nose down toward the target, quickly rolls right side up again, drops his bombs, and heads for home.

To one who has never executed such a maneuver, it would seem much simpler for the pilot to pop up and then push the nose back down toward the target without rolling upside down and back up again. There are two reasons for the quick roll. One is that the plane can stand about five times as much pressure exerted toward the bottom of the plane as it can in the other direction. This means the pilot can point his nose at the target much more quickly with the rolling maneuver. The other reason is that popping up and back down subjects the pilot to negative gravity and that is very uncomfortable. Blood rushes to his head, and his lunch heads in the same direction.

Field followed the standard bombing approach. He popped up, rolled upside down, and pointed the nose at the ground. Then he discovered what the engineers, in their dry way, labeled the "roll rate problem." The Hornet was rolling back right side up more slowly than it should have—and Field was headed for the ground, less than 400 feet below him. Summoning all his skill, he managed to pull out before hitting the ground and, still shaken by his near miss, hurried back to tell the engineers about their problem.

Ideally, the Hornet should have had a roll rate of at least 180 degrees a second. In other words, it should have been able to do a complete 360-degree roll in two seconds. What Field found was that this strike-fighter had a ponderous roll rate of only about eighty degrees a second. It took the plane all of four and a half seconds to do what it should have done in two.

As Field's experience demonstrated, the new plane's roll rate was too slow for it to be an effective bomber. But the agility with which a plane can roll is also vital in a dogfight. If an enemy gets on a pilot's tail, and the pilot can roll more quickly than his pursuer, even by a fraction of a second, he can spoil his opponent's aim and perhaps even get in a shooting position himself. A pilot flying a plane as sluggish as the F/A-18 against a skilled adversary would probably have only moments to live.

If the Hornet's lethargic roll rate could not be fixed, it wouldn't be able to do either job for which it was intended. And even if it could be fixed, the fix might be so expensive that the Hornet would be doomed politically.

When the engineers got back to their computers and wind tunnels, they found something very weird indeed. There was a basic flaw in the design of the wing that permitted it to bend during abrupt maneuvers in the dense air at low altitudes. This was partly due to one of the compromises involved in attempting to build a plane that would be both a fighter and a bomber, and partly due to a failure to understand how some of the new materials used in the wing would perform in flight.

The original design called for a wing that would be as thin as possible to make it a good fighter, but also as strong as possible so it could carry a heavy bomb load. In their effort to build a very thin, very strong wing, the designers used far more composite materials, rather than the traditional aluminum and titanium, than had been used in previous planes. Much of the wing is made up of a lightweight honeycomb material covered by graphite epoxy panels. The result is a wing four inches thick at its thickest point. As one pilot says, "We fly on razor blades."

At the time the design work was done in the early and mid-1970s, industry was still learning about composite materials and how they work. One thing that was not understood clearly is the flexibility of these new materials. The unexpected bending of the wing of the F/A-18 taught an important lesson. The manufacturers of golf clubs learned the same lesson when they first used these new materials. The graphite was plenty strong enough for the shaft of a golf club. But when the head of the club hit the ball, the shaft twisted almost like the wing of the Hornet.

Normally, if a pilot wants to roll his plane, he moves his control stick in the desired direction. That activates two flaps, known as ailerons, attached by hinges to the rear of the wings at the outer ends. One aileron is pressed down and that tends to raise the wing. The other aileron is pressed up and that lowers the wing, causing the plane to roll in that direction.

In the F/A-18, the wings proved so flexible that, when the ailerons were activated, the wings bent in the opposite direction, in effect tending to make the plane try to roll the wrong way.

Fixing the roll rate proved to be a difficult and expensive affair. It involved making the ailerons bigger, adding several hundred pounds of composite fabric material to stiffen the wings, and modifying the computer instructions to involve other adjustable parts of the wings in helping the ailerons to roll the plane quickly and crisply.

The result of all this effort was a roll rate so high that a pilot could actually damage the plane by snapping it around too fast. To keep that from happening, the computers were programmed to prevent the plane from rolling faster than 220 degrees a second—a 360-degree roll in a second and a half.

Serious as the problem was, it was not as bad as it might have been. Almost as soon as Field reported his brush with disaster, word spread in the navy and on Capitol Hill that McDonnell Douglas had recommended the plane be given an entirely new wing of a different design. That was not true. If it had been, the entire F/A-18 program would very likely have been killed.

Like all very big Pentagon weapons programs, the Hornet was threatened repeatedly with a cutoff of funds. Almost every year, such an effort came to a vote in one or both houses of Congress. All of those efforts failed. But, in contrast to other big ticket items, the F/A-18 suffered more death threats more often, and it really did hover on the brink of death on a number of occasions.

One of the most serious threats came from the very highest levels of the navy itself late in 1977. As final decisions were being made on the budget that would go into effect the following fall—the budget that would provide funds to move from development into production of the F/A-18— Navy Undersecretary R. James Woolsey wrote an extraordinary five-page memo to Defense Secretary Harold Brown, urging him to cancel the F/A-18 program outright and fill the carrier decks with F-14 fighters and A-7 attack planes.

"Although the F/A-18 provides some capabilities that we would like to have, in light of the fiscal constraints we surely face, it is far preferable to terminate it than to suffer the disproportionate loss in other aviation and non-aviation programs which otherwise seem inevitable," Woolsey wrote.

The navy's top admirals were careful not to take a public stance on Woolsey's proposal. If the F/A-18 remained in the budget, they would have to defend it on the Hill and support its use in the fleet. But many of the admirals had favored a fighter force made up of F-14s all along, so Woolsey's recommendation was not entirely unwelcome.

Although Woolsey's memo had some harsh words for the F/A-18 in comparison with the F-14, he later insisted that the recommendation to kill the program stemmed from the money crunch rather than any vendetta against the Hornet.

Extraordinary as Woolsey's proposal was, the outcome was perhaps even more extraordinary. Instead of grasping the navy's offer to sacrifice the biggest item in its budget, Brown accepted the advice of Russ Murray, his assistant for program analysis and evaluation. Although once a sharp critic of the F/A-18, Murray had gradually become convinced of its value. In a four-page memo of his own, he convinced Brown the plane was worth building. Brown okayed production of the first five Hornets—and cut F-14 production nearly in half.

One can only wonder whether Brown, trying to make ends meet on a tight budget, would have made the same decision to go from development to production if he had been able to see a few years into the future.

Almost as soon as production began, both McDonnell Douglas and Northrop found it was taking longer to assemble a plane than had been expected, and the cost started to go up. The problem at Northrop was truly alarming. According to the original plan, it should have required 67,500 hours of labor for Northrop to assemble its rear section of the plane. On the assembly line, however, the work actually required as much as 147,000 hours.

Thomas Burger, manager of the F/A-18 program for Northrop, blames much of the trouble on the fact that the central portion of the fuselage—a heavy, dense structure full of complicated plumbing for the fuel system—is difficult and time-consuming to assemble.

"We've got some of the hard stuff," he says. "The central fuselage is the worst part of the plane because it has all the heavy structural stuff, the critical fasteners, the tightest density of stuffing things in."

At the heart of the central section of the fuselage, right behind the cockpit, are three large metal bulkheads. Instead of a single wing extending right through the fuselage, there is a separate wing on each side and they are attached to each of the three bulkheads with two-and-a-half-inch diameter titanium pins, one at the top, one at the bottom, for a total of six pins for each wing. The three bulkheads and those dozen pins must take all the stress of gravity during the plane's violent maneuvers.

Production had barely begun when cracks developed in one of the bulkheads in a test rig. This meant work on the plane was delayed while the design was reworked and the bulkheads strengthened. Burger says a conscious decision was also made to incorporate about 200 improvements into the first plane on the assembly line and this caused further delay.

As reports of the rapidly soaring labor hours at Northrop reached St. Louis and Washington, teams of experts were sent to help out. John Capellupo, who had worked with Northrop earlier on development of the plane and who was later to head McDonnell Douglas's F/A-18 operation, was dispatched to Hawthorne with a large group of McDonnell Douglas engineers.

To both the navy and McDonnell Douglas, the prime contractor, there were two critical issues: First, if planes could not be produced on schedule, the flight test program would be delayed. Second, if the time and labor involved could not be reduced, there could be a major increase in the cost of the plane. The possibility that the entire program might be cancelled was very real.

To the experts from St. Louis, it seemed clear that Northrop's problem was not only the difficulty of assembling the dense central section of the fuselage, but also a lack of recent experience in setting up a major production program. Northrop had last gone into production in a big way on the F-5, and that had been many years before. McDonnell Douglas, on the other hand, had had a steady stream of major production contracts, including the F-4, the F-15, and the AV-8.

Lenox took a worried look at the situation and concluded that Northrop's managers had failed to realize the F/A-18 was much more dense, much more complex than the F-5, and that they "were too damn proud to admit it."

The influx of outside experts, insisting that Northrop change its way of doing business, was a direct affront to the professional pride of the Northrop managers, and the cause of a good deal of resentment. The ill-feeling was intensified by a bitter legal dispute pitting Sandy McDonnell and Tom Jones in a fight over foreign sales.

Even after losing the air force competition for the lightweight fighter and ending up playing second fiddle to McDonnell Douglas on the navy plane, Jones still pursued his dream of selling a new fighter to the many countries whose F-5s and other planes were in need of replacement. The two companies agreed that Northrop would be free to develop and sell a lighter, less expensive, land-based version of the Hornet called the F-18L.

Jones went vigorously to work trying to market the F-18L. He even obtained the blessing of the Joint Chiefs of Staff for a sale to Iran, but the White House blocked the deal because the land-based version of the plane was not in use by an American service.

Tom Jones tried to get around this problem. In a "Dear Davy" letter to Gen. David C. Jones, then chief of staff of the air force, on 22 February 1977, he offered to sell the F-18L to the air force at a remarkably low fixed price: $4.77 million apiece for any quantity between 600 and 1,000 aircraft, and $3.8 million apiece between 1,000 and 1,500 planes. The air force, already committed to the F-15 and F-16, passed up the offer.

The F-18L was, of course, in competition with the F/A-18 in the foreign market, and Northrop suspected McDonnell Douglas of working with the navy to sell the Hornet at the expense of its land-based sibling. Any foreign sales would help reduce the cost of the plane to the navy. On 26 October 1979, Northrop filed a suit against McDonnell Douglas, accusing its partner of fraud, economic coercion, unfair competition, industrial espionage, and antitrust violations. It asked for more than $400 million in damages. McDonnell Douglas filed a counter suit accusing its partner of similar offenses. It upped the ante to more than $2.3 billion in damages. The dispute dragged on for nearly six years in an atmosphere of suspicion and animosity. A series of navy officers tried to push Sandy McDonnell and Tom Jones to agree on a settlement, but they resisted. At one point, they were forced to sit down together with an admiral acting as arbitrator, and they actually reached an agreement. But it fell apart almost as soon as they left the room, apparently because of a lack of trust between the two men.

Finally, a settlement was reached on 8 April 1985, after Navy Secretary Lehman let the companies know the government was not about to pay their rapidly mounting legal bills. McDonnell Douglas agreed to pay Northrop $50 million in return for the uncontested right to sell the F/A-18 wherever it could. Northrop would, of course, share in these sales, but that was not the same as producing its very own plane for the export market.

While the case was being contested, it was obvious to those in the know that production problems, plus the rise in inflation, were pushing the cost of the plane upward, although no one seems to have realized—or dared to imagine—how high costs threatened to go. Adm. Wes McDonald, who was DCNO for air warfare in the late 1970s, says he didn't sense any dramatic increase, "just continuing soft growth."

Late in 1979, as required by law, the navy had to calculate the cost of its major programs and report the numbers to Congress. That forced the navy to face up to a startling increase in the projected cost of the entire program. Early in 1980, the nervous admirals appeared on Capitol Hill to report the bad news: the program was projected to balloon by $5.1 billion.

Lenox broke it down this way: The total cost of purchasing 1,366 aircraft, with deliveries through 1991, would be $26.9 billion. Of the $5.1 billion jump from the previous year's estimate, he blamed $3.5 billion on inflation and $1.6 billion on increases caused by the troubles on the assembly lines.

Congressman Chappell, one of the most persistent critics of the F/A-18, seized on the report: "There is no question, of course, that the program cost has just gone out of sight."

"No question," a glum Admiral McDonald agreed.

One of the interesting characteristics of the F/A-18 program is that each of the program managers seems to have left at least one big, and often unexpected, problem to his successor. In this case, Lenox was reassigned early in 1980 to take over as commander of the shore facilities of the Pacific Fleet's attack squadrons at Lemoore NAS in California. In that position, he would oversee the introduction of the Hornet into the fleet. He passed on the program manager's job to Capt. John C. Weaver, and, for the next three years, one of Weaver's biggest jobs would be to deal with questions about the cost of the plane and try to satisfy Congress that he was not playing a shell game with appropriated funds.

The appointment of Weaver was part of the navy's effort to correct the problem so quickly identified by Willoughby, the expert on reliability: that program managers learned on the job and then were reassigned. Weaver was a fighter pilot, but he also held advanced degrees in aeronautical engineering and electronics, and he had spent a decade and a half working on some of the navy's most important development programs, including the F-14 and the Phoenix missile. He was not just a fighter pilot brought in from the fleet for on-the-job training as a program manager.

One of Weaver's most urgent tasks was to try to reduce production hours. Although it took longer than everyone had hoped, Northrop did manage to bring about a dramatic decrease in the time needed to build its part of the plane. Northrop's Burger says proudly: "The way we went down the learning curve will probably go down in the annals of aircraft assembly as unbelievable."

As the Navy scrambled to complete development and go into production of the Hornet in the face of the high inflation rates of the late 1970s and early 1980s, it moved more than 300 million dollars from the weapons and spare parts accounts into the accounts needed to pay the bills coming due from the aircraft factories. Later, Congress had to appropriate more money to pay for the spare parts and weapons. To the critics, it seemed a clear case of paying twice for the same thing. The House Defense Appropriations Subcommittee and the Pentagon inspector general's office both issued sharply worded reports questioning the legality of these transfers.

The navy's actions had been strongly influenced by Vice Adm. Richard Seymour, who was commander of NAVAIR from April 1980 until the summer of 1983. A veteran attack pilot, Seymour had served in Washington since the mid-1970s, learning his way around the political no-man's land between the Pentagon and Capitol Hill.

"A big thing I learned is that if Congress says something in a report, it does not bind you to do it," Seymour says. "If they put it in a law, you have to do it. I used that a number of times later in my career. They used to write all this stuff in reports. I would sometimes ignore it at my own risk. If the sensible thing to do was not to do what they said to do, we would not do it. They clearly did not want me to do something stupid."

Seymour's philosophy guided the navy as it shuffled around the money to keep the F/A-18 on track. Weaver was held in his program manager's job for an extra year to answer questions from the Hill about the funds transfers. In the end, he convinced skeptical members of Congress that what had been done was legal and that the navy had avoided doing "something stupid."

During this difficult period, every technical problem with the plane cost money and only added to the task Weaver faced in keeping the budget under control.

The year he took over, 1980, when a number of bad things happened to the F/A-18, was a particularly dicey period. There was the roll rate issue and the engine problem revealed by the crash in the English countryside, both matters of deep concern. And then, on 14 November, Lt. Travis Brannon, a pilot brought in from the fleet to conduct operational testing of the F/A-18 at Patuxent, accidentally discovered that the Hornet would do something it was not supposed to do.

Brannon and another pilot were engaged in a simulated dogfight when Brannon racked his plane around in a sharp turn with the nose pointing upward at a steep angle. Suddenly, it felt as though someone had jammed on the brakes. The plane went into a flat spin and began to drop toward the Chesapeake Bay, four miles below, at 500 feet a second.

Under the rules, Brannon should have ejected at 10,000 feet, but he fought to control the plane for thirty-four seconds before finally abandoning the craft at 5,000 feet. He descended safely and was quickly rescued. But the plane pancaked into the bay.

The crash occurred during a hectic period at Patuxent. Development and testing of the plane had fallen several months behind schedule and there was pressure from Washington to hurry things along. In any such program, there is always tension between the testers, who want more time to make sure that everything is just right, and the managers, who fear that any slip in the schedule will mean higher costs and political problems. In this case, Brannon and other fleet pilots were brought in to begin operational testing of the plane—trying to determine how it would perform in actual service in the fleet—before the professional test pilots working for both the navy and McDonnell Douglas had explored the outer edges of the flight envelope. At least one pilot protested in writing against turning the plane over to the fleet pilots without further testing.

The test pilots insisted after the crash that they had carefully described the regions in which it was safe to fly the plane. They blamed officials in Washington for trying to rush the program and Brannon for exceeding the limits they had set. Brannon, who later left the navy to go to medical school, felt he was being blamed unfairly for stumbling onto something that was actually wrong with the plane.

Whether or not, in the excitement of a dogfight, he pushed the plane into a maneuver that had not been explored by the test pilots, he certainly did find something seriously wrong. The F/A-18 not only could fall off into a spin, but it spun in such a way that recovery was very difficult, perhaps even impossible. If Brannon had not lost a plane at Patuxent and Hornets with this deadly defect had found their way into the fleet, a number of pilots and planes might have been lost in mysterious crashes at sea before the problem was identified and corrected.

The task of trying to duplicate what had happened to Brannon and then find a way to recover from the subsequent spin fell to Denny Behm, a fighter pilot who had left the navy in 1967 to become a test pilot for McDonnell Douglas.

Behm, the assistant program pilot, had been assigned to the F/A-18 from the beginning. In September 1979, he obtained one of the first planes off the assembly line, a craft specially rigged to explore its performance at high angles of attack, and flew to Pax River, where he was to remain for three years, performing some of the most demanding tests. At the end of almost every flight, he would turn off his engines at 20,000 feet, glide down to 8,000 feet—dropping at a rate of about 34,000 feet a minute— then do one full turn and test the performance of the plane in a dead-stick landing. "It's a lot of fun—like a shuttle approach," Behm says.

For the tests of the high angle of attack, in which he would deliberately push the plane to its limits to see if it would spin, Behm's plane was equipped with a huge parachute in a compartment in the tail. If he got into a spin, he could pop the parachute. That would pull the plane out of the spin and leave it hanging vertically. He could then release the parachute and fly away. Earlier, Behm had tested the parachute to see if it worked properly, and he had found that being jerked up by the tail and left dangling nose-down was an extremely uncomfortable experience. Behm recalls listening to a tape made during the chute test: "The calm test pilot pulls the handle and his voice goes to 3,000 rpm and three pitches higher. I sounded like a mouse squeaking." He didn't want to do that again unless his life depended on it.

At the moment when a plane ceases to fly and falls off into a spin, it is said to "depart." In most planes, departure is fairly benign. "When a pilot gets his brains shook up a bit," Behm says, "that's a normal departure." But a few planes, such as the A-7, have a violent departure. The nose wanders left and right, then the plane snap-rolls and corkscrews through the air, banging the pilot's head violently against the canopy.

When Behm went out to attempt to recreate the situation that had gotten Brannon in trouble, he already had done almost everything he could to see if he could make the plane depart and spin. He had even tried to spin the plane upside down.

In the NASA wind tunnel at Langley Air Force Base, Virginia, engineers had tried what they called the "frisbee test" on a scale model of the F/A-18. They held the model upside down and then flipped it into a vertical stream of air to see if it would spin inverted. The tests indicated it might. So Behm was told to try it in the air.

He went straight up at 300 knots and then let the plane slow down. As it slowed, he crossed his controls, pushing the stick as far forward and to the right as he could and, at the same time, pushing hard on his left rudder. In effect, he was telling the plane to go one way with his right hand and the opposite way with his left foot.

"It is a terrible thing to do," Behm says. "It causes the plane to start to yaw, then cartwheel once and tumble, or vice versa. Talk about brain scrambling! It is just very, very difficult to tell what is going on. You're far from the center of rotation, with motion about several axes. I did not like that at all. That was not fun. We never got a stabilized inverted spin, so after some thirty attempts at scrambling my brains I called it off."

As Behm headed out to the spin area, which stretches from eight to fifteen miles off the end of the runway where the Patuxent enters the

Chesapeake Bay, he was confident he would not experience the extreme discomfort involved in trying to make the plane spin upside down. But he also knew he was heading into the unknown.

He leveled off at 30,000 feet and then pulled the stick back until the plane was aiming upward at about fifty degrees and, at the same time, made it rotate about its axis. Abruptly, the plane stalled and fell off into just the kind of flat spin Brannon had encountered. Most fighter planes, when they spin, whip completely around in three or four seconds. But the F/A-18 was rotating at a lazy rate of about twelve seconds for a complete turn. Behm had decided earlier that he would deploy the big chute in the plane's tail at 20,000 feet if he had not broken out of the spin by that time. That gave him about twenty seconds to solve the problem that had sent Brannon's plane into the bay.

As soon as the plane departed, Behm pushed his control stick in the direction of the spin and kicked the opposite rudder. That should have brought him out.

"At 25,000 feet or so, it was apparent to me that this thing was not recovering normally," he says. "I decided we were in trouble."

He cut back on one engine and increased power on the other, using the thrust of the engines to do what the controls refused to do. That was enough to stop the spinning motion and permit Behm to regain control of the plane.

Fortunately, Behm's flight turned out to be the hard part of understanding and dealing with the spin problem. Unlike the roll rate problem, where expensive modifications of the plane were required, this new problem was dealt with by changing the computer software to make the plane much less likely to spin and easier for the pilot to recover in the event he did get into a spin.

Even as Weaver worked to solve the technical and financial problems of the Hornet, he could not ignore one large obstacle that would have to be surmounted before the plane could join the fleet. That was a review, set for the spring of 1983, of the entire program by a top-level Pentagon committee.

Two years earlier, on 28 June 1981, the Pentagon board had given approval for full-scale production of the fighter version of the plane, but it held back approval for the attack version. Since, by that time, the two versions had become identical, the decision really involved how many planes would be produced. It permitted production to go ahead in an orderly way, and it meant that the marines would get their new plane after having agreed to wait for it. But it left open the question of how many planes would be produced for the navy. In fact, it left open the question of whether the F/A-18 would ever go to sea as a navy strike-fighter.

In preparation for that final review, the navy ordered a major operational test of the plane by pilots from the fleet, not by professional test pilots. Most of them were combat veterans, and it was their job to use their experience to evaluate how the plane would perform if it ever went to war. Two operational test squadrons—VX-5, which focused on the attack role, and VX-4, which focused on the fighter role—joined forces in a combined squadron. That meant there were fourteen pilots with ten airplanes, two of them two-seaters.

The Operational Test and Evaluation or, in the Navy acronym, OPEVAL, took place from May to October of 1982. Since this was the first time a new fleet airplane had ever been subjected to this kind of through-the-wringer testing, the pilots had to make up their own test program. Through the spring, summer, and into the fall, they flew at the naval air stations at China Lake, Yuma, Pt. Mugu, Lemoore, and Oceana, at Nellis Air Force Base, and off the carrier *Constellation*. For the final test, they moved to Fallon Naval Air Station, Nevada, to simulate the operations of the F/A-18 with an air wing. They flew a long cross-country navigation flight with extensive tanking (refueling), and then they were joined by a score of other planes for three major bombing strikes similar to that conducted a few years later against Libya.

It was a big, expensive test, involving 1,232 sorties and 1,648 flying hours. It was marred by the fact that more than half the sorties were flown in early, pre-production models of the plane, so a good deal of time was spent discovering and reporting on problems that had already been fixed.

The test became one of the most contentious issues in the history of the Hornet, pitting admiral against admiral in nasty personal attacks. And again, as it had before, the issue focused on personalities.

One of those in the center of the maelstrom was Holly Hollandsworth, the A-6 pilot who had long been known as a foe of the F/A-18. He happened to be the skipper of VX-5 at the time the test was ordered, and so he became one of those most involved in setting up the test program and carrying it out. "A lot of people say we were primed to kill the thing, primarily because I'm an A-6 guy," Hollandsworth says. "We did not. We went out with the idea that if we can make it work, we'll make it work."

The other key actor was Rear Adm. Edward W. Carter III, who took over as commander of the Operational Test and Evaluation Force (COMOPTEVFOR), which is responsible for testing all naval weapons, after the testing of the F/A-18 had begun but well before the all-important evaluation of its performance.

Carter, a surface warfare officer and weapons specialist—a black shoe and a cannon-cocker in naval jargon—was not a favorite among the aviators, who referred to him derisively as "Yosemite Sam." He also had picked up other nicknames during a career that began when he joined the navy as an enlisted man in 1945. At the Naval Academy, where he graduated in 1951—a year before Lenox—he was known as Red, for the shock of hair that has now turned auburn, with gray on the sides. On the destroyers and cruisers where he spent most of his career, he was known as Bulldog or, sometimes, the Tasmanian Devil. "All," he says, "imply a certain degree of stubbornness and tenacity, which I guess is deserved."

He came to his new job after a tour of duty as inspector general of the navy. "The IG's job was a great preparation for becoming COMOPTEVFOR," he says. "I didn't have any friends left to lose."

By the time of the operational tests, the F/A-18 had picked up a strong body of support among naval aviators. The "hate and hostility," as Carter puts it, came primarily from the office of the DCNO for air warfare, then headed by Adm. Dutch Schoultz—the same office from which most of the opposition to the new plane had been heard six or eight years earlier.

The fliers were irritated that the fate of their new plane might rest, in the case of Carter, with a non-aviator and, in the case of Hollandsworth, with an aviator who had long been a foe of the plane. Carter rejects the concerns about his role. As commander of guided missile cruisers, he says he knew more about air defense and the command of air attacks than most aviators. In fact, the cruiser he commanded off Vietnam in 1972 claimed responsibility for destruction of thirteen MiGs—two shot down by the ship itself and the remainder by aircraft guided to their targets by the ship's radar. As an aviator friend told the critics: "He shot down a goddam sight more MiGs than you did."

What really divided Carter and many of the aviators was a basic dispute over the role of the F/A-18. Carter, coming new to the issue in the summer of 1982, approached his job almost as though he were dealing with two planes. He insisted on testing and evaluating it in its two separate roles, fighter and attack. Schoultz and many of the aviators by that time had learned to think of the Hornet as Kent Lee had thought of it in the beginning—as a single strike-fighter in which performance in each role had been compromised to provide the carriers with a dual-role plane.

When the tests were done, Carter called together his immediate staff at his headquarters at the Norfolk Naval Base in a building known as the Mattress Factory, because Italian prisoners had worked there during World War II making mattresses for the fleet. To Carter, the results seemed obvious. The Hornet was a superb replacement for the F-4 as a fighter. But the navy should not buy it for the attack role because of its limited range and load-carrying capacity.

Carter held back on submitting a written report because he knew it would be explosive if it leaked, which it was sure to do. Instead, he called his old shipmate, Adm. Jim Watkins, the CNO, and asked to meet with him. Watkins knew he was bringing bad news.

Carter's basic objection was that the limited range of the F/A-18 would force carrier commanders to come in close to shore to attack targets on land, and this would greatly increase the danger to the carriers.

"It is crystal clear when you look at this airplane, using this airplane in the attack mission, you're going to have to make your force more vulnerable in order to deliver the same effects on an enemy that you can with what you've already got," Carter says. "That doesn't take any genius to figure that one out. But that certainly sparked a hell of a lot of disagreement."

When word of Carter's negative report got around, the supporters of the F/A-18 were alarmed. To Lenox and a number of others, the real worry was Lehman. They had long suspected that the secretary opposed the plane and feared he would use this report as an excuse to kill it. They weren't sure what he would do or say from one day to the next. When Lehman was scheduled to testify on the Hill, Schoultz, who became DCNO for air warfare in the fall of 1982 when this whole affair was coming to a head, would often don a business suit, sneak into the back of the hearing room, and take notes to "make sure I wasn't on the wrong side of the street." Relations between Schoultz and Lehman finally became so strained that, late in 1984, Watkins called Schoultz in and suggested he either retire or take an assignment outside Washington. Schoultz opted for a job in London.

The worries about Lehman were intensified in September 1982 when he abruptly announced in a newspaper interview that he intended to force the contractors to produce the sixty-three planes to be funded that year for $22.5 million apiece. Otherwise, he said, he would kill the program and spend the money on A-6s. Lenox and those who shared his suspicions saw this as Lehman's way of doing away with the F/A-18.

To outside observers, Lehman's threat seemed to be a grandstand play, a way of furthering his own future political ambitions by putting on a public show of getting tough with the defense contractors. But those close to Lehman knew he was deadly serious. Admiral Tom Hayward, who was chief of naval operations then, says he had no doubt that Lehman would kill the program if he didn't get his price—and that his price was probably a couple of million dollars lower than a reasonable figure for the plane.

The contractors reacted with predictable cries of outrage and alarm. Then they caved in. Lehman and Sandy McDonnell held a press conference at the Pentagon on 4 October to announce agreement on a fixed-price contract of $22.5 million apiece for sixty-three planes. The price included $18.1 million for the airframe and $4.4 million for the engines and other government-furnished equipment. That was a "fly-away" price that did not include each plane's share of the costs of development or spare parts.

The agreement on price ended Lehman's threat to kill the program outright, but it didn't end the fears about what he might do next. In the fall of 1982, just after the negative OPEVAL report, Lehman ordered the navy to make a test flight to demonstrate whether or not the range of the F/A-18 was adequate. To the consternation of almost everyone involved, Lehman dictated the profile to be flown and picked Hollandsworth to fly it.

Rear Adm. Paul T. ("Punchy") Gillcrist, a deputy for air warfare and a late-blooming enthusiast for the F/A-18, was shocked. In effect, Lehman seemed to be putting the fate of the plane in the hands of a man who was already convinced the navy shouldn't buy it. "I want Holly to fly it," Lehman insisted. Carter resented being told how to conduct the test and even Hollandsworth himself had his doubts. He had more than 5,500 hours in the air and had flown 246 combat missions. But, as skipper of the test squadron, he had only forty-nine hours in the Hornet's cockpit; much less than the pilots working for him.

On the day set for the test, Hollandsworth reported to the flight line at Patuxent River. His plane was jacked up so it could be gorged with every last ounce of fuel. Then it was towed out to the end of the runway. Although critics later accused the navy of cheating, it made sense to tow the plane because it would not have had to taxi a mile or so if it had been operating from a carrier. Hollandsworth and the pilot of another F/A-18 operating as a chase plane planned to fly down the Atlantic Coast and around Point Hatteras, to an ocean bombing range off Beaufort, South Carolina. There, Hollandsworth, who was carrying six 500-pound Mark 82 bombs and two 400-gallon drop tanks, would make his bombing attack.

Then they would fly back up the coast to Atlantic City, New Jersey, before turning around for the return to Patuxent. By flying along the coast, they would always be within easy reach of an airfield if they ran low on fuel. Hollandsworth, skeptical as always about the plane's range, figured that point would come as they passed Patuxent on the way back up north.

The test got off to a questionable start. The two pilots chose a runway heading in the direction they wanted to go. But that gave them a slight tail wind and forced them to use their fuel-guzzling afterburners on takeoff.

The flight was uneventful until they reached the target area. There, Hollandsworth's flight plan called for him to turn on his afterburner while just above the waves and fly a tight circle, pulling six Gs. Carter thought it a tough assignment even for a younger man, and Hollandsworth almost blacked out. He also misjudged the tightness of the turn and pulled only about four Gs. That meant the turn required an extra fifteen seconds in afterburner and a drain on the plane's supply of fuel.

Moments after Hollandsworth had made his bombing run, the pilot of the chase plane called "bingo." He was running short of fuel. The two pilots broke off the test and flew straight back to Patuxent. Reports of the flight very quickly leaked to the press. It was represented as a failure of the plane to fly the required distance even though it was the chase plane that had run short on fuel.

Gillcrist, alarmed that the distorted reports of the test, added to the negative OPEVAL, might doom the Hornet, confronted Carter. "I told him that if that guy [Hollandsworth] worked for me, I'd fire his ass," Gillcrist recalls.

"I don't understand why Gillcrist was unhappy. It was the chase plane that ran out of gas. I guess I've missed the point some way," Hollandsworth says. But then he adds: "We did not part the best of friends. That's too bad. It is a lot of hard work for those guys up in Washington to push something through and then have your own navy types shoot it down."

Actually, the test flights ordered by Lehman had almost nothing to do with aeronautics and almost everything to do with politics. From at least the time the navy had set about converting the YF-17 into a strike-fighter, it had been obvious that, since its "fuel fraction" would be lower than was desirable, its range, or radius of action, would be a matter of concern. Test flights, depending on how they were flown, would demonstrate that the range was somewhat short or just about what the specifications called for, but they added very little to what was already known about the plane's performance.

Range continued to be the center of controversy, however, as the time approached for a decision on production of the plane for use in the attack role. In fact, that decision was coming very late in the program. The plane had been in production for five years and flying for four years and was scheduled to become operational with the marines in January 1983.

Hollandsworth, who continued to believe the F/A-18 was a mistake, felt increasingly that the program was going ahead and that "we were kicking a dead horse" in raising objections.

But the top-level Pentagon board had yet to make its decision, and that decision remained in doubt to the last minute. Normally, the program manager presents all the evidence, pro and con, on his weapons system at such a meeting. In this case, in an unprecedented move, Carter and several of his pilots were invited to attend the meeting and make their case against the plane. "They got it straight with all the bark off," Carter says.

Then it was Lehman's turn to speak. If, as many of the aviators suspected, his real goal was to kill the Hornet, this was his clearest—and last—chance.

Perhaps the best witness to the role Lehman played at that point is Rear Adm. George Strohsahl, Jr., who was then a captain. He was at the time Weaver's deputy and was soon to become program manager himself. Strohsahl, who was an A-6 pilot and an early skeptic about the F/A-18, had known Lehman for a number of years before he became secretary, and the two men had flown in the A-6, Strohsahl as the pilot, Lehman as the bombardier-navigator.

"The only fair thing," Strohsahl says, "is not what he thought, but what he did. What he did, when the chips were down and he had to make a stand, was he supported the F/A-18, and he supported it very strongly. Had he not, I'm not sure it ever would have made it through."

As both Strohsahl and Carter recall, Lehman spoke only briefly. "I've looked at it a lot, and that thing goes just as far as it needs to for a strike-fighter. We want it," he told the assembled Pentagon brass. On 17 March 1983, approval was granted for production of the Hornet for the attack role.

One last obstacle remained before it was safe to say that the F/A-18 was assured of an important part in the navy arsenal. On 14 June 1983, Carter and a group of pilots from the test squadrons met in a closed session of the House Defense Appropriations Subcommittee, still the center of opposition to the plane. The subcommittee had twice in the previous months issued its own hostile reports on the plane's performance—much of it based on information provided by foes of the Hornet within the navy. Carter and the pilots listed the problems they had found with the plane and emphasized their deep concern with its range.

That afternoon, the proponents of the plane paraded up to the Hill to meet with the same subcommittee. By the time the session ended late in the day, the majority of the subcommittee had been convinced that production should go ahead.

The production decision in March and the subcommittee's day-long session in June marked the end of most of the political opposition to the plane. And it left to the fleet the question of how to get the most out of a plane that carried less fuel than most of the pilots would have wished for.

When Strohsahl took over from Weaver in the fall of 1983, he had every reason to look forward to smooth sailing during his tour of duty. All the big problems—technical, political and financial—seemed to have been solved. He couldn't have been more wrong. The old jinx, in which every program manager leaves an unpleasant surprise for his successor, had not gone away.

CHAPTER SEVEN

"A Tremendous Amount of Grief"

To the designers of the F/A-18, the strict rules laid down by the experts at the Naval Air Systems Command seemed to be a bad case of overkill.

If the designers had had their way, they would have taken full advantage of the new way of building airplanes by using as much lightweight, honeycomb material as possible, and then gluing on large sheets of graphite epoxy to form the outer covering of the plane. The result would have been a structure that was very strong, impervious to corrosion, simple to manufacture, and relatively cheap.

But NAVAIR said no. The experts insisted that many of the external panels be attached by titanium screws rather than glued on. This way, the panels could be removed for a look at the innards of the plane. They were especially concerned about the ability to inspect the bulkheads that carry the heavy loads imposed by the wings and tail. One aircraft generation earlier, they had forced Grumman, when it wanted to use the new plastic technology in its F-14, to carry out parallel development of metal structures in case the new system didn't work out. The substitute panels had not been needed, but NAVAIR remained distrustful, and the Hornet was designed so mechanics can routinely look at its inner structure.

NAVAIR's caution paid off during one such routine inspection in the summer of 1984 at the El Toro Marine Corps Air Station in southern California, where the first Hornets had entered active service early in the previous year. A mechanic removed Panel No. 88 from one of the F/A-18s. The panel covers the metal beams to which the tall vertical tails are attached.

Peering inside, the mechanic was startled to see a crack several inches long in one of the structural I-beams that support the vertical tail. Finding a crack there was almost unbelievable. The plane was nearly new—only a little more than 400 hours in the air. It was designed to fly 6,000 hours without structural failure, and that part of the plane had already experienced nearly 12,000 hours of simulated flying in a test rig without any problem.

Within minutes, the phones were ringing at McDonnell Douglas in St. Louis, at Northrop in Hawthorne and Century City, and at NAVAIR in Crystal City. The rest of the Hornet fleet was quickly examined, and similar cracks were found in the tails of a number of other planes. On 26 July 1984, the Navy grounded its Hornets and stopped accepting delivery of new planes. The experts said none of the cracks posed an imminent danger of a tail breaking in flight, but the grounding order was so sweeping that two instructor pilots from the training squadron at Lemoore were stranded at Fallon, Nevada, and had to get a special emergency order to permit them to make the short flight back to their base in California. Canada and Australia, which had purchased some of the earliest planes off the production lines, also grounded their fleets and angrily demanded action from St. Louis and Washington.

Once again, John Capellupo was called in to deal with a serious problem. This time, he was made the leader of a McDonnell Douglas "Tiger Team," so-called, he says, because "a tiger is a ferocious animal." He was given authority to spend money as needed and draft experts from other parts of the company to find what had caused the problem and find a way to fix it—fast.

"It was a very large problem, a major deficiency, a problem we should not have created," Capellupo says. "Planes were piling up at St. Louis and they were grounded in the fleet. We were causing ourselves and our customers a tremendous amount of grief."

Defense Secretary Caspar W. Weinberger and Navy Secretary Lehman threatened to sue McDonnell Douglas if the company refused to absorb the cost of fixing the tails. If the issue had gone to court, the government might well have lost because of a side effect of Lehman's triumph, two years before, when he forced the manufacturers to agree to a fixed price of $22.5 million a plane. As part of that deal, the warranties provided by the manufacturers were drastically watered down. But McDonnell Douglas apparently gave little, if any, thought to the possibility of refusing to fix the tails and fighting the issue in the courts.

"They were just plain embarrassed," says George Strohsahl, the navy's program manager at the time. "Sandy McDonnell was very embarrassed to build a fighter plane that had the tails crack after a few hundred hours.

Legally, contractually, McDonnell Douglas wouldn't have to pay. Sandy McDonnell stepped up to that, whether contractually obligated or not."

Capellupo felt the pressure. Planes were scheduled to come off the production line at a rate of more than one a week, but the navy wouldn't accept or pay for them until the tails were fixed. And naval pilots at Lemoore were in a critical phase of their training in preparation for the Hornet's first deployment at sea.

All the other problems experienced in developing the new plane and getting it ready to go to sea—cracked wing carry-through bulkheads, the flat spin, the roll rate, landing gear failures, corrosion and exploding engines—seem to fade into insignificance when compared with the difficulties posed by the tail cracks. An old timer at McDonnell Douglas told Capellupo it was the worst problem he had seen in forty years in the business. Once again, the possibility that the entire F/A-18 program would be scrapped seemed very real. "It was like a chicken on a June bug. I was the June bug," Capellupo recalls.

His number one priority, of course, was to find out why the tails were cracking. To understand what had happened, it is useful to go back to the early 1970s when Northrop was involved in the air force-financed effort to develop and demonstrate new ways of designing and building fighter planes. This is before the YF-17 came into existence and years before the YF-17 was converted into the F/A-18.

Although there were many in the military and in the aircraft industry who were convinced that radar and the long-range missile had made the dogfight a thing of the past, the Northrop engineers deliberately set out to design a dogfighter. Inevitably, they reasoned, pilots will find themselves in close-in, one-against-one combat—what the pilots call "a knife fight in a telephone booth"—ending only when one plane has been destroyed.

In such a fight, with the planes turning as tightly as possible and zooming up and down, in a maneuver known as the "yo-yo," both planes rapidly bleed off energy. The planes move slower and slower, like two groggy heavyweights groping for a knockout punch. The airplane designer can do a couple of things to help a pilot survive such an encounter. First, he can provide him with engines powerful enough to regain lost energy faster than the other fellow. But the designer can also help the pilot immeasurably by making the plane so it will perform well at very slow speeds.

That accounts for Northrop's decision to use two large vertical tails. Because they are set off on either side of the fuselage, they receive air that is not blocked by the body of the plane. This enables them to maneuver the plane more precisely at all speeds. This idea of using two tails was not unique to the Northrop plane. Twin tails are a distinctive feature of the American F-14 and F-15 and of the new Soviet fighters, the SU-27, the MiG-29, and the MiG-31. The major exception to this trend is General Dynamics' F-16, which has a single vertical tail.

The innovative contribution of the Northrop designers was to combine the advantages of the twin tails with a new shape for the wing. With their YF-17, they added a narrow section to the wing extending forward along the side of the fuselage, almost to the nose of the plane. They called this the "leading edge extension," better known by its acronym, LEX.

This small section of the wing, extending far forward, helps to support the nose of the plane when it flies slowly, with the nose pointing sharply upward. With its LEX, the YF-17 was able to continue flying with its nose pointing almost straight up—an attitude at which other planes depart and fall off into a spin. Moreover, the plane didn't simply hang there. The pilot remained in control, able to maneuver, bringing his nose around for a snap-shot at his adversary with his gun.

The LEX also has another effect on the performance of the plane. It churns up the air passing over the junction between the wings and the fuselage and sends it swirling back toward the vertical tails in a stream so violent that a pilot, looking back over his shoulder, can actually see it as a kind of churning, grayish fog. Aircraft designers spend much of their effort trying to prevent air from becoming turbulent and trying to calm it down when it does. But in this case, the vortex, as it is called, is highly desirable because it gives the vertical tails an added bite on the air when the plane is aimed sharply upward and flying very slowly.

The Northrop designers knew that this turbulent air would batter the vertical tails. In the F-14, the twin tails had, on occasion, moved so far that the tips had banged together. And equipment such as lights and radar antennae attached to the vertical tails of the F-15 had often broken. But, with the vortex coming from the LEX, the tails of the YF-17 and, later, of the F/A-18, were subjected to a much more severe battering.

Even for someone accustomed to flying in a modern combat aircraft, it is disconcerting to look back and see the vertical tails shaking violently from side to side as much as ten times a second. Hornet pilots say you look once, and that's enough. But that visible buffeting is not something to worry about. The tails have built-in flexibility designed to withstand stresses at their tips of more than a hundred times the force of gravity.

What the designers didn't realize is that the movement of the vortex past the tails would also set up an invisible high-frequency vibration, at the rate of forty to sixty vibrations a second, and that is the kind of stress that breaks tails.

"No one ever visualized the extreme loads that would be placed on that tail," says Corky Lenox, who was the program manager throughout all the early test and development phase. "The loads were underestimated to begin with, and the plane flies so well at low speed and high angle of attack that the pilots fly in that regime far more than we ever dreamed they would. The environment there is more severe than envisioned, and it's more severe more often. It was a great surprise to me that we had that problem."

Using his authority as leader of the Tiger Team, Capellupo drafted some 400 experts from throughout the McDonnell Douglas operation. If he needed a specialist in metallurgy or vibration analysis, he simply took him. The result was close to chaos in other parts of the plant. Work was not only disrupted on the F/A-18 production line but on the F-15 and the AV-8B as well.

Working with the experts at Northrop, Capellupo's Tiger Team came up with a fairly straightforward solution for the weakness in the tails. Three strips of metal, called cleats, were bolted to the base of each tail where it is attached to the plane. It was not a very elegant solution. In fact, the cleats, attached where they could be seen on the outside of the tail covering, looked like an example of country carpentry. But they did the trick. By increasing the amount of metal at the point where the cracks were occurring, they increased the safe flying time of the plane by several thousand hours.

A special team of 250 mechanics took over a hangar at Lemoore, where the Navy pilots were preparing to take the plane on its first deployment. They quickly added cleats and put the planes back into service. By the end of November, delivery of new planes, with the strengthened tails, resumed. McDonnell Douglas announced that it would absorb the $25 million cost of fixing the tails.

All in all, it seemed a fairly quick and relatively painless ending to a very serious episode. Unfortunately, it was only the beginning of a problem far more serious than anyone imagined—or cared to think about.

True to the jinx that has afflicted each F/A-18 program manager, Strohsahl left the office on 30 September 1986, to be succeeded by Capt. J. A. ("Spider") Lockard, one of the pilots who had helped introduce the F/A-18 into the fleet and who had been involved in the plane's baptism of fire. He took over just as it was becoming apparent that the quick fix had not really been a lasting fix.

Adding the reinforcing cleats was a fast way of getting the planes back into the air and resuming deliveries. But there had been no time for exhaustive analysis and testing to see whether the cleats really did solve the problem and to determine how much they added to the lifetime of the plane. To believe that the addition of the cleats, which strengthened the tails without decreasing the stresses to which they were subjected, had solved the problem involved a good deal of wishful thinking. The cleats had probably increased the service life of the tails from 400 or 500 hours to some 2,000 hours. But that was still well short of the 6,000 hours the plane was supposed to be able to fly.

As the engineers should have realized, stresses migrate. With the base of the tails beefed up with the cleats, the stresses went looking for somewhere else to show themselves. Soon, there were alarming reports from the fleet of new cracks in other parts of the tail. Mechanics on the flight lines speculated that the stresses from the tail were even migrating far enough to cause cracks in the engine mounts and the landing gear.

"I personally feared that we were going to have to make large portions of the vertical tail and aft fuselage from titanium," Capellupo says, recalling his reaction when the reports of new problems with the tails began coming in. "That would have been a terrible thing. We were only halfway to where we had to be when we learned that the tail would just not live in that environment. Those were very, very tense times."

The cleats obviously were not the solution they had seemed in the fall of 1985. But they had bought time. With them, the plane could continue to be flown safely and deliveries could continue while efforts were made to find a permanent solution. There was no need to ground the planes, with all the unfavorable publicity that comes with such a move.

Instead, this second act of the drama of the cracking tails attracted little outside attention, even in the trade press. McDonnell Douglas waited until 11 November 1987, and then quietly issued a press release announcing it was developing modifications to the plane "to sharply reduce stress on its aft sections and thereby increase its service life." The press release was issued on the deadline for the company, as required by law, to file a Form 10-Q with the Securities and Exchange Commission, revealing that it expected fixes in the tail to result in a "material charge" to its earnings. Later, it reported that charge had amounted to $13.6 million in a single quarter of 1987.

Neither the press release nor the statement to the SEC came close to reflecting the anguish suffered by McDonnell Douglas executives when they were confronted with the fact that the problem with the vertical tails had not been fixed after all. Capellupo worried that the company might have to embark on a massive effort to remanufacture the planes already delivered. McDonnell Douglas, the biggest manufacturer of combat aircraft in the free world, was strong enough that it would not have been forced into bankruptcy. But there was no question that rebuilding several hundred planes already delivered would have, as Capellupo put it, "done major surgery to our earnings."

By the time the press release was issued, McDonnell Douglas was well along in the development of what it hoped would be a lasting fix to the problem of tail cracks. This time, the effort focused on changing the forces at work on the vertical tails, rather than trying to beef up the tails themselves. Using wind tunnels and computers, the McDonnell Douglas engineers experimented with as many as fifty different shapes of fences and vortex generators to change the flow of air over the wings so it would not beat the tails to death. Since all these gizmos would be attached on the forward part of the plane, the work was done at St. Louis.

The Northrop engineers watched all this with concern. They wanted to be sure that nothing done up front had an adverse impact on the performance of the tail on their section of the plane. It was the vortex, after all, that helped give the plane its superb performance at high angles of attack. The trick was to make the vortex more benign, not to weaken or deflect it away from the tails.

The solution finally settled on was what is called the "LEX fence." It is a narrow chunk of steel thirty-two inches long and a little over eight inches high, attached to the wing where it narrows and extends forward along the fuselage. The fences on both sides of the plane are interchangeable. Together with the internal structure to which they are bolted, they add fifty-two pounds to the plane's weight.

If the fences worked as the designers hoped, they would smooth the flow of air and spread out the vortex to reduce its impact on the vertical tails while still providing enough turbulent air for the tails to do their job. But there was real fear that the fences might cause other serious problems. Wind tunnel tests hinted that the fences might make the horizontal tail—the stabilator—less effective. That would make it harder to bring the plane aboard an aircraft carrier. There was also concern that the fences might make the plane more likely to fall off into a spin.

The earlier solution involving the cleats had been approved after only half a dozen test flights. But this time, a much more elaborate test program was set up, both to assure that the fences would do what they were supposed to do and to assure that they would not cause some other problem.

The tests involved forty-five flights checking the plane's performance at 3,000 combinations of speed, angle of attack, and altitude. F. Alan ("Al") Frazier, McDonnell Douglas's chief experimental test pilot, flew some seventy-five percent of the test flights in a plane loaded with stress gauges. Each day, carrying a card listing the points to be checked, he would climb to altitude, pull the nose back, and snap the stick sharply to one side in two-tenths of a second. The result was a seven-G snap-roll. Then he would change the speed or angle of attack slightly and do it again—over and over and over.

Since the fences are held on with bolts, it was possible to go through the same tests with the same plane, with and without the fences.

When the tests were complete, it was clear that the fences reduced the load on the vertical tails and extended their life, actually improved the plane's performance at very high angles of attack, and did not make it more difficult to come aboard a carrier. The only serious adverse effect was to increase the vibration of the LEX itself. But even so, it was calculated, the LEX would last for twice the design goal of 6,000 flying hours.

The test program was conducted with a good deal of urgency. Every plane that left the factory without being fixed would have to be modified later at company expense. Even so, the flight tests continued from October 1987 into April 1988. On 20 May 1988, the navy gave its approval to the modification, and planes in service were quickly fitted out with fences.

In addition to developing and installing the fences, McDonnell Douglas also took on a major job of checking hundreds of planes already in service and repairing any damage caused by stresses on the tail.

How could such a terrible defect slip past some of the best engineers in the business?

Donald Snyder, vice president for aircraft engineering at McDonnell Douglas and director of engineering on the F/A-18 from 1982 to 1985, says: "Our management questioned if we should have found it. No one has come forward and said, 'you could have found it.' I was not there, in charge of engineering. I have no reason to be defensive. I'm the fellow who came in and had to fix it. It would have been easy to blame the previous administration, but I don't think that's fair."

Strohsahl, the program manager during this difficult period, puts the primary blame on Northrop. "They goofed on it," he says. "They clearly did. The navy doesn't hold Northrop responsible. But in all fairness, we really know where it came from."

A big part of the problem can probably be traced back to the sudden switch from a technology demonstration to a fly-off between the YF-16 and the YF-17, and the navy's subsequent attempt to convert a lightweight fighter into a heavier strike-fighter. Northrop, in the early development of the YF-17, focused heavily on the development of new technology, and then demonstrated it in a prototype designed to fly for only a thousand hours or so.

As Tom Burger, the Northrop manager for the F/A-18 program, explains it, the company was struggling to find the best combination of the size and shape of the leading edge extension and the placement and angle of the vertical tails to give the plane superior performance at high angles of attack and low speeds—all without beating the tails to death.

Could the Northrop engineers have done a better job with the tail design? Burger shrugs: "It's hard to say. I don't know."

Throughout this entire episode, the Northrop engineers remained possessive about the tail. They relied on McDonnell Douglas to tell them what stresses the tail must withstand. But they insisted on doing the engineering on the tail themselves.

When McDonnell Douglas became the lead contractor on the Hornet, however, it had assumed responsibility for the performance of the entire plane, and it did a good deal of design and test work on the vital tail structure.

In addition to thousands of hours of wind tunnel tests, the engineers also had the advantage of sophisticated new computer programs that impose a fine-mesh grid over the entire plane and then analyze the stresses in each square of the grid. Finally, actual airplanes were built and then sent to a torture chamber, where they were dropped repeatedly to test the landing gear and where the wings and tails were shaken and twisted, so they would go through all the strains of flight and expose any problems long before a pilot encountered them in the air—or a mechanic saw a crack when he opened an inspection panel.

But all of this clearly wasn't enough.

One reason may be that McDonnell Douglas relied too heavily on the fact that the YF-17 had flown successfully, even though the F/A-18 was in many ways a new airplane. But Len Impellizzeri, a vice president of the company who was responsible for structural work during the design phase, says he doesn't think the McDonnell Douglas engineers were misled by the work already done on the YF-17. "None of us was clever enough to see the problem," he says.

In using the powerful vortex created by the LEX to help the vertical tails control the plane, the engineers were stepping off into new territory. In hindsight, Impellizzeri says they should have done a better job of testing. "But," he says, "we just didn't know enough to do the right kind of testing."

Even now, the question remains: Have the fences really fixed the Hornet's tail problems for good? The engineers think so, but they admit they are working at the outer edges where aeronautical engineering is as much art as science. It is still an area where the fleet sometimes learns of problems before the engineers.

CHAPTER EIGHT————————————
"A Deep-Seated Drive to Kill"

As a pilot banks his Hornet and turns toward the carrier, ten miles ahead, for a nighttime landing, everything seems to happen in slow motion. The carrier comes into view as a postage stamp-sized apparition, floating in the darkness. A single line of strobe lights marks the center line of the deck. A vertical line of lights—the drop light—marks the stern. There is a faint glow off to the right from the sodium vapor lights around the island.

Just to the left, a round amber light—the meatball—is centered between two green lines if the pilot is on the proper guide slope.

Near the stern of the ship, two landing signals officers huddle behind a barrier that shields them from the wind and the jet blast of landing planes. Far astern, a single red light atop a destroyer provides an artificial horizon for the landing signals officers. As the incoming pilot approaches the ship, he announces his plane number and how much fuel he has left and says, "ball," to indicate he sees the meatball. The LSO responds: "Roger, ball," giving the pilot permission to land.

If the approach is normal, those will be the only words spoken.

The pilot concentrates on three things: his airspeed, the center line of the deck, and the meatball. On a dark night, there is no horizon, and there are no other points of reference except those disembodied lights hanging out there in the darkness.

In the Hornet, he can set his throttles, much as a motorist sets the cruise control in an automobile, and the engines automatically maintain his speed as he comes toward the carrier.

If he flies so the lights marking the center of the deck form a straight line with the vertical lights on the stern, he is properly aligned for his landing.

Most crucial of all is the meatball, which tells if he is on the proper guide slope. If he comes in too high, he will miss the arresting wires and have to go around again. If he comes in too low and does not add power in time, he risks crashing into the stern of the ship.

Inside the mechanism that holds the meatball, gyroscopes automatically compensate for the movement of the ship, sending the beam of light through a series of mirrors similar to the lenses originally designed to boost the power of a lighthouse beacon.

On either side of the amber light are green stripes. In an ideal approach, the meatball is centered between the stripes. If the plane is too high, the meatball appears to rise above the stripes. If too low, it drops below them. If the approach is dangerously low, the meatball turns an angry red.

As the pilot comes closer to the carrier, it is suddenly obvious that he is pursuing a moving target. Not only is the carrier sailing away from him into the wind at some thirty-five miles an hour, but, since he is headed for an angled deck, his landing area is moving away from him at an angle. This means he must not only fly in a curve to compensate for the movement of his landing place, but he must also compensate for a slight crosswind caused by the fact that the deck is set at an angle to the movement of the ship.

The space for which he is headed is incredibly tiny. The runway of a military jet airfield may well be more than two miles long. The landing space on a carrier such as the U.S.S. *Coral Sea,* one of the first to take the Hornet to sea, is only 120 feet long. For a plane crossing the stern at 200 feet a second, that is only a fraction of a second's worth of space in which to set down. Width of the landing area is also critical. Other planes are parked on both sides of the deck, leaving a strip only eighty feet wide. This means that if a Hornet, with a wingspan of forty-three feet, including Sidewinders, is more than a few feet to one side or the other of the center line, it is probably going to break something.

Normally, the landing signals officers set the meatball so the plane will catch the third of four cables stretched across the deck. For a perfect landing, the pilot must maneuver his plane so precisely that, when he crosses the stern, his tail hook is fourteen and a half feet above the deck, and his head passes through an imaginary three-foot square.

In those last few moments, what had been an almost leisurely process abruptly changes. Everything goes into fast motion. The shape of the carrier suddenly looms out of the darkness, lights flash past, and the landing gear crunches down on the deck. If the pilot has been focusing almost all his attention on the meatball, as he should, the actual touch down will come as an abrupt surprise.

The natural instinct, at that moment, is to cut off the engines, slam on the brakes and stop. But what if the tail hook has not caught the wire? Following one's instinct would send the plane careering down the deck and off into the sea. Instead of trying to stop, the pilot does just the opposite: he tries to fly. He slams the throttles into full military power and steels himself to go hurtling off into the darkness to make another landing attempt. If he has caught the cable, the sudden burst of power from the engines will force him backward, and then he will be thrown forward hard against his restraining harness as the plane comes to an abrupt stop.

Quickly, as the deck crew checks under the plane, he releases the cable, folds his wings, and moves forward to make room for the next plane, already heading in for a landing exactly sixty seconds later. Then follows an experience that many pilots find even more stressful than the landing itself. Out in front, a teen-aged member of the deck crew waves the pilot forward with a lighted wand. As he taxis over the catapult toward his parking place at the bow of the ship, he feels his wheels slip on the oily deck.

Onward the baton beckons him, into the darkness, part of the process of making the most use of every square foot of some of the most intensively utilized real estate on earth. At the edge of the abyss, the pilot pivots the plane and parks with the tail hanging out over the ocean. Even pilots with hundreds of landings to their credit make those last few movements with one hand on the ejection handle. They know that, if the plane slips over the side, the only realistic chance of survival is to eject and hope to be rescued.

Afterward, down in the squadron ready room, it may take half an hour or more before the adrenalin stops pumping. Studies conducted during the Vietnam War confirmed that a night carrier landing is the most stressful part of military flying—even more than the tensest moments of combat itself.

Daylight landings, when the pilot can usually see the horizon, the carrier, and other ships and planes, are demanding, but not nearly as stressful as coming aboard in the dark of night. In the daylight, instead of making a long, straight run at the ship, pilots fly parallel to the deck, then turn toward the ship while half to three-quarters of a mile astern, and then make their approach. One trick that Hornet pilots have adopted is to put the velocity vector—that little symbol in the heads up display that shows where the plane is actually going—just ahead and to the right of the bow of the ship. That helps to compensate for the way the angled deck is moving away to the right. Landing signals officers say they can spot the pilots who move the velocity vector to the center line of the deck and use it—instead of the meatball—to land, because they usually trap on the second rather than the third wire.

With experience, daylight landings become fairly routine, even fun. But a pilot's feelings during a nighttime landing are never far from the edge of sheer terror. Even those with hundreds of landings to their credit think about dying.

Much of what the navy does to prepare a new plane to go to sea is concentrated on that one task: landing on a carrier. The plane itself has been beefed up to withstand the impact. Engineers have worried over the responsiveness of the engines and the way the plane handles as it approaches the deck. How well a plane comes aboard the carrier is not merely a matter of safety. A squadron of planes that can land predictably on the first pass needs less fuel to go around again, and they require the carrier to keep its nose into the wind for a shorter time.

By these measures, the Hornet comes aboard well. Its relatively short wingspan and the maneuverability built into it as a fighter plane make it much easier to handle in those last moments before touchdown than the F-14, with its sixty-two-foot wingspan. And its very responsive engines make it much easier for the Hornet to maintain the proper airspeed than the sluggish response of the single-engined A-7.

But the plane itself is only half the equation. From the first flight of the Hornet in November 1978 until the first deployment of two squadrons on a carrier in February 1985 was a span of five years. And much of that time was spent selecting and training pilots to fly the new plane and mechanics to service it.

Two years after the first flight, the first training squadron—VFA-125—was commissioned in November 1980, at Lemoore, under the command of Capt. James W. Partington, a veteran A-7 attack pilot. Four months later, on 10 March 1981, Partington and marine Capt. Doug Tyler picked up their first two-cockpit training plane in St. Louis, flew it to Lemoore, and immediately turned it over for the maintenance crews to study for a month.

For the next year and a half, thirty-two hand-picked navy and marine fighter and attack pilots taught themselves to fly the Hornet so they, in turn, could train the "nuggets"—the new pilots just out of the training schools—and the experienced pilots moving over from their older A-7s and F-4s to the new F/A-18.

The one great advantage the instructors had, beyond their combined experience with the fleet, was the presence of very realistic simulators that permitted them to put in hundreds of hours in the cockpit of a Hornet before they first left the ground. In the past, simulators had most often come along months, or even years, after a plane went into service, and even then they often provided only a pale approximation of what it was like to actually fly the plane. In this case, a determined effort was made to have the simulators available well before the planes themselves were ready, and to make them as realistic as possible.

Three different simulators were developed. Gould Simulation Systems provided a relatively simple part task trainer to familiarize the pilot with the cockpit and permit him to practice manipulating the switches and other cockpit controls—to learn his "switchology," as they say.

The Sperry Corporation's Flight Simulation Division (later a part of Hughes Aircraft) built a more complex operational flight trainer to provide practice in all the basic flying skills. The trainee sits in a cockpit inside a large dome, and an operator at an outside panel controls what the pilot sees. With a flip of a switch, he can create daylight, a moonlit night, or total darkness. He can present the image of a carrier so the pilot can practice landing time after time, and then the operator can change the scene inside to permit the pilot to navigate back to his home airfield and land.

The most advanced simulator is the weapons tactics trainer developed by Hughes Aircraft. In this device, the pilot again sits in a cockpit in the center of a large dome. But here he is able to practice both aerial combat maneuvering—dogfighting—and attacks on ground targets.

The computer that forms the brains of the trainer can automatically present the pilot with foes of varying levels of skill. At the most basic level, a hostile plane appears off to the side and then flies smoothly around in front of the simulated F/A-18. Even a novice can maneuver the plane, center the target in the sights, and pull the trigger when the strobe in his HUD flashes "SHOOT . . . SHOOT . . . SHOOT." The result is a satisfying flash as the enemy plane explodes. But as the controller ratchets up the skill level of the hostile pilot, it becomes harder and harder even to keep an eye on the other fellow, let alone get in a shot at him. He may disappear one moment and then flash past head-on, large as life, with gun blazing.

The system was designed so that two or more pilots, each in a separate dome, can fly together or fight against each other. In each dome, the images of the planes controlled by the pilots in the other simulators are flashed on the inside surface of the dome, growing larger or smaller, depending on their distance.

The controller outside can complicate the combat by triggering cockpit warnings such as "bingo"—low fuel—or an engine fire. The simulator itself monitors altitude—very realistically. If a pilot forgets to watch his altitude, he may suddenly hear a crashing sound in his earphones and be startled to see his altitude indicator reeling off negative numbers.

Both the device developed by Sperry and the Hughes simulator provide a remarkably realistic sense of actual flying except for the extreme pressures of gravity that are a constant part of the fighter pilot's life.

Creating these realistic simulators was a daunting challenge. If they had had their way, the designers would have rigged actual airplanes with instruments and gathered the data they needed to duplicate the flying characteristics of the plane in a dome on the ground. But the flight test program was already so crowded that there was no room for special flights for the simulator designers. Instead, they took whatever information they could gather while tests were being flown for other purposes.

They also faced a firm deadline. The navy planned to begin training the instructor pilots early in 1982, and it insisted on having Sperry's operational flight trainer installed at Lemoore by that time.

Pilots who flew the plane and then tried the same maneuvers in the simulator were surprised to find that "flying" on the ground was almost exactly the same as flying in the air throughout the plane's entire flight envelope. The one major discrepancy cropped up when pilots involved in the early carrier landing tests of the Hornet stepped into the simulator and found that it didn't match the guide slope they had flown in their actual flights. By the time the simulator went into service at Lemoore, that and a few other less serious discrepancies had been found and fixed.

When the initial small group of pilots had taught themselves to fly the Hornet, their first job was to train the marines who would form the first operational F/A-18 squadron. The marines, who had made a conscious decision to keep flying their aging F-4s while waiting for the new Hornet, deserved to be first in the new plane. But the marines felt the fact they came first was also a great help in getting the Hornet off to a good start.

Unlike the navy pilots, traditionally segregated into fighter and attack squadrons, the marines, with their strong commitment to close support of their fellow leathernecks on the ground, expected their pilots to perform both fighter and attack missions. Although the navy bomber pilots doubted the marines' skill at dropping bombs, the marines were comfortable stepping into a new plane designed to do both jobs.

Even as training of the pilots for the first squadron began in 1982, however, there were many in the navy who continued to doubt that a pilot could be taught to be as good at both aerial combat and ground attack as pilots trained separately for the two jobs. Their doubts were buttressed by the navy's decision to give the pilots the "firehose treatment"—teach them to fly the plane, to dogfight, and to deliver bombs and missiles, all in about thirty-six weeks, the same time that other training squadrons had traditionally used to train pilots in just one of those skills.

Today, this introduction to the F/A-18 is conducted by two squadrons—VFA 125, the Rough Raiders, at Lemoore, and VFA 106, the Gladiators, formed at Cecil Field on 27 April 1984, to serve the East Coast carriers. Each is known as a RAG, for Replacement Air Group, but that is actually a misnomer, harking back to the days when entire air groups were trained as a unit. The proper name for today's training squadrons is the seldom-used Readiness Training Squadron.

Before a nugget comes to the RAG, he has spent about 200 hours in the air and has taken off from a carrier and landed again—just enough to know what it feels like.

Much of the time he spends in training in the RAG, of course, is devoted to learning how to fly the plane skillfully. In this sense, the training is much like that offered earlier to F-4 or A-7 pilots preparing to fly fighters or bombers. On every landing, for example, the pilot "flies the meatball," simulating his approach and landing on a carrier. Navigating to and from the training area and flying in formation are also the same, whether the training involves aerial combat or bombing. The instructors were pleasantly surprised to find that nuggets, with the help of the Hornet's computerized controls, were quickly able to fly as smoothly and efficiently as pilots with long experience in other planes.

In the past, fighter and attack pilots argued endlessly over which of their skills was most difficult. But most Hornet pilots now agree that what they call "ACM"—Aerial Combat Maneuvering—is the most demanding. Partly, this is due to the fact that the computerized bombing system in the F/A-18 is so good that even the rawest nuggets, on their first day at the bombing ranges, often do better than veteran pilots in older airplanes. The same is not true in aerial combat. Personal skill is most often the factor that distinguishes winners from losers or, in actual combat, the living from the dead.

Surprisingly, despite all the advances in aerodynamics and weaponry, fighting in the air has changed remarkably little from the days of the Spads and the Fokkers, three-quarters of a century ago. The major difference is that the time that planes may be engaged in combat has shrunk, while the volume of air space in which they fight has greatly expanded.

An indication of how little things have changed is the fact that an important part of the manual used by pilots in training at Cecil Field and Lemoore includes a comparison of rules for aerial combat set out at four different periods. First is a list of eight rules submitted to the German chief of war aviation in 1915 by Oswald Boelcke, the foremost theorist of aerial combat in World War I; another set of ten rules written by Adolph (''Sailor'') Malan, a South African pilot who scored twenty-nine kills during the Battle of Britain; an expanded list of twenty-five offensive and nineteen defensive rules written by Frederick (''Boots'') Blesse, an American air force pilot who downed ten planes in Korea and an even longer set prepared by the authors of the manual now used to train F/A-18 pilots.

Basically, today's rules, while taking account of changes in aircraft and weapons performance, are still about eighty percent consistent with Boelcke's list.

The pilots in training are told: ''Above all (and taken for granted in Boelcke, Malan, Blesse, and anything intelligent written about fighter combat) is aggressiveness. It should be patient; it may even be cautious, but the absolute essential is a deep-seated drive to kill.''

Much of the training, both on the ground and in the air, is focused on teaching pilots how to win in aerial combat against another fighter. And yet pilots are warned that is the last thing they want to do. They are told, over and over: ''Don't fight one versus one unless it's a matter of life or death.''

Lt. Comdr. Dave Jones, an instructor at Cecil Field, puts it this way: ''I never want to fight. My ideal—and this may sound crude in civilian terms—is an assassination. I'm going to come sneaking up on this guy and kill him before he even knows I'm around. I'm not out there to turn and burn and do Top Gun stuff. I'm out there to put 'em down, and I don't want them to ever know I'm around. I want a guy to be flying along and then next thing he knows he's hanging in his parachute wondering what the hell happened. That's my idea of a perfect day in combat. My ideal is, when he's six or eight miles away, he just goes up in a puff of smoke, and I just keep right on going.''

To understand what it is like to go into combat, first accompany a section of two Hornets on a combat air patrol. Before they ever take off, the two pilots spend hours preparing for the flight, learning everything they can about their potential enemy: How many planes will they face? What type? Do they carry missiles capable of firing head-on, or only from the rear quadrant? How skilled are the other pilots? Will the enemy be under ground control? How much antiaircraft fire should be expected, and where?

Attention to the tiniest detail pays off. Deck crews carefully clean and polish the cockpit canopies so there won't be a speck of dirt to confuse the pilot in the heat of combat. Helmets, already personally contoured to fit the individual, are tightly cinched so the helmet and visor won't shift position under the stress of gravity.

As part of their preparation for the flight, the two pilots enter into a series of "contracts" that spell out what they will do in a variety of circumstances. This means they may not even have to exchange radio messages: they will act almost as though they were both in the same plane. As much as possible, these "contracts" between the lead pilot and his wing man are designed to make up for the fact that the Hornet is a one-man plane.

As they head out on the patrol, the wing man flies slightly to the rear of the lead plane, from three-quarters of a mile to a mile and a half away, and within 3,000 feet above or below the lead plane's altitude. If the two pilots get any further apart, it is hard for them to see each other and difficult to coordinate their actions. But, by spreading apart, they make it much more difficult for an enemy pilot to see both planes. They have been careful to pick an altitude just below that at which contrails would be formed. That way, they will not give away their position but will be able to see planes flying at a slightly higher altitude.

The lead pilot sweeps the area ahead with his radar in the relatively short range at which his Sidewinder missiles will be effective. The wing man, in effect, looks over the lead pilot's shoulder, using the longer range setting of the Sparrow missile. This way, they will be able to sort out the enemy planes. If the lead pilot picks up one plane, the wing man will look for the second. If they spot two planes, they will search for a trailing section of two more planes.

Even with the Hornet's superb radar, good eyesight makes all the difference when hostile planes come within visual range of each other. The pilot who can see the other fellow first and keep him in view is the one who is most likely to live. The two men on the combat patrol constantly scan the skies, trying to overcome the eye's natural tendency to focus a few inches in front of a person's face.

If they pick up the enemy planes on radar at twenty to thirty miles, they will be about a minute and a half apart, time to swing carefully off to the side—but not so abruptly as to signal their presence by the flash of sunlight from a wing—and fire missiles that will hit the other planes from the rear quadrant. If they don't spot the other planes until they are fifteen miles away, they will be only forty-five seconds apart and will have to use their head-on missiles.

One of the most dangerous mistakes is to turn to fight the first enemy plane you spot. Novice pilots are warned: "Never turn your belly up to a trail group." Much better is to fire head-on missiles at the first enemy section, put on speed, and "blow through" to engage the other planes trailing eight to ten miles behind.

But what if the first shot misses and, as the pilots say, "the bogey is alive at the pass"? There may be no choice but to fight. Suddenly it is one against one, and the odds are very high that one pilot will have to knock the other plane out of the sky before he can go home. It is at that moment, as the training manual says, that "you are so scared you want to puke, and your IQ drops to fourteen."

It is also at that moment, as the two planes hurtle past each other at a combined speed of more than a thousand miles an hour and so close that the two men can see each other, that skill and training pay off as the Hornet pilot sizes up his adversary. Does he have a gun? Is he carrying missiles? Then stay so close he won't have room for the missiles to arm themselves. What is his energy state? If he is making very tight turns, he is bleeding off energy at a rapid rate and may not be able to respond to your next maneuver. Is he pushing his plane to the limit or is he holding something in reserve?

Most critical: How good a pilot is he?

All those questions flashed through the mind of Lt. Randy Cunningham on 10 May 1972, one of the most intensive days of aerial combat in the Vietnam War. Cunningham, flying an F-4 Phantom from the U.S.S. *Constellation* with Lt. William Driscoll in the back seat as radar intercept officer, attacked air defenses as part of a major "Alpha" strike against the Haiphong rail yards. Then, as they came off the target, they were almost immediately jumped by two MiG-17s.

Cunningham's homework paid off. He knew that it is almost impossible for the pilot to move the stick of a MiG-17 when he is going very fast. Cunningham turned sharply toward the first plane and the pilot was unable to respond. Then he hit the second MiG with a Sidewinder.

Moments later, Cunningham fired a second Sidewinder and shot down another MiG-17 just as it was about to attack a fellow Phantom.

When four MiG-21s dove on them from above, Cunningham and Driscoll decided it was time to head for home. As they turned toward the carrier, Cunningham spotted a MiG-17 heading toward him. In training, Cunningham had often flown against A-4s simulating the performance of a MiG and had found one of the most effective tactics was to fly straight at the other pilot in an effort to intimidate him. The tactic almost got him killed.

"I bored in on the 17 . . . head on," Cunningham later recounted. "Suddenly, his whole nose lit up like a Christmas tree. I had forgotten that the A-4s didn't shoot at you, but this guy was really spitting out the 23-mm and 37-mm."

Cunningham pulled back hard on the stick and zoomed into the vertical. But the MiG pilot came right with him, followed him over the top and started shooting again. Up and down the two planes went, with the Vietnamese pilot shooting every time they came over the top. Very quickly it became obvious to Cunningham that his opponent was not just lucky. He was good!

Finally, the other pilot, apparently running low on fuel, decided to bug out and went into a vertical dive. Cunningham followed him down and loosed a Sidewinder at the fleeing plane, even though he knew that the missile, with its heat-seeking nose, would almost certainly be distracted by heat sources on the ground. But, as Cunningham and Driscoll watched, the other plane blew up in a flash of flame and a cloud of black smoke, and dove straight into the earth. They later learned that their adversary had been a Colonel Tomb, at that time the leading North Vietnamese ace, with thirteen American planes shot down.

The three victories that day, added to the two MiGs they had shot down earlier in the year, made Cunningham and Driscoll the first American aces of the war. They were, unfortunately, wet aces. As they headed seaward after their victory over Tomb, they were hit by an antiaircraft missile and forced to eject. Both men were quickly rescued by helicopter and returned to the *Constellation*.

On a combat air patrol, the chances of knocking out the enemy at long range with a missile are good. But on a bombing mission, it may be impossible to avoid a dogfight, or even one dogfight after another, as Cunningham and Driscoll learned.

On every attack where opposition is expected, several of the Hornets will be designated as fighters to protect the planes carrying bombs. If the likelihood of running into enemy fighters is slight, all the planes will carry bombs, but the pilots of several of them will be prepared to jettison their bombs and become fighters if they are jumped.

A pilot assigned to protect the attacking force must, if he sees an enemy plane that threatens the heavily laden bombers, react to the threat even though he, with a lighter load, might easily avoid a fight. If he can't drive off the enemy or knock him out with a missile, he may well find himself in a dogfight.

Even more likely is that the attacking planes will be jumped near the target by enemy fighters, just as Cunningham and Driscoll were. If the defenders can force the Hornets to dump their bombs before they reach the target, that is almost as good as shooting the attacking plane down. And the enemy fighters are likely to be waiting as the bombers come off the target, trying to escape and head back home. If that happens, the pilot of a Hornet has the great advantage of being able to convert his plane into a fighter with that one flick of the switch on his control stick. But he is still in trouble.

Even if he has already dropped his bombs, he will be carrying at least one fuel tank on the center line, his Sparrow and Sidewinder missiles, and a load of ammunition for his gun. All that weight and resistance to the air degrades the plane's performance. His hope is that the enemy plane, even though it requires less fuel because it is close to home, will also be hampered by the drag of its weapons.

A Hornet pilot is justified to think that his plane is still markedly superior to any other plane he will meet in combat. He can rightly figure that, as a dogfight begins, the odds in his favor are about seven to one. But he faces not just one enemy—the hostile pilot—but another more insidious enemy, time.

Each second the fight lasts, the odds drop precipitously, like sand running out of an hourglass. The reason is not only the flow of fuel through the afterburner, but the fact that a dogfight is like a big neon sign drawing attention to itself.

Picture two planes involved in a dogfight. They fly up and down, around and around, all the time twisting and turning, losing energy and moving slower and slower. As the fight degenerates in this way, the Hornet, with its superior performance at a very high angle of attack, has the advantage. But if the pilot cannot exploit that advantage quickly, he is in deadly trouble. With each twist of the planes, there is a flash of wing, calling attention to the fight. Every enemy pilot within a ten-mile radius—418 square miles—can be there within a minute. By that time, the odds of survival are one to one, at best. If the fight lasts two minutes, the circle of danger expands geometrically to more than 1,800 square miles.

The first goal of a pilot who finds himself in a dogfight is a quick kill—the quicker the better. But even a quick victory can be dangerous. The fireball of an exploding plane is a more powerful magnet for hostile pilots than the wing-flashing signals from a dogfight. If a fight begins to drag out, even a pilot confident of victory should turn his thoughts to the best way to bug out and go home. If he breaks contact skillfully, he may be able to get away, even if he has to outrun or outmaneuver an air-to-air missile as he escapes.

The key to a successful bug out, as to everything connected with aerial combat, is a poorly understood quality called "situational awareness," or SA. Basically, it means the ability of a pilot to carry in his mind a total picture of what is going on around him.

Imagine how critical it is for a pilot to have a full grasp of the situation when he tries to leave the scene of a dogfight, whether or not he has scored a victory. How much fuel does he have left? How many enemy fighters are in the area and where are they? Are there any friendly planes to provide protection?

Most basically, he must know the way to the carrier. Before the skilled pilot ever gets into a fight, he will have in his mind the relationship between the position of the sun and the course to the carrier. Thus, if he decides to bug out, he will know generally which way to go without bothering with a compass heading. But he should also have in mind the location of enemy defenses. The long way home may be the safest way to go.

Successful fighter pilots have this kind of awareness almost as an inborn instinct. No one is quite sure why some men have it and others have it in a lesser degree.

Robin Olds, an ace in World War II and a near-ace (four MiGs destroyed) in Vietnam, is often cited as an example of a pilot who had an almost uncanny ability to keep track of everything that was happening, even when fighting for his life. In one instance over North Vietnam, Olds was busy hassling with two MiG-17s. Ten thousand feet above them, another American plane made a slashing gun attack on a MiG. Olds calmly radioed congratulations on a nice shot.

In today's high-performance planes such as the Hornet, situational awareness is vital not only in combat but in everyday flying. By the mid-1980s, there was growing concern about the loss of SA among otherwise experienced pilots. There had been eleven cases in which F-16 pilots had flown into the ground—and in nine of those cases investigators concluded that the pilot had lost contact with reality: he didn't know where his plane was or where it was headed. What happened at Patuxent River on 22 October 1986 provided chilling evidence that this was not just a problem for the air force.

On that hazy afternoon, marine Maj. Rick Shows and his boss, navy Comdr. Keith E. Crawford, each piloting an F/A-18 as part of a test program to check out the plane for use by the Blue Angels aerobatic team, were flying in close formation where the Patuxent enters the Chesapeake Bay.

Both men were among their services' most skilled pilots. Shows was a graduate of the Top Gun aerial combat school, a low-altitude tactics instructor and a graduate in the top third of his class at the U.S. Naval Test Pilot School. Crawford had graduated first in his class at the test pilot school and then served as an instructor of other test pilots.

Shows, flying lead, did a mild wingover maneuver and headed down toward the water, rolling first to the right and then back to the left, intending to level off at 1,000 feet. He later described what happened next:

At that instant I was getting ready to do the next maneuver and thinking about what I was going to do next. . . . I looked in the mirror because I had my mirror set up to watch Keith, and I turned my head to Keith to see if he was still in a good position, the position we had briefed, probably ten feet or so away from my wing. When I glanced back—this is only a number of seconds—I looked at the HUD and I saw 600 feet. I couldn't believe it. Where did that come from? At the very next instant when I realized that I was at 600 feet and couldn't understand it, I was in the water. I saw calm water, I saw pieces of wood floating in the water. I was in the water! Instinct took over. I pulled back on the stick and at the same instant the realization hit me that I had a wing man; Keith was on my wing.

I immediately looked over to the left and Keith was still in perfect formation with me. He had pulled [up] with me. . . . I realized the horror of everything and what had occurred. I don't know how I had gotten there. All of a sudden I was in the water, wings level, and I pulled back on the stick. I knew he was there. I immediately looked to my left and Keith was still in position on my wing fifteen feet away or so. His airplane was entering the water and mine wasn't. . . . It looked like he may have been five degrees more nose down, pitch attitude than my aircraft. I thought I was a dead man, but he was in the water on my left wing and I saw that I wasn't.

A report on the accident included this transcript of Shows's radio transmissions in the forty-six seconds leading up to the crash:

"Okay, let's reverse right coming nose high.

"A little more G and then roll right.

"More roll.

"A little drive here.

"Let's reverse it left.

"A little more pull."

And then, three seconds later: "Oh, my GOD!"

An eyewitness later told investigators he had seen the first plane hit the water, followed immediately by the second. And then, he said, a third plane flew away from the wreckage. What he saw, of course, was Shows's plane emerging from the plume of water sent up by his engines and Crawford's fatal impact with the water.

Shows later told investigators he had often, in his flying career, been frightened and even thought of dying. But in this case, his situational awareness badly awry, he felt none of those fears: "I thought everything was perfect, everything was fine, everything was going good."

Once a pilot in a plane like the Hornet loses situational awareness, he may be only moments from death. If a pilot flying at more than 400 miles an hour, as Shows and Crawford were, at a supposedly safe 10,000 feet, inadvertently heads toward the earth, he has less than twenty seconds to realize his error and pull out.

In many ways, the "glass cockpit" of the F/A-18 is an enormous advantage to the pilot in helping him to keep totally aware of the situation around him. At the flick of a switch, his radar can search near or far, high or low, in a broad area or in a narrow beam. The heads up display permits him to follow up the clues from his radar so he will see other planes as they come in view. This is especially important if air crews are required, as they were in Vietnam, to identify a potentially hostile plane visually before firing a weapon. In the case of most MiG-type targets, this involves coming within about two miles of the other plane—a few seconds apart. Unfortunately, the glass cockpit may also detract from situational awareness at critical moments. In the accident in which Crawford was killed, Shows apparently misread the information on his HUD. He might have had a clearer picture of his situation with the old-fashioned instruments, in which a large ball in the middle of his panel showed him which way his wings were tilted, and the needle of the altimeter, spinning counterclockwise, alerting him to the closeness of the ground.

A navy study done two years before that accident called attention to possible confusion resulting from use of the HUD as the primary flight instrument. It also noted that the F/A-18 flies so smoothly that the pilot is even less able than in other planes to "fly by the seat of his pants," sensing what the plane is doing. The result is that he may experience large, sudden changes in airspeed, altitude, or attitude and not be aware of them. These factors, the study concluded, "make this airplane particularly susceptible to pilot's loss of situational awareness and subsequent CWG." In the navy, which has an acronym for everything, CWG equals "collision with ground."

Fortunately, younger pilots who have grown up with computers and video games seem to be much more comfortable with the glass cockpit, with its digital displays and symbols, than pilots who learned to fly with the old steam gauges.

The loss of situational awareness is not the only problem faced by those who fly the F/A-18 and other very high performance planes, and it is probably not the most severe or dangerous problem. The Hornet is capable of taking the pilot right up to the edges of human endurance, and perhaps a little beyond.

Probably the most insidious problem—one that has cost the lives of a number of pilots—is the sudden loss of consciousness caused when the force of gravity prevents sufficient blood from reaching the brain.

In the past, a pilot might experience as much as nine Gs if he put his plane in a steep dive and then pulled back on the stick as hard as he could. Such a maneuver gave his body time to adjust to the pressure. But in the Hornet, a pilot can subject himself and his plane to more than seven Gs simply by turning sharply.

Computers in both the Hornet and F-16 Falcon automatically limit the amount of gravity the pilot can impose on the plane—seven and a half Gs in the F/A-18, nine Gs in the F-16. While these limits protect the plane from damage, they also leave the pilot free to push himself to the limit or beyond, and to do it quickly and often. In either plane, it is possible to go from the normal one unit of gravity to the plane's limit in less than half a second, with the pressure of gravity increasing at the rate of fifteen or sixteen Gs per second. A Hornet pilot who weighs 150 pounds one moment will weigh 1,125 pounds the next. The poorly understood effects of repeated instances of the sudden increase of gravitational force has flight surgeons and aircraft designers deeply worried.

All pilots of high-performance combat planes now routinely wear a tight-fitting garment called a G suit. As the force of gravity increases, the suit automatically fills with air and pushes blood upward toward the head. Without the G suit, a normal person will begin to black out shortly after the pressures exceed four times the force of gravity. With the G suit, an experienced pilot in good condition can withstand about nine Gs for a minute or so.

Under such pressures, the first faculty to go is eyesight. The pilot is still conscious, and he can hear and think, but he seems to be peering through a gray tunnel. Then, without any warning, consciousness may go, and the pilot has blacked out.

Losing consciousness while flying a plane is extremely dangerous. Blacking out in a dogfight means death.

Al Frazier, the McDonnell Douglas test pilot who has specialized in studying the effects of gravity, tells what it is like to black out:

"I was in the back seat of a T-38 on takeoff, when the pilot did a real fast climb. When I woke up, I looked around and I couldn't believe it. I'm in an airplane! I had no realization of where I was, what I was doing. Then, after a few seconds, I thought, 'Oh my God, am I flying? Am I the pilot?' It takes thirty to forty-five seconds after a pilot wakes up to gain his senses back enough to fly the plane. If you're pointed at the ground, you don't have thirty to forty-five seconds. That's why we're losing airplanes."

The G suit is no longer adequate to protect pilots of today's combat aircraft. Even if it keeps the pilot conscious, it does not protect his bones from the type of stresses to which they are subjected when he does a high-G turn while straining to look over his shoulder. All the aircraft manufacturers are working to develop better suits, but they seem to be reluctant to spend the money to go into production for fear that something better will come along quickly. In the meantime, the emphasis is on training pilots to protect themselves from blacking out.

One of the best protections is provided by nature. The short, stocky person, with a short, thick neck and a tendency toward high blood pressure has a much better chance of remaining conscious than the tall, thin pilot who has to pump blood a longer distance from heart to eyes and brain. Pilots are being warned to avoid long-distance running and, instead, to spend time in the weight room developing strong abdominal muscles. One air force pilot who ignored his flight surgeon's advice and continued to run marathons later blacked out and crashed.

When pilots pull Gs, they are taught to strain and grunt to push blood upward, almost like a little boy straining to make his face turn red. Air force fighter pilots and all test pilots actually practice this maneuver in a centrifuge, but the navy does not yet require centrifuge training for its pilots.

Since there is no way to eliminate the possibility of blackouts, Mc-Donnell Douglas is testing a system for the Hornet that will recognize when the pilot blacks out and releases his pressure on the controls, sense where and how far away the ground is, and instruct the automatic pilot to level the plane off and fly it until the pilot recovers. The system could be a life-saver in peacetime but not much help in a dogfight.

Whether routinely pulling Gs, especially now that the sudden onset of Gs has become so common, will have any effect on the long-term health of pilots is still unknown, because the planes capable of such stresses have not been around long enough for pilots to spend a career pulling high Gs and then to grow old. One predictable effect is hemorrhoids—a near-universal affliction of fighter pilots. There is also a folk belief among pilots that those who frequently experience high G loads tend to father girls.

Far from worrying, along with the flight surgeons and the designers, about the effects of gravity, pilots learning to master the Hornet at Lemoore seemed to revel in their ability to survive these enormous pressures and to do things few other mortals have the chance to do. They even purported to find it pleasurable to pull Gs. The truth is probably closer to the experience of Mike Tkach. He told friends that it was not until he stopped flying as a McDonnell Douglas test pilot that he realized how much he hurt all the time.

As the initial group of instructor-pilots finished their own training at Lemoore and were followed into the Hornet's cockpits by the first marine squadron and then the first two navy squadrons, there was suddenly a vast flow of information about how this new strike-fighter behaved in the hands of the fliers who would actually take it to sea for the first time. They flew far more hours, in a greater variety of missions, than the test pilots in their precisely monitored test programs. And they were far freer to experiment and improvise than the pilots of VX-4 and VX-5 in their operational evaluations.

One crucial discovery was that the Hornet lends itself to new ways of bombing with a much higher chance of survival than the methods used by the A-6 and A-7. These new tactics were refined in a 1,500-square-mile instrumented range east of Fallon Naval Air Station in the Nevada desert.

Standard tactics in the past had called for a thirty-second separation between attacking planes. This permitted time for the fragments of the bombs dropped by the first plane to reach their zenith and fall back to earth before the next plane attacked. If he came in any sooner, the second pilot would fly through the "frag envelope" of the first plane's bombs and run the risk of being shot down by debris from a "friendly" bomb. But the thirty-second separation gave gunners on the ground time to aim and shoot at the follow-on attackers.

The obvious solution was to streak in toward the target at a low altitude to prevent detection, then pull up sharply to avoid ground fire and bomb fragments. The attack would be made from a safer altitude, and the planes would need only a few seconds of separation rather than a half-minute. But the older A-6 and A-7 bombers didn't have the energy for such a maneuver. As the pilots at Lemoore began to experiment with the F/A-18 with its two powerful engines, they found they had the energy to do what they had never been able to do in the older planes. What evolved is called the "Hornet high pop."

In this tactic, the pilot begins his run toward the target about five miles out and 200 feet above the ground (or lower in combat), and flying about 600 miles an hour. As he approaches the target, he kicks in his afterburners, pulls hard back on the stick, and streaks upward at a forty-five-degree angle to 10,000 feet. There, two miles above the target—and well above the threat of small-arms fire and the frag envelope—he rolls, recovers, and drops his bombs from about 8,000 feet.

Increasingly, Hornet pilots are relying on tactics that take advantage of the plane's power to keep them out of the range of deadly small-arms fire from the ground. They also attack from different altitudes. In one experiment at Fallon, thirteen planes dropped their bombs from 16,000 feet, with all of them in and out of the target area in forty-five seconds.

In an actual bombing attack, the planes fly in a "battle box," with two Hornets in the lead spread 4,000 to 6,000 feet apart, followed by one or two trail sections of two planes each, flying three to four nautical miles back. The approach is at high altitude to conserve fuel. Then, at about a hundred miles out, each of the two-plane sections takes a different route, adjusting their airspeed so they will all reach their goal from a different direction at the same time, about twelve minutes later.

Despite the rule drilled into the consciousness of every attack pilot that "speed is life," the fliers experimenting at Lemoore found that it may be better to approach the target at a comfortable speed of about 500 knots and as high as 500 feet, rather than to fly faster and lower where the increased sensation of speed, cockpit noise, and increased sensitivity of the flight controls all make the pilot's basic job of controlling the plane more difficult.

In a well-coordinated attack, a flight of Hornets can be in and out of the target zone in a few seconds, flying at different altitudes and from different directions, presenting a dizzying problem for the defenders.

As they leave the target area, the pilots go to full power and jink rapidly from side to side so they don't remain on the same heading for more than three to five seconds. The Hornet is capable of putting on speed rapidly as it climbs away from the target, and here it is very true that "speed is life." This burst of vertical speed makes the F/A-18 a difficult target for enemy aircraft. It is safer from surface-to-air missiles (SAMs), however, if it stays low. Tactics will depend on which threat seems most dangerous.

If the SAM threat is severe, the pilots are likely to see telephone pole-sized missiles rising toward them, riding a plume of fire. The standard tactic is to turn sharply toward the missile, trying to make it stall out in the attempt to follow the wildly jinking plane. An A-6 or A-7 may be able to make one or two such violent maneuvers, but then they run out of energy. The Hornet, on the other hand, has the power and agility to outmaneuver a missile if the pilot sees it in time.

The pilots in training also began to find some encouraging answers to questions about the Hornet's range.

In the spring of 1981, Admiral Gillcrist, then a wing commander at Miramar, visited Lemoore, where Lenox held a similar post. He found two air force F-15 pilots whom Lenox had invited in to engage them in a dogfight. This was part of Lenox's continuing campaign to "sell" the Hornet to the navy. Flying in a two-seat plane with another pilot, Gillcrist's inclination was to enter the fight at about 600 knots. He was alarmed when his co-pilot suggested they hold their speed to about 340 knots, the speed at which the Hornet turns best, as the F-15s streaked toward them at almost twice that rate.

"I felt absolutely obscene staying at 340 knots while the enemy, now in full view, were roaring in at twice our velocity," Gillcrist says. As his adversary passed about a hundred feet to his right, the Eagle pilot broke toward him, streaking almost straight up. Gillcrist slammed his plane into afterburner and followed the F-15. As they completed a full circle, he had turned tightly enough to put the F-15 at a clear disadvantage. Moments later, Gillcrist pulled in behind him and the fight ended.

Three more encounters brought the same result. Then the battle ended abruptly when one of the F-15 pilots called "bingo." His plane, with its larger load of fuel, had run out of gas. The two F/A-18s still had enough fuel left for another round of combat between themselves before they had to go home.

"I was totally astonished," Gillcrist recalled later. "Here I was flying in an airplane that had been highly criticized for its lack of internal fuel capacity, and I just ran the highly touted long-range Eagle out of fuel. Amazing! The real operational significance of the Hornet had finally sunk in."

When Gillcrist was assigned to the Pentagon the following year as director of aviation plans and requirements, he didn't realize at first that he had walked into a big controversy over the results of the operational evaluation run by Admiral Carter. His suspicions were raised, he says, when Carter ordered his pilots not to answer calls from Gillcrist. So Gillcrist called Lemoore and arranged for the pilots there to fly their own simulated missions to check the range.

The data they sent back provided a much more optimistic picture of the Hornet's range than that coming from Carter, and Gillcrist used it to the utmost in the debates within the navy. "That saved the plane," Gillcrist concluded.

The controversy was still going on in Washington when the marines finished their training at Lemoore and moved to their own base at El Toro, where VMFA 314, the first squadron of Hornets, was commissioned on 7 January 1983. The commander was Lt. Col. Pete Field, who, as a test pilot, was the first to encounter the roll rate problem at Patuxent three years before.

When the first Hornets came on the scene, pilots of the new plane were not permitted to participate in the Navy Fighter Weapons School at Miramar. The school—popularly known as "Top Gun"—had been formed in 1969 in a successful effort to improve the combat skills of navy and marine pilots, whose performance against MiGs in Vietnam had left much to be desired. By the early 1980s, Top Gun had become an F-14 enclave, and Hornets were not welcome. As soon as this parochial rule was sensibly set aside, the marines, from their vantage point at nearby El Toro, made it a practice to volunteer to fill any vacancies in the Top Gun classes. As a result, marine Hornet squadrons have a higher percentage of these highly skilled fighter pilots than any other fighting units in the world.

It was not very long, as we have seen, after the marines began flying the Hornet in their normal operations that the first tail cracks were found. The discovery of this problem could not have come at a worse time because the pilots and mechanics forming the first two navy squadrons were under a tight training schedule, preparing to go to sea early in 1985.

Strangely, the disruption resulting from the grounding of the planes caused more distress for the mechanics than for the pilots. While the pilots continued with their ground school and flew the plane frequently in the simulators, the mechanics had become emotionally attached to "their" planes and fretted as they were taken away from them to be modified by McDonnell Douglas experts.

Master Chief Don Leap, who was at Lemoore then, says: "We got very possessive of the aircraft. When there was talk they might be giving us another aircraft, morale of the squadron went down real quick. We wanted to take our own planes on the cruise, the ones we'd groomed, the ones we'd babied."

The mechanics' fears, as it turned out, were not justified. They got their own planes back and the navy's first two Hornet squadrons, VFA 113, the Stingers, and VFA 25, the Fist of the Fleet, or Fisties, embarked on the U.S.S. *Constellation* and set sail for the western Pacific and the Indian Ocean late in February 1985.

For Leap and many of the other mechanics in the two squadrons, the cruise was, for the large part, almost boring. All the effort put into making the plane reliable and easy to maintain paid off. Often, at the end of a day of flying, the F-14s and A-6s were in for repairs, but the F/A-18s were ready to fly again.

Two serious problems did, however, require far more work by the mechanics than had been expected.

The first problem involved the fuel cells inside the plane. During the Vietnam War, North Vietnamese infantrymen were taught to lie on their backs as a plane approached, point their rifles skyward and fire in unison on a whistled signal. It was a simple, primitive tactic—and it brought down more planes than MiG fighters, missiles, and rapid-fire antiaircraft guns. To make the Hornet less vulnerable to such cheap kills, the plane's fuel is contained in self-sealing cells with most of the plumbing inside the cells. Thus, if a cell is hit it seals itself; if a fuel line is hit the leak is inside the cell, and fuel is not lost.

The result is a complex maze of plumbing with many points where fuel lines go through the side of one cell and connect into another cell. These connections turned out to be highly susceptible to leakage. Poor quality control in the manufacture of the rubberized cells themselves created even more leakage problems.

Will Willoughby, the navy's reliability and maintenance guru, had quickly spotted the fuel leak problem. When one of the first Hornets was put on view for the assembled brass at Patuxent, Willoughby noted a McDonnell Douglas employee, wearing sparkling new coveralls, standing under the wing of the plane and surreptitiously reaching up from time to time to wipe leaking fuel from the wing so it would not form a visible puddle on the hangar floor.

With an admiral in tow, Willoughby indulged a fiendish sense of humor by approaching the man and engaging him in conversation, pretending not to notice the fuel slowly flowing, drip, drip, drip, on the man's head.

The fuel leakage was finally brought under control but not before mechanics had spent thousands of frustrating hours tracking down and fixing leaks.

Even more surprising when the Hornet went to sea was the amount of corrosion that occurred in a plane that had been carefully designed to be corrosion-proof. One particularly puzzling problem was the corrosion where the plane's composite skin covers the avionics and radar compartments. Supposedly, the composite material, which doesn't corrode, would protect the metal underneath. To their surprise, the mechanics found instances in which the metal was badly corroded. Tests revealed that an electrical current, much like that in an automobile battery, was flowing between the skin and the metal, eating away the metal. The problem was finally solved by carefully coating the joint between the two with a special sealing material.

Fighting corrosion became a constant battle. With the limited supply of fresh water on a carrier, it was impossible to run out a hose and wash down the planes, even though they became coated, overnight, with a visible residue of salt. Instead, crews attacked the planes with backpack sprayers, trying to get the salt off the most susceptible areas without rubbing it into the cracks. Crews also kept canopies closed to protect the cockpits from salt spray. Even when pilots sat in their planes on five-minute alert, they raised the canopies only enough for a slight breath of air to blow through.

Normally, five-minute alert is one of the least sought-after assignments on a carrier. The pilot gets dressed in all his flying gear, checks out his plane, climbs into the cockpit, and then sits there, ready to be catapulted into the air at any moment. Finally, after four boring, uncomfortable hours, another pilot takes his place. Since the Hornet was not expected to stay aloft for very long, it was built without a relief tube. If the pilot has been imprudent enough to drink too much before climbing into the cockpit, he is forced to unloosen his gear as much as possible and relieve himself into his "piddle pack"—a plastic bag containing a sponge.

As the *Constellation* sailed out across the Pacific and came within range of Bear bombers flying out of bases in the western Soviet Union, assignment to five-minute alert suddenly became prized duty. One of the pilots on alert would be the first Hornet driver to make contact with a Soviet plane.

For several tantalizing days, Bears showed up in the vicinity of the ship, although they did not fly over it, and it was not clear if they had spotted it. On several occasions, Tomcats from the *Connie* rendezvoused with the Bears, but the F/A-18s sat on the deck. Battle group commanders had decided to use the F-14s, with their longer loiter time, to watch the Bears. On 18 March 1985, about a month out of San Diego, between Guam and the Philippines, Comdr. Tom ("Smooth Dog") Vaughn, maintenance officer of the Stingers, was on five-minute alert. As his four-hour stint wore on, he heard a tap on the side of the plane and his relief made the unusual gesture of offering to take his place early. Vaughn declined. Nearby, Lt. Dave ("Red Bone") Martin of the Fisties sat in his F/A-18.

Suddenly, about fifteen minutes before their time was up, Vaughn and Martin heard the order: "Launch the F/A-18s!" Vaughn tells what happened next:

"Within seconds, we launched. The Bears were out quite a way, and they had turned back. We're seeing opportunity slip between our fingers. I told old Red Bone, 'light the burners, we're going after these guys.' We plugged in the burners and started zorching out there after the Bears. For whatever reason, they turned around."

Vaughn, then a lieutenant commander, outranked Martin, so he was the first to pull up alongside a Bear. Martin, who had cameras loaded with both color and black-and-white film, snapped the historic encounter. Vaughn could see a Soviet crewman just as eagerly taking his own pictures of the new American planes. Then Vaughn and Martin changed places. But Vaughn had only black-and-white film, and his pictures didn't turn out very well. It was Martin's shots of Vaughn making the contact that were published. Squadron mates later accused Vaughn of planning it that way.

The Bear is, of course, an old, lumbering, propeller-driven bomber now used primarily for long-range patrol. A still-unanswered question was how well the Hornet would perform if it were called upon to protect the fleet against the fast, modern Backfire bomber, a plane built in a naval version specifically for attacks against American carriers. Would the F/A-18, with its relatively limited range, be able to reach out far enough to take on the Backfires before they launched their missiles and headed for home?

This was precisely the question raised more than a decade before, when Kent Lee argued that the ability of a carrier skipper to arm all his Hornets as interceptors would greatly increase his protection against air attack. Lee had, of course, been laughed out of the room by the F-14 proponents, who contended that only the Tomcat could reach out and hit the enemy bombers far enough from the fleet.

Adm. Leon Edney, who was commander of Carrier Group One, aboard the *Constellation,* and later vice chief of naval operations, was aware of the attention focused on this first test of the Hornet, and he was very concerned about the range. In an attempt to answer the question of the F/A-18's effectiveness against a Backfire raid, Edney set up a series of exercises in which the Hornets were called upon to help protect the *Constellation* from simulated attacks by a regiment of Backfires, as many as twenty-five to forty planes.

In an extreme case, he found the Hornet could pick up attackers as far as 800 miles from the carrier, and it was used often as a deck-launched interceptor to go after planes 450 miles away. In such a role, the Hornet would be most effective in a head-on shot, trying to hit the Backfire before it launched its missiles. The F-14, on the other hand, with its greater ability to loiter far from the carrier and its longer-range radar and missile, would be the first line of defense.

In wartime, he concluded, the range of the Hornet could be stretched at least another fifty miles by reducing the amount of fuel reserved for return to the carrier. In peacetime, pilots like to keep an extra 1,500 pounds of fuel or so to permit as many as three passes at landing on the ship. But, during the *Constellation*'s deployment, the Hornets routinely made it aboard the ship on the first pass more than ninety percent of the time, even at night. In combat, they would use that fuel rather than bring it back aboard.

In other training exercises, Edney sent Hornets out on strikes against targets 500 miles away, using refueling. But unlike an A-6, which, in "truck mode," carries as many as sixteen 500-pound bombs to blanket the target, the F/A-18s carried a small number of bigger bombs—three to five 1,000-pounders—and relied on their computerized bombing system to drop them precisely on the target.

One of the most interesting experiments conducted aboard the *Constellation* involved mixed sections in which an F-14 and an F/A-18 flew together. At first, it seemed logical to put the Tomcat, with its more powerful radar and its two-man crew, in the lead, with the single-place Hornet flying wing. That was soon recognized as a bad idea. Pilots found it much better to put the Hornet out in front, leaving the added burden of flying formation to the pilot of the two-man plane.

Quickly it became apparent that the Tomcat-Hornet team is a deadly combination. The F-14's radar can see farther, but the radar on the F/A-18 is better able to separate out individual targets. The F/A-18's radar also does a better job than that in the F-14 in picking out surface targets, especially over land. The two planes also have two different methods for identifying distant targets. The F-14 has a telescopic television viewer that can see well beyond the range of human eyes, and the Hornet has a still-secret method for telling friend from foe at long ranges.

But while, in many ways, the two planes work beautifully together, pilots also learned that they have to be careful. The Tomcat quickly runs low on fuel if it tries to keep up with the Hornet's high cruising speed. But the F-14 has a higher top speed than the F/A-18, which can go just under twice the speed of sound, so the pilot has to be careful not to run away from his teammate when it is time to bug out and go home.

Knowledge about the strengths and weaknesses of the navy's new strike fighter grew rapidly during the *Connie's* cruise. But the cruise also demonstrated the value of the kind of meticulous training that preceded and continued throughout the deployment.

All this preparation was put to the test one very dark night, as the carrier sailed in the western Pacific about 400 miles from the nearest land.

Lt. Rodger Welch came in out of the dark, touched down on the deck, then boltered and took off again for another pass. The second time around, he made a perfect landing—"right in the spaghetti," as the carrier crews say of the cables crossing the deck—and kept right on going. There weren't even any sparks where his tail hook scraped the deck. The startled landing signals officers took one look and saw the problem: On the previous pass, the tail hook had hit the catapult track and been knocked off to the side. Later tests revealed that the spring that is supposed to snap the hook back into place was not strong enough for the job.

Vaughn was in air ops when the word came from the flight deck.

"There was no way to get him on board," Vaughn recalls. "We scrambled the tankers and figured how much gas it would take to get to Cubi [an American base in the Philippines about 450 miles away.]"

Welch rendezvoused with the tanker, took on about 4,000 pounds of fuel, and turned onto the course for Cubi. The ship told him he would pick up the beacon from shore about 300 miles out, and from there in it would be an easy, although lonely, flight.

Officers in the operations room began drifting off to other parts of the ship. Suddenly Welch radioed an alarming message: "I have a low fuel light." He turned back toward the carrier while deck crews frantically refueled a tanker to try to meet him before he went into the sea. A helicopter was sent out to be on hand for the rescue.

Vaughn called his friend, Lt. Comdr. Bill Shepherd, the squadron operations officer, and they began puzzling out what had gone wrong. Comdr. Craig ("Panda") Langbehn, the squadron commander, arrived, sized up the situation, and concluded: "He's going to have to eject." In the backs of their minds, everyone was aware of the reaction in Washington if a $30 million Hornet fell into the sea on its first deployment because it had run out of gas.

The cause of the problem quickly dawned on the group in the operations room: As a safety measure, the fuel in the plane's drop tank can't be pressurized with the hook down. The load of fuel Welch had taken on had, naturally, gone to the lowest point, the drop tank. So, while he had plenty of fuel aboard, he couldn't pump it up into the plane.

The tanker, finally refueled, was launched and headed outward. Welch radioed that he had the tanker in sight, but he was down to 400 pounds of fuel in one feed tank and zero in the other—both within the gauge error. At any moment, he would radio that his engines had flamed out, and he was ejecting into the dark Pacific.

Suddenly, Shepherd grabbed the microphone and gave him crisp instructions: "Hey, Rodger. Pull the hook circuit breaker, raise the handle, and go to override on the pressurization."

The operations room fell silent. Then Welch's voice crackled over the radio. The fuel was flowing up into his feed tanks: 500 in one, 200 in the other . . . 600 and 300. He was going to make it.

Shepherd later explained the source of his sudden inspiration. Days before, a group of pilots had gathered for one of the "emergency of the day" discussions frequently held during the cruise. One of the questions discussed that day was what prevented the transfer of fuel from the drop tank into the plane. Shepherd remembered the conclusion: It is not the position of the hook, but the position of the hook handle in the cockpit that controls whether the external tank can be pressurized. Thus, even though Welch's tail hook remained useless, he was able, by moving the hook handle, to trick the plane into feeding fuel up into his internal tanks. He took on a load of fuel and landed safely later that night at Cubi.

Broken tail hooks caused several other pilots to fly to shore bases later in the cruise. One pilot twice landed at a British base and returned to the carrier to regale his comrades, who hadn't had a drink for months, with accounts of the hospitality provided by his hosts.

The *Constellation* returned to the West Coast on 23 August 1985, and the pilots flew their planes ashore to Lemoore. Even as they were reunited with their families, navy pilots on the East Coast and marines at El Toro were preparing for the Hornet's maiden voyage aboard the U.S.S. *Coral Sea*. They did not know it then, but they were headed for the F/A-18's first test in combat.

CHAPTER NINE

"It Starts Raining F/A-18s On You"

For two ear-splitting days in the middle of April 1986, two carrier battle groups put on a typical American show in the Tyrrhenian Sea north of Sicily. Planes roared on and off the carrier decks. The air waves crackled with radio messages and the beams of high-powered radar. The crews of the three Soviet radar picket ships north of Sicily and those of the trawlers assigned to shadow the individual carriers could have kept track of the Yankees in their sleep.

Then, as soon as it was dark on the night of 14 April, the U.S.S. *Coral Sea* (carrying three squadrons of Hornets and a heavy squadron of A-6 bombers) and the U.S.S. *America* (carrying a more traditional mix of F-14 fighters and A-6s plus A-7 light bombers) headed south toward Libya. With all their electronic equipment shut down, they steamed through the narrow Straits of Messina, between the boot of Italy and Sicily, in total EMCON [Emission Control], at thirty miles an hour.

Ships in the two battle groups stayed at least twenty-five miles away from each other. To the sailors aboard the Soviet ships, the American fleet seemed to have vanished from the face of the earth.

Chief Petty Officer Kurt Benson, in the *Coral Sea*'s aircraft control center, recalls: "We just blowed the horn and everyone got out of the way. We weren't slowing down for nothing."

As the ship cleared the straits and sped south into the Mediterranean, Benson heard the voice of Capt. R. H. Ferguson, the skipper, come over the 1 MC, the general announcement system: "We're gonna go south and kick some ass."

As the Soviet trawlers and picket ships reported they had lost contact with the two carriers, a Soviet Sovremennyy-class guided-missile destroyer, stationed south of Sicily, began a frantic search. Even with the help of long-range surveillance planes, it milled around for seven hours without making contact.

As soon as darkness shielded the ships from prying eyes, conveyor systems began disgorging bombs and missiles from the magazines, deep in the bowels of the ship, to the hangar deck. They were loaded onto dollies and then lifted to the flight deck on the aircraft elevators. Crew members, excited with the knowledge their ship was going into action, took time to paint messages on the bombs: "FROM NICKI" . . . "FROM JEFF" . . . "THIS ONE'S FOR RHONDA" . . . "FROM UNCLE CHARLIE" . . . "DIAL 911" . . . "JULIE" . . . "FROM MEMPHIS."

To most crew members, this sudden transformation from peacetime exercises to war was a real surprise, even though planning with the air force for a joint attack on targets in Libya had begun in January after terrorist bombings at the Rome and Vienna airports. In all, 162 contingency targets were considered, with attacks involving one or two carriers, with and without air force planes, and both day and night. But all of this planning had been kept a deep secret—up until the time for action in retaliation for the bombing of a discotheque frequented by American troops in Berlin.

Rear Adm. Jerry Breast, commander of Carrier Group Two, aboard the *Coral Sea,* insisted that all information be classified at least Top Secret and compartmented. This meant that even the skippers of some of the ships in his battle group were kept in the dark. But, in the days immediately before the operation, leaks from Washington turned into a deluge.

"It seemed the press stayed ahead of us darn near the whole time— about two or three days ahead," Breast reported later.

> I'd be holding something very, very close, and it would come out in the *Washington Post* or CNN or ABC. They seemed to be way ahead of us. It hurt our morale, it hurt our security efforts. It hazarded us operationally if the Libyans had really been listening or reading or believing what they were hearing. I conjectured it might have been a purposeful effort to prepare the American people for those things we might be going to do over the mainland of Libya or convince the Libyan people what would happen if they didn't get their act straight.

As the two carriers sped south, there was good reason for concern that their fliers might be heading into defenses alerted and primed to knock them down. That was an especially unnerving thought because the whole affair had been planned to avoid American losses. On several occasions earlier, when the U.S. fleet carried on operations inside the so-called "line of death" in the Gulf of Sidra, Adm. Frank Kelso, commander of the Sixth Fleet, visited the *Coral Sea* to speak personally with the ship's pilots to make sure they knew the rules of engagement. As preparations for the Libyan raid intensified, Kelso tapped Breast forcefully on the chest and insisted: "I don't want any U.S. aviators walking through the streets of Tripoli with a noose around their neck."

Aboard the *Coral Sea* that night, there was a more immediate question. Down in the humid, 120-degree engine compartments, shirtless crewmen sucked on ice cubes as they monitored the temperature and fuel-flow gauges and checked the long nozzles that feed oil into the white-hot furnaces. The engineering plant, with its twelve boilers and four main engines capable of turning out 212,000 horsepower, had been designed in 1929 for use in a battleship, and sent to sea in the *Coral Sea* in 1947, more than twice a lifetime ago to the young sailors. When ordered to take part in the Libyan raid, the *Coral Sea* had been at sea, sailing hard, for most of the previous 200 days. The ship and her crew were tired. Would the "Ageless Warrior," as she had been dubbed, get there in time?

The whole operation would be imperiled if anything went wrong. But that ancient engineering system ground out the knots, hour after hour. Right on schedule, the *Coral Sea* reached its assigned position 180 miles off the coast north of Bengazi, fifteen minutes before the 1:30 A.M. launch time. Both the position and the timing were critical because strikes by planes from the *Coral Sea* and the *America,* further west, off Tripoli, had to be meshed precisely with those of F-111 bombers flying all the way from England, seven hours away.

At the appointed hour, the *Coral Sea* turned into the wind and began launching its strike force, including 20 F/A-18s, into the dark Mediterranean night. Breast took a chance. He ordered a destroyer, twenty-five miles away, to turn on a radio beacon to make it a little easier for the pilots to form up in their battle boxes before heading toward the beach. They were careful to stay below 5,000 feet—beneath the beams from the Libyans' shore-based radar.

There are two ways to suppress enemy defenses. One way is to make enough noise on the way in so the defenders will turn on their radars and send their fighters aloft—and then knock them out. The second is to rely on total surprise.

Breast decided on a combination of the two—with heavy emphasis on surprise.

Leading the raid were the carrier's EA-6B Prowlers. The Prowler is an expanded version of the A-6, carrying four crew members and loaded with powerful electronic gear to search out and jam enemy radar. As they approached the coast, some degree of surprise was lost, and the Libyan air-defense radar reacted. But the Prowlers immediately blanketed the radar with their jamming devices.

This gave a margin of safety for the F/A-18s following close behind to swoop in along the shoreline and launch their new HARM missiles to home in on the emissions from the air-defense radars and surface-to-air missile sites. Two missiles apiece streaked down toward a dozen installations, opening a hole in one of the world's densest and most sophisticated air defense systems for the heavily laden A-6 bombers. The defenders fired more than fifty missiles without a single hit.

Other F/A-18s, carrying both air-to-air and antishipping missiles, were aloft to guard the attacking force from both enemy airplanes and missile-firing surface ships. The A-6s from the *Coral Sea* hit the Benina Airbase outside Bengazi, destroying a number of aircraft and damaging several hangars. Other A-6s from the *America* hit the Jumahirayah barracks in Bengazi. At the same time, the F-111s, which had flown around France, Portugal, and Spain from their bases in England, hit targets in the Tripoli area, including the tent compound where Col. Muammar Qaddafi, the Libyan leader, was believed to be.

The whole operation took less time than it takes to read about it. From the moment the first bomber crossed the shoreline until the last one cleared the coast, the elapsed time was only thirteen minutes. As one pilot involved put it: "It was all designed to happen at once. The bombers are there, the HARMs come down, the bombs come down, and everyone gets the hell out of there."

Qaddafi, who moves around frequently, was not injured, although an adopted child was killed. One of the F-111s crashed, and its two-man crew was lost, but all the other aircraft returned safely to their bases or carriers.

Back on the *Coral Sea,* an anxious quiet had settled over the ship. The launch had been almost exactly like a normal exercise except that a few more planes had been launched, and all their weapons were armed. Benson, in the aircraft control center, responsible for the placement of planes on the deck before and after the strike, was reminded of Vietnam: "You wonder whether the same number that went off are going to come back.

Will the same faces be seen tomorrow? More importantly, are they going to find what they're looking for and get it done? We were pretty excited."

Probably no one aboard the ship was more interested in the performance of the F/A-18s in this first venture into combat than John Lockard, the ship's executive officer. He had worked on the F/A-18 program in the early days in NAVAIR, was one of the pilots who had helped introduce the plane at Lemoore, and was soon to become program manager. He monitored the operation from the dimly lit Combat Direction Center, just above the hangar deck and two decks below the flight deck. This is the large room from which the crew manages combat operations.

In many ways, the operation was for Lockard a gratifying demonstration of the performance of the Hornet. After all the agonizing over the plane's range, the F/A-18s flew that night without tanking. Instead, it was the longer-range A-6s that were refueled in the air, permitting them to carry a heavier bomb load.

Earlier in the *Coral Sea*'s deployment, Breast had experimented to see how the F/A-18 could be used to protect the carrier against air attack. He found he could keep seven planes, each carrying a full combat load of 8,000 pounds of fuel and four missiles, on station in a grid about 150 miles from the carrier, without refueling. But, he concluded, once the shooting started, he would have to supply them with fuel.

Fortunately for the Americans, the Libyans did not get their fighters into the air the night of the raid. If they had, Breast was counting on the *Coral Sea*, with more than a score of Hornets in reserve, to launch its planes quickly to deal with the threat from enemy fighters. As a result of their earlier exercises during this deployment, crew members had begun to boast that their ship, one of the oldest and smallest in the fleet, could put more fighters in the air than the much bigger, nuclear-powered, *Nimitz*-class carriers.

Lt. Comdr. Dave Jones, one of the pilots flying fighter cover for the strike that night, says pilots from other ships complained to him: "When you get within 200 miles of the *Coral Sea,* it starts raining F/A-18s on you."

In preparations for the operation, the F/A-18 pilots were specifically ordered not to fly over land, and all of the navy bombs were dropped by two-man A-6s and not by Hornets. One of the criticisms later made was that the operation had demonstrated that the navy's two carriers had relatively little offensive capability and needed the help of the air force to carry out the raid.

The navy bombing force could have been significantly increased, however, by using F/A-18s as bombers and sending them to hit targets on land. The F/A-18 is designed to fly under the weather at night, over relatively flat terrain, and Hornets often carry out such nighttime missions in training. But sending a one-man plane on a low-level attack in the dark is somewhat more hazardous than it is for a two-man plane, and the admirals' concern about avoiding losses led to the decision to keep the Hornets offshore and to supplement the bombing force with F-111s.

Although the navy's part of the operation took little more than an hour from launch time to recovery of the returning planes, the attack, together with earlier operations off the Libyan coast, provided a major test of new weapons—the F/A-18, HARM and Harpoon missiles, and the Lamps Mark III helicopter—and of the way the navy goes to war.

During the raid, Lehman and Admiral Watkins, the chief of naval operations, waited in the Navy Command Center at the Pentagon until word came that the planes had returned safely to their carriers. Lehman later termed the operation "an overwhelming success."

This was in sharp contrast to what had happened two and a half years earlier, when planes from the U.S.S. *Independence* and the U.S.S. *Kennedy* attacked targets in Lebanon. The operation was poorly conceived and poorly coordinated. Two planes were lost, one pilot was killed and one officer was captured. Immediately afterward, Lehman found money to create a new school at Fallon NAS in the Nevada desert. Known as the Strike Warfare Center, or Strike U, the school runs senior officers through an intensive two-week course that teaches them how to plan and coordinate the ships and planes involved in an attack by an air wing. Each air wing also practices there before deployment.

When the navy is ordered into action, decisions on how to carry out the operation are made by commanders on the scene—and not, as in the case of Lebanon and often during the Vietnam War, by military officers far from the scene or even by politicians in Washington.

Breast was told what targets to hit and when to do it. But his contingency plans had been approved without tampering by higher officials, and he was left free to decide how many planes to use, what aiming points to employ, and precisely when to make the attack.

The Libyan raid has now become part of the curriculum at Strike U, an object lesson in how to conduct a surprise attack against shore targets.

One of the most impressive parts of the whole operation was the navy's demonstration of its ability to spirit two battle groups across the busy Mediterranean without anyone knowing they were coming. In 1941, the

Japanese moved a much larger fleet into position for their surprise attack on Pearl Harbor. But there were no satellites overhead in those days, and there were no trawlers constantly shadowing the carriers.

As recently as the mid-1970s, the U.S. Navy had great difficulty shutting down all the emissions from its ships. Now, after years of practice, it can be done in moments. The navy has also become a master of deception. A carrier may suddenly turn off its radios and radar and speed away while a destroyer continues on the carrier's course, broadcasting what sounds like a carrier's normal radio traffic.

An impressive demonstration of a combination of EMCON and deception was put on by the U.S.S. *Ranger* shortly after the Libyan raid. During exercises in the Pacific in the summer of 1986, the ship sailed from San Diego, bound for Hawaii, and then disappeared for fourteen days despite an intensive air, sea, and satellite search by the opposing side. During its furtive voyage, it continued to fly its planes in mock attacks on surface, submarine and land targets.

Strict EMCON, of course, makes life more difficult for the pilots. They complain that the first switches pulled shut down the beacons and radar that help them to navigate and to find the ship when they are returning, low on fuel. The pilots say that anyone who thinks it is easy to find a carrier in EMCON, even if you know where the ship is supposed to be, ought to try it on a dark night. Except in their early training, pilots now routinely operate "zip lip," with no radio communications and even with their own radar turned off. When planes return from a mission, the pilots place themselves into a holding pattern near the ship and then come in, one after the other, without a word spoken.

To help them get aboard safely in these conditions, Hornet pilots have at their fingertips an automatic landing system in which the plane's computers bring the craft right down onto the deck without a human hand on the controls. The system is so good it seems almost uncanny.

During a shakedown cruise before the *Constellation*'s first deployment, a sudden fog enveloped the ship off the San Diego coast while many of its planes were in the air. Admiral Edney, who had seldom seen weather so close to zero-zero—no visibility and no ceiling—sent all but two of the airborne planes to bases on shore. Then he asked two of his most experienced pilots to try to bring their Hornets onto the carrier using the automatic landing system. One plane landed perfectly on the first pass. The second boltered the first time and then came aboard the next time around.

Despite this dramatic demonstration, pilots on those first two deployments—of the *Constellation* in the Pacific and the *Coral Sea* in the Mediterranean—seldom used the automatic system. One pilot, "Smooth Dog" Vaughn, became so enamored of the system that he used it all the time aboard the *Connie* until he was told that he was being paid to take his plane off from the pointy end of the ship and put it back on the dull end.

Most pilots seem to resist using the system. One reason is the fear that it might not work when it is needed most. They feel that the more they practice landing on their own, the safer they will be. There is also the macho factor. Pilots are rated on the quality of their landings—"Okay," "Fair," "No Grade," "Wave Off," and "Cut Pass" (unsafe but too close for a waveoff)—and the competition among pilots and between squadrons is intense. But a landing in which the computer does all the work doesn't qualify for a rating.

Rear Adm. William A. Dougherty, Jr., commander of the Atlantic Fleet's Carrier Group Four, says he doesn't want his young pilots to rely on the automatic system as a crutch. But he says they should use it routinely as they approach the ship. This is the way he puts it:

> I can use it and break out of it. That's what I like. If I can get myself in to a quarter of a mile, the game's won. The hard thing in night or bad weather is to get set up. The last portion is a piece of cake. I feel better landing it myself. When you're in the goo, at night, and you have a rolling, pitching deck, and you have a system that will get you in so you can see the ship and the deck, that is worth its weight. The only contention is the last quarter of a mile. Someone who doesn't use it to come within a half-mile or a quarter-mile is not smart. But you still ought to be able to get the plane into the basket with your own skills.

In practice, on most carriers the system is not kept in tip-top operating shape all the time, and pilots use it far less than they should if they are going to have full confidence in it when the weather turns bad, and they need all the help they can get to come aboard safely.

The *Coral Sea*'s first deployment with the Hornet not only took the plane into combat for the first time but, if anything, provided an even rougher test for the plane than the first cruise in the *Constellation*. The weather in the Mediterranean was the worst Lockard had ever seen. He was aghast when he saw blue water breaking over the deck and drenching the Hornets with salt. Although corrosion was much less than on other planes, it still caused far more maintenance work than had been expected.

Particularly disturbing was the discovery that the edges of the wing carry-through bulkheads, where the wings are attached, were corroding. The problem was found before the corrosion ate away enough metal to cause a plane to lose its wings, but it did require each plane to be pulled out of service while the bulkheads were treated to avoid further damage.

The seven-month cruise also had its share of landing gear problems—an average of one a month. At first the crew thought the problem was metal fatigue, and then they suspected corrosion. Breast called the problems "strange." Years after the cruise ended, Lockard acknowledged that he did not think the navy had seen the end of its landing gear problems.

While the Libyan raid answered many questions about the performance of the Hornet and other new weapons, it fell far short of demonstrating how the navy would perform if it had to go to war against the Soviets.

While the general easing of tensions between Moscow and Washington seems to make such a conflict only a remote possibility, the navy, mindful of the speed with which international relationships can change, still considers a confrontation with the Soviets the ultimate challenge, and plans its forces and its strategy with that in mind. This is the way navy planners think such a conflict might unfold and how the Hornet would fit in:

War does not come without warning. First, there is a period of growing tension between East and West. Soviet troops in Germany go on higher alert. Soviet reserves are called up. Civilian trucks begin moving men and equipment into position.

In the West, reservists are called to active duty, and the U.S. begins flying troops across the Atlantic to draw tanks and other pre-positioned equipment and then move toward the East-West border. The navy cancels all leaves and prepares to escort supply ships across the Atlantic and to protect ports on both sides of the ocean.

The attention of most military men and much of the world is focused on the central front in Germany, where war could come at any moment with the movement of armies of tanks and regiments of attack aircraft. But navy leaders look nervously toward the north—toward the sparsely populated area of Norway above the Arctic Circle; toward the approaches to Iceland through the Sea of Norway; toward the Red navy's big, missile-carrying nuclear submarines in their sanctuaries in the Barents Sea and under the polar ice—and toward the buildup of ships, planes, and troops on the Kola Peninsula. The military force concentrated here seems to loom over the narrow, lightly defended stretch of Finnish, Swedish, and Norwegian territory lying between the Soviet Union and the Sea of Norway.

If, as seems likely, the millions of men facing each other in Central Europe are fairly evenly matched, what happens on the northern flank, in the vast open reaches of the Sea of Norway, in the narrow wind-swept fjords along the Norwegian shore, and in the air over the craggy snow-clad mountains of northern Norway, may determine the outcome of the entire conflict.

It is here, far from the major land battles, that the navy expects to make its contribution.

As tension rises, the president confers with leaders of the NATO alliance, and then gives the order for three carrier battle groups, together with a force of American, British, Dutch, Norwegian, and Danish surface ships, to move past Iceland and across the northern tip of Scotland toward Norway. Marines, equipped for fighting in the far north, accompany the task force, prepared to set up defensive positions on shore. Norwegian law bars the stationing of foreign troops on its soil, but the marines have practiced fighting in the harsh Norwegian weather during peacetime exercises. Scouting ahead of the flotilla are aircraft from the carriers and planes from bases in the British Isles. Moving silently under the sea, American submarines listen for the faint sounds of Soviet subs lying in wait up ahead.

The task force commander gives a prayer of thanks. His greatest fear has always been that his orders to move north would come too late, after fighting had already broken out. He now has the chance to prevent enemy occupation of Norway and Iceland, rather than the much more difficult task of dislodging forces already in place.

As the task force moves north, the individual ships are spread out over thousands of square miles. To enemy analysts poring over satellite photography and reports from listening posts on shore, in the air, and at sea, there is no discernible pattern. Ships seem to be moving almost aimlessly. What appears on one pass of a satellite to be a carrier is nowhere to be seen on the next pass.

Even the task force commander doesn't know exactly where his own ships are. Before moving north, he called the leaders of his three battle groups together aboard his flagship. He told them where he wanted them, when they should be there, and what he wanted them to do. How to get there was left up to them.

And then most of the ships and planes went into strict EMCON. But there were exceptions. Some of the surface ships were assigned to broadcast signals that would make them seem to be something they weren't. With destroyers sounding like aircraft carriers—and then suddenly going off the air—it was difficult for the enemy analysts even to count the number of ships in the flotilla, let alone know exactly what types they were, where they were, or where they were headed.

With silence or deception the rule, the admiral in charge of the entire operation would seem to be as much in the dark as anyone else. Actually, a steady flow of information comes to him from E-2C Hawkeye aircraft flying out hundreds of miles from the fleet. The Hawkeye, like the air force's airborne warning and control system [AWACS], is a flying command post, sporting a huge radar dome and sprouting communications antennae. With its radar, the Hawkeye is capable of keeping track of aircraft and ships within a circle of hundreds of square miles. But the Hawkeye is old and inadequate for the job. Hornets and Tomcats, borrowed from their primary jobs, are assigned as scouts and they report in with high-speed bursts of data to fill out the picture of the battle scene.

In effect, the admiral becomes an "information sponge," soaking up data about the situation facing his task force. His ship remains silent, its radio and radar systems shut down. It is the duty of his subordinate commanders to communicate with him only if they are unable to carry out their assignments. Otherwise, he assumes they are where they are supposed to be.

If the Soviet commanders can move quickly enough, before this powerful force is in place, they will gain a major advantage. If they can take Iceland and the isolated Norwegian bases such as Bodo, they will not only be in a strong position on the northern flank of the allied forces in Central Europe. They will also have air and sea bases from which to attack the approaching task force and then strike at shipping in the Atlantic.

But the mere fact that a powerful allied force is moving northward presents them with serious problems. They have no choice but to move planes and troops that might otherwise be positioned along the German border far to the north to protect their own northern territories. They must also worry about the possibility of devastating air attack from the American carriers anywhere along a broad arc extending from northern Germany to the ports for their Northern Fleet and their air bases in the area around Murmansk.

Even discounting its nuclear weapons, the task force steaming northward represents a formidable array of military power. Many of the surface ships and submarines bristle with Tomahawk cruise missiles that can be launched to slip in under defensive radar to hit targets far inland. Each of the three carriers has nearly a hundred aircraft. With the F/A-18s capable of operating as fighters or attack planes—or both on the same mission—that means a potential attack force of more than 100 aircraft.

The danger of air attack on the approaching force grows rapidly, once it comes within about 1,200 miles of Soviet bases. The latest model Backfire bombers, recently assigned to the Northern Fleet, rise from their bases along with older Bears and Badgers in swarms of as many as forty planes, seeking to get close enough to the American carriers to launch their air-to-surface missiles. The Bears and Badgers lead the way, firing subsonic cruise missiles.

Part of the Badger force complicates the fleet's air defense problem by firing Kingfish missiles from altitudes above 35,000 feet. The missiles, flying at three times the speed of sound, soar upward to nearly 60,000 feet before diving toward the ships below. This attack from above, while the attention of the ships' crews is riveted on beating off surface-skimming missiles, is eerily similar to the American dive bombers' attack on Admiral Nagumo's carriers in the Battle of Midway.

Many of the missiles fired in this first-wave attack are launched at extreme range, and most of them are older weapons, relatively easy to confuse or shoot down. But even if most of the missiles don't get through to the carriers, they create confusion and may even saturate the defense with more targets than it can handle.

In the early stages of the battle, the planes can only come from the direction of the Soviet Union because of the distance they have to fly. F-14s, with their long-range Phoenix missiles, are sent out to loiter on station, several hundred miles in advance of the fleet. On the carriers, pilots sit strapped into their F/A-18s on five-minute alert, ready to join the Tomcats as soon as the approach of the enemy planes is detected.

As American commanders such as Admiral Dougherty picture the confrontation, the Soviet pilots face a daunting challenge. They are approaching an extremely powerful force—but they don't know exactly where it is. All they know is that it is out there somewhere. And yet, between them and the fleet is a picket line of fighter planes armed with a variety of missiles as well as guns.

"Think about this," Dougherty says.

Here you are sitting on land, and you know there's a pretty potent force out there you want to try to get. Well, if you know their guns are cocked and they're going to shoot you, you don't just go blundering out there, because you're liable to get shot down and never even find the ships. That's one of the beauties of the whole battle group. The advantage is in my favor. I'm floating around there, I've got my guns cocked, and the burden is on him to come out and find me. All he has to do is get within my lethal range, whether that be with fighters or guns or missiles, and he's a grape. I mean, that's a turkey shoot.

The first obstacle Backfire pilots face is the threat from the Phoenix missiles, capable of reaching out scores of miles. But the launch of a Phoenix can be detected—and if it is detected, it can be defeated. If a Backfire pilot detects the Phoenix in time, he turns sharply right or left and forces the missile to chase him in a long arc until it runs out of fuel. But the Backfire pilot has also burned precious fuel, and he has had to turn away from his target. Perhaps a Phoenix that runs out of gas and splashes into the sea has still paid its way.

As the Tomcats seek to knock down or drive away the incoming Backfires, they are soon joined by scores of F/A-18s armed with Sparrow and Sidewinder missiles to increase the odds against the attacking planes.

As pilots run low on fuel, they pull back to refuel. They may find big air force KC-10 tankers waiting to fill their tanks. When ammunition runs low, the fighters are forced to withdraw from the battle and return to the carrier, but only for a brief visit. As soon as they have been refueled and fitted with missiles and more ammunition, they move up to the catapult again. In a couple of days of combat, a pilot flies more hours—and takes more Gs—than during an entire month in peacetime. Every bone and muscle aches, and he feels like a Redskins tackle after a Super Bowl game. Exhaustion begins to take its toll in combat and accidents.

For the F/A-18 pilots, the pace is even more strenuous than for those flying other planes. Peacetime experience indicates the Hornets will keep on flying when other planes begin to break down and remain on the deck for repairs. The Hornet pilots also have more different jobs to do—dropping bombs; dogfighting; launching HARM, Harpoon, and Maverick missiles; serving as scouts—than pilots of other planes, and the struggle to do all of those jobs well is a constant strain. Fortunately, the Hornet is a comfortable plane to fly—except for the webbing of the parachute harness criss-crossed under the pilot's buttocks. When the Australians bought the F/A-18, they found the harness so uncomfortable that they modified the ejection system so there is only a cushion beneath the pilot. They also use sheepskin seat covers on long flights. The American pilots make do with sheets of the kind of plastic filled with bubbles that is used as packing material.

The Americans may well succeed in beating off the first assault. But that will not be the last battle. As the task force moves forward, the danger arises that the allied ships may be attacked not just from one predictable direction but from any point of the compass. As the situation changes, the F/A-18s may be called on to play a new role.

Instead of spreading his F-14s out in a grid pattern all around the carrier, a battle group commander may instead decide to assign his more numerous Hornets to that job. As soon as an attack is detected, the F-14s, either loitering in the air near the carrier or on deck-launched alert, can all be sent to intercept the attacking force.

As the task force moves closer to Soviet bases, it comes under repeated assault by waves of bombers accompanied by long-range fighters. The outer air battle, many miles from the carriers, degenerates into a series of swirling dogfights as the bombers press forward to get within missile range of the carriers and the defenders try to beat them back. The goal of the Backfire pilots is to cross an invisible line in the sky where their missiles will come within range of the carriers, to launch their weapons, and then turn for home. The goal of the Americans is to prevent a single plane from crossing that line. Unfortunately for the defenders, they cannot be sure where the line is. Some of the missiles may carry a small warhead but a large supply of fuel and be capable of flying nearly 500 miles. Others, with a big warhead and limited fuel, may be rigged to fly only a hundred miles.

Down below, American cruisers fitted with Aegis antiaircraft systems monitor the battle with their powerful radar and help to beat back the attack with barrages of missiles. But once the cruisers turn on their electronic equipment and enter the battle, they signal their location and put themselves in danger of attack.

Inevitably, a few of the attacking planes get close enough to fire their antishipping missiles. Like the kamikaze planes of World War II, the missiles streak toward their targets, oblivious of the missiles fired by the vessels defending the carriers and of the rain of bullets poured out in a last-ditch defense by the ship-based Phalanx gun system. EMCON is cast aside as electronic signals seek to confuse the missiles and cause them to go astray. But even one missile making its way through this curtain of fire is enough to disable or sink a destroyer or frigate or to put a carrier out of business for at least several hours. Even a relatively brief disruption of carrier operations could be a disaster if planes cannot find room on another carrier and the pilots are forced to ditch in those frigid northern waters. In the Battle of the Coral Sea, it will be recalled, the Japanese carrier *Zuikaku* survived the battle but lost most of its planes and experienced aviators.

If the task force survives this initial battle, the attacks by Backfires and other land-based planes gradually diminish, a result of the fierce air battles along the Norwegian coast. Then it is the turn of the attack planes aboard the carriers to strike at the naval bases, air fields, and army staging areas from which a Soviet attempt to capture Norway's North Cape would come.

Planners in Moscow have for decades assumed that Soviet cities could come under attack by carrier-based planes, although the U.S. Navy has long since given up its plans to take part in such a major assault. But one important result of this fear has been the creation of an extremely formidable air defense system. The allied fleet has already met the first line of defense. As planes take off from the carriers and head inland, they encounter one layer after another of defenses.

In effect, the roles of the two forces have been reversed. But there is one major difference. When the Backfires came out to repel the task force, they didn't know where the carriers were. But the American pilots have been briefed in detail on the fixed land targets they are to attack. The coordinates of their targets and their aiming points have all been punched into their inertial navigation systems so they know precisely where to go.

The first attacking force is made up of A-6 bombers, accompanied by F-14s. The F/A-18s come along on this first long-range mission, carrying both air-to-air weapons and HARM antiradiation missiles to knock out the defenses, but no load of heavy bombs. The goal of this first wave of bombers is to crater the enemy airfields, destroy as many planes as possible on the ground, and put radar and missile sites out of action.

The threat to the attacking force is not limited to the surface-to-air missiles and antiaircraft guns down on the ground. High overhead, modern Su-27 Flanker and MiG-31 Foxhound interceptors circle. With their state-of-the-art radar, they are able to detect low-flying planes and then shoot down at them with supersonic missiles. As the attacking forces come closer, they swoop down, guided by traffic controllers on the ground, to join in the battle to keep the bombers from reaching their targets.

The ensuing air battle strains the situational awareness of even the best-trained pilots. The F/A-18 and the Flanker look remarkably alike, each with tall, twin vertical tails and a leading edge extension sweeping forward below the bubble canopy. In fact, the most distinctive feature of each of the four planes—the F-14, F/A-18, Su-27 and MiG-31—is its set of twin vertical tails.

Losses in this first attempt to penetrate the Soviet defenses are severe, especially among the A-6s. But the attack serves its purpose in knocking out defending aircraft and missile sites.

The carriers, facing less threat from enemy bombers, move closer to shore. With a shorter distance to fly, many of the F/A-18s are loaded with bombs and sent off to hammer away at the naval and army installations from which an attack on Norway and Iceland might come. Each day, missile and antiaircraft sites and airfields are subjected to repeated attack. The mistake committed so often in Vietnam, of permitting the enemy to rebuild his defenses, will not be repeated here.

As the threat on the northern flank recedes, the allies have a choice. The carriers can be sent further north to provide air cover for an assault by submarines and perhaps even by surface ships on the Soviet "boomers"—their big, missile-firing submarines. Or, if the threat that the conflict will degenerate into a nuclear exchange seems slight, the carriers are moved south off the coast of Denmark. From there, the F/A-18s and A-6s join in the battle to attack Warsaw Pact land and air forces threatening Western Europe, and hammer away at Soviet ships in the Baltic Sea.

In the Far East, a similar scenario unfolds. The U.S. goal there is to control the straits that connect the Sea of Okhotsk and the Sea of Japan with the open Pacific. If those straits can be blocked, this will bottle up the Soviet Far Eastern Fleet and prevent it from attacking the lines of communication between the U.S. and Japan and South Korea.

The Soviet goal is twofold. The first effort is to control the straits so their ships will be able to move back and forth but American ships will not be able to enter the inland seas to attack the missile submarines in their sanctuary in the Sea of Okhotsk. The second goal is to keep the U.S. carriers at bay so they will not be able to come within easy striking distance of such major military centers as Vladivostok and Petropavlovsk.

The U.S., with land-based aircraft already on hand in Japan, Okinawa and South Korea, attempts to gain air control over the vital straits both to prevent movement of hostile ships through them, and also to try to beat back missile-carrying bombers flying out in search of the approaching carriers.

As the carriers move within 1,200 miles of Soviet bases, they come under attack by missile-launching planes and submarines. Again, the fate of the carriers depends on the outcome of the outer air battle in which F-14s and F/A-18s team up to knock down the Soviet Backfire and Badger bombers before they come within missile-launching distance of the carriers.

Those two battles, off the coast of Norway and in the northwestern Pacific, play out in an ultimate way the navy's Maritime Strategy. It is a high-risk strategy that deliberately puts the carriers in harm's way in the knowledge that the sinking of even two or three of the big ships (with their crews of more than 5,000 men and nearly a hundred planes) would be a grievous loss. Just as in the 1940s and early 1950s, the navy sees itself having a major role in taking the battle to the Soviet Union in the event of war. This is a distinct change from the long period of the 1950s, 1960s, and 1970s, when the major focus for the navy was in keeping open the supply routes to Europe with the line to be drawn from Greenland to Iceland to the United Kingdom in an effort to bottle up Soviet forces in the Sea of Norway.

The switch back to the older, more ambitious strategy began with a plan developed in 1977 by Adm. Tom Hayward when he was commander in chief of the Pacific Fleet. When he became chief of naval operations in 1979, he outlined what came to be known as the Maritime Strategy.

"It is important," he told Congress, "that we make the Soviets understand that in war there will be no sanctuaries for their forces. Keeping the Soviets preoccupied with defensive concerns locks up Soviet naval forces in areas close to the USSR, limiting their availability for campaigns against sea lines of communication or for operations in support of offensive thrusts on the flanks of NATO or elsewhere, such as in the Middle East or Asia."

When the Reagan administration came into office in 1981, Navy Secretary Lehman spoke out as the most vocal advocate of the navy's reborn aggressive strategy, with all that it implied in the way of big carriers, a 600-ship force, and even surface action groups built around four battleships resurrected from the mothball fleet.

Both the strategy and the type of fleet needed to support it are certain to become matters of increasing debate during the 1990s. The dramatic changes in the Warsaw Pact alone will raise questions about what kind of navy the U.S. needs and how big it should be. Just as the defeat of the Japanese in 1945 deprived the navy of its role as the nation's defense against a major naval power, the easing of tensions between East and

West brings into question the navy's mission to defend the U.S. against a major land power. But even if the rapidly changing relationship between East and West did not force such a debate, the effects of time on today's fleet certainly will.

Between now and the end of the century, the U.S. could have available what would be, in many ways, the most powerful naval force ever to put to sea, with as many as eighteen deployable carriers, half of them nuclear powered. But in the first decade of the new century, half the carrier force will go out of service. From the time the decision is made to buy a new carrier until it puts to sea is nearly a decade. So, if the ships scheduled to be retired between 2000 and 2010 are to be replaced, the decisions on what size ships to build, how many to build, and when they are to be built will all have to be made in the next few years.

The admirals have already begun to be heard, arguing that a powerful navy will still be needed to deal with third-world countries that are increasingly arming themselves with first-rate modern weapons. With a price tag of perhaps $20 billion or more for a carrier, its air wing, and support ships, the debate over the navy's future is sure to be a fierce one. Even friends of the navy may well argue, as many have in the past, that new carriers should be smaller and therefore cheaper.

But Vice Adm. Richard M. Dunleavy, who took over as assistant CNO for air warfare in the spring of 1989, argues vigorously in favor of supercarriers—about 1,000 feet long, 160 feet wide, and with a flight deck of about 250 feet. Only such a large vessel is big enough and stable enough to permit flight operations in any weather anywhere on the world's oceans, he says.

How does the Hornet fit into this uncertain future?

Despite all the early controversy, the seven years that the F/A-18 has been in service have demonstrated the value of its versatility. For a task force commander, the ability to change a plane—even in mid-air—from a bomber to a fighter or interceptor dramatically multiplies the forces he has available—whether to defend the fleet or do damage to the enemy. New models of the plane now coming off the production lines or planned for the future provide even more flexibility. One version is a single-seat plane with improved cockpit displays that enhance the pilot's ability to carry out low-level attacks at night. The other is a new, two-seat version with weapons controls operated by a naval flight officer in the rear seat so the plane can be used for night attacks under the weather. In use by the marines, the two-seat version will replace the all-weather A-6 Intruder.

Both planes are designed to carry a package of reconnaissance equipment that can be inserted to replace the gun in a few minutes, further increasing the number of different jobs the same basic aircraft can be called upon to do.

Both the navy and McDonnell Douglas have done a good deal of research on a follow-on version of the plane, called the Hornet 2000. With a larger airframe, improved engines, more fuel, and improved electronic equipment, the Hornet 2000 would be virtually a new airplane. Whether it will ever be built is questionable, given the increasing pressure to hold down defense expenditures. What is more likely is that the basic F/A-18 will continue to be improved. The fact that improvements, even in the flying qualities of the plane, can be made by writing new computer software rather than by bending sheet metal, makes this an attractive possibility.

In addition to improving the F/A-18, the navy is also at work on two new planes. The A-12 will be a new, medium bomber to replace the A-6. The Naval Advanced Tactical Fighter will be a new fighter to replace the F-14.

But both will build on the lessons of the F/A-18, because both will be dual-purpose planes. Although its basic role is to serve as a bomber, the two-man A-12 will also be capable of engaging in air-to-air combat. Similarly, the one-man tactical fighter will also be able to drop bombs.

"We're not going back to having separate aircraft for different missions," Dunleavy says. "We'll have, as far as I can see into the future, multi-mission aircraft. The strike-fighter is the wave of the future. Depending on how things work out with the budget, I think you'll find us buying more strike-fighters, whether they be F/A-18 or some follow-on aircraft." Although he is a naval flight officer—the first non-pilot to hold the navy's top aviation job—Dunleavy has become an enthusiastic supporter of the F/A-18 and often flies in the rear seat of the two-man trainer version. "We love it," he says.

The navy of course faces a difficult—and familiar—task, because it has been ordered to adapt the air force's Advanced Tactical Fighter for carrier operations, despite the lessons of the 1960s and 1970s that should have convinced everyone that it makes much more sense to develop a plane for use aboard a carrier, and then adapt it for use on land, than to do things the other way around.

The F/A-18, in fact, has achieved widespread acceptance as a land-based strike-fighter. Canada has purchased 138 planes, with three squadrons in Europe. Australia has bought seventy-five and Spain seventy-two.

Kuwait has forty on order, with deliveries beginning in January 1992, and Switzerland has expressed its intent to buy thirty-four Hornets after an exhaustive comparison with the F-16. In December 1989, South Korea chose the F/A-18 over the F-16 and plans to acquire 120 of the planes. In a deal worth $3.5 to $4 billion, the Koreans will buy twelve complete airplanes, assemble thirty-six more from parts purchased from the U.S., and build the remaining seventy-two planes in its own factories.

France, whose navy strongly favored the purchase of F/A-18s to replace the 1950s-vintage F-8 Crusaders on its carriers, decided late in 1989 to develop and build its own new plane as a way of keeping its aerospace industry competitive in the world's arms market.

The early emphasis on reliability and maintainability by a few stubborn men such as Admiral Lee and Will Willoughby has paid handsome dividends in the fleet.

The F/A-18 has turned out to be at least twice as reliable as other navy warplanes and to require less than half as many manhours of maintenance. While the older F-14 suffers an equipment failure of some sort every half-hour it flies, the latest model of the Hornet, the F/A-18C, is expected to fly five times as long before anything goes wrong.

But it is not at all certain that the navy, the Pentagon, and Congress will be willing in the future to spend the money that is needed up front to build in reliability, so that planes will be ready to fly when they are needed. Willoughby is devoting his formidable energies to institutionalizing his doctrine of reliability and maintainability, and Dunleavy says he is even willing to buy fewer planes if that is what it takes to build in reliability.

But Vice Adm. Richard Seymour, who served as commander of the Naval Air Systems Command in the early 1980s, put it this way in an interview shortly before his death in 1989: "We talk life-cycle costs, but we don't really believe it. In this kind of climate, it just doesn't work. For me to reduce the costs of the P-3s [antisubmarine aircraft] I was buying, I would have to lose two F/A-18s. I would not make that choice."

The F/A-18 in the fleet today is a far cry from the cheap, lightweight fighter envisioned in the early 1970s. With all expenses, including research and development, counted, each Hornet costs about $30 million. But almost all of the increase from the cost projections made in the mid-1970s was the result of the high inflation rates that continued into the early 1980s. A Congressional Research Service study found that the actual cost increase, between 1975 and 1985, was just four percent.

As the inflation rate came down, the navy also benefited from a relatively high production rate and even more from the fact that foreign buyers were helping to share the cost of operating the aircraft, engine, and radar factories.

Whatever the decisions on the navy's future, whether there will be more carriers or fewer, bigger carriers or smaller, the Hornet seems assured of a major role well into the next century. If the decision is to continue to build supercarriers, the F/A-18 will have an important place in the carrier air wings. If the decision is to build smaller carriers, the Hornet strike-fighter will fit in perfectly, as the experience with the *Coral Sea* in the Libyan operation demonstrated.

APPENDIX I
F/A-18 Vital Statistics

Speed: Mach 1.8-plus

Combat Ceiling: 50,000 feet

Ferry Range, unrefueled: 2,000-plus nautical miles

Combat Radius—attack: 575 nautical miles

Combat Radius—fighter: 400 nautical miles

Maximum Payload: 17,000 pounds

Length: 56 feet

Height: 15.2 feet

Wingspan: 40.7 feet

Originally produced as a single-place A version and a two-place trainer B version. Now produced as an improved single-place C version and a two-place night, under-the-weather D version.

APPENDIX II

The Author Learns to Fly Back Seat

Al Frazier, the chief experimental test pilot for McDonnell Douglas, made an unexpected comment at the conclusion of an interview during my research for this book.

We had just spent an hour or so talking about his adventures testing the F/A-18 at extremely high angles of attack (a regime where other planes routinely fall off into a spin) and his work on the poorly understood physiological effects on today's combat pilots of the frequent and sudden onset of extreme pressures of gravity—loads that, within half a second, can multiply a man's weight by as much as nine times.

As we stood and shook hands, Frazier looked at me and said, "You certainly have an interesting job."

Rear Adm. William A. Dougherty, Jr., commander of the Atlantic Fleet's Carrier Group Four, made a similar comment at the conclusion of an interview aboard his flagship, the U.S.S. *Coral Sea:* "I know why you're writing this book . . . so you can do all these neat things."

Frazier and Dougherty were both right about on the mark. Writing a book on the Hornet has been not only a fascinating job of research and reporting but a physically demanding series of adventures as well.

In a long career as a newspaper and magazine reporter, I have always believed it was the reporter's job to go where the action was and then report back to the reader as accurately as possible. Research on the Hornet has taken me where the action is: An arrested landing and catapult takeoff from a carrier; streaking across the Nevada desert at 600 miles an hour, 200 feet above the sagebrush; hours "flying" the F/A-18 in simulators; down into the engine rooms of the *Coral Sea;* to the factories where the plane, its radar, and its engines are made, and to the air bases where the plane was tested and where the pilots are trained.

Before the navy would let me ride in the back seat of one of its $30 million strike-fighters, it sent me across a demanding set of hurdles. First was a flight physical that would result in an Up-chit—qualified to fly as a passenger—or a Down-chit—not qualified. Dr. James M. Craven, a flight surgeon at Patuxent River Naval Air Station granted me an Up-chit.

With Up-chit in hand, I was subjected to two days of lectures on the physiology of flight. I learned a good deal about what happens to the human body in flight, including some things one would rather not know, such as: at high altitude, a person's blood boils, and a wound bleeds a kind of froth. From the lecture room, the next move was across the hall to the flight training area.

First was a session in the altitude chamber, where the air is pumped out to simulate flight in an unpressurized plane at 25,000 feet. Next, I was strapped into an ejection seat and fired up a rail to simulate ejection from a plane. This part of the training was fun, only a pale approximation of what it is like actually to eject from a plane, where the ejectee is subjected to a momentary force of 200 Gs. The ejection seat was the last fun part of the training.

Next came the water survival course, all of it conducted in full flight gear, including heavy steel-tipped boots, parachute harness, G suit, and helmet. First was five minutes of treading water, with all that gear wanting to go to the bottom, followed by five minutes of the dead-man's float. This was all preparatory to the real test: a seventy-five-yard swim covering three lengths of the pool. The first length was done in the breast stroke, the second in the side stroke, and the third in a relatively relaxing back stroke.

The scene then moved to the water survival building at Norfolk Naval Air Station. On one floor was a large indoor pool equipped with an array of fiendish devices.

There, I stood on a tower about ten feet above the water, attached my parachute harness to risers connected to an overhead cable, and then was jerked off the platform and into the water face-first. As the cable dragged me down the pool, I had to twist the risers to turn on my back, disconnect the so-called Koch fittings from the risers, and swim to the side of the pool.

Then came underwater breathing. While another trainee held me down, I learned to clear my oxygen mask and breathe underwater. Then I put my legs, bent at the knees, over the edge of the pool and went through the whole procedure again, upside down. That was not fun.

Next came the helicopter rescue. Up above, large shower heads simulated the down draft from a helicopter. I was taught to grab a line dangling from a platform, signal that I was ready, and then be lifted about twenty feet to the platform. At Pensacola Naval Air Station, this training is conducted out in the Gulf of Mexico, with a real helicopter churning the water with its down draft. They say sharks come hurrying to see what all the excitement is about.

This was followed by the parachute escape. I attached myself to a parachute suspended from the ceiling. Then I was swung out over the pool and dropped, with the chute and the tangle of lines falling on top of me. I released myself from the chute and then followed a seam, pulling the chute forward over my head while sculling backward. I was taught to be careful to clear all the lines, which can easily become entangled with the seat bottom dangling below me and containing survival equipment. More than one pilot has ejected safely and then been dragged to his death after becoming entangled in his parachute lines.

Our damp, shivering group of trainees then climbed the stairs to a large room containing a pool about fifteen feet deep. Suspended above the pool was an object that looked like a huge metal barrel. This was the Dunker, about which we had all heard fearsome stories. It is designed to teach navy people how to escape from a helicopter that has crashed in the water and then turned upside down—which a helicopter, with its engine up top, is almost certain to do. A friend had described it to me and added: "It's not bad after you get over the idea you're going to die."

On the first ride, the six of us in our group were assigned seats and strapped ourselves in. We looked around and found we were in a cabin about twenty feet long and ten feet in diameter, with four large openings on one side to represent windows, and three windows and a door on the other side.

The Dunker seemed to drop into the water rather gently. As the water rose to chest level, I took a big breath, waited until the violent motion had stopped, unfastened my seat belt, grasped the edge of the nearest window opening, and propelled myself out and up. I swam to the side of the pool and grabbed the yellow safety line before I remembered I was still holding my breath.

On the second dunk, I had seat number eight, in the right forward corner. This time, as the Dunker entered the water, it slowly rolled upside down. I thought I had a slight edge as I watched the water rise first on the man across from me, as I rolled over the top and entered the water head-first. It gave me a few less seconds to hold my breath. The goal this time was to find and exit through the large doorway. For me, this involved avoiding a large box protruding from the floor (now the ceiling) and pulling myself hand over hand diagonally across the cabin to the exit. When I bumped into the protrusion, there was a moment of confusion and panic, but I worked around it and out.

On the third dunk, a new hazard was added. We had to wear blackout goggles. As I felt the Dunker drop into the water and begin to invert itself, I realized that, as I rolled over the top, I would not be able to see or feel the water rising. How would I know when to take that last deep breath? What if the water reached my face while I was inhaling? Perhaps I took that breath a moment too soon, but I had plenty of air to slip out the nearest window as soon as the Dunker came to rest. I felt sorry for one young woman who had taken swimming lessons and worked very hard to qualify to fly. But when she was told to put on the goggles, she decided this was too much for her and walked out. Actually, as my friend had said, it was not that bad after you decided you weren't going to die.

There was one more dunk, again with goggles. The Dunker entered the water right side up, but all of us had to find and go out the main door. I thought I was fortunate when my seat turned out to be right next to the door. But then the instructor gave us the ground rules: First out would be the one from my old seat, number eight, diagonally across from the door. As he went out, he would pat the leg of the man across from me, who would then go out. He would hit my leg, I would tap the fellow next to me, and then go out.

All very neat and orderly, except that the man who was supposed to exit first and begin the knee-tapping routine got disoriented and went out a window, leaving the rest of us sitting there in the dark in fifteen feet of water. The fellow across from me finally decided it was time to go, and I felt him swim past. I tapped the man next to me and went out with enough air left to reach the side of the pool.

To my Up-chit, I added two sheets of paper proving that I had successfully completed the water survival course. I felt like Houdini. My sense of accomplishment was diminished only slightly when one of the instructors explained that they also had a device to simulate escaping from a fighter plane that has crashed in the sea. But they didn't use it, he said, because the chances of survival were so slight that training for that eventuality wasn't worth the effort. Later, when I was catapulted off the *Coral Sea* in a small cargo plane called a "Carrier-On-Board-Delivery" [COD], it was comforting to know what to do if the plane crashed in the sea.

After the ordeal of the Dunker, my actual flight in the Hornet was a pleasant adventure. But more than that, it helped me to gain some appreciation of what a pilot experiences when he takes the F/A-18 into combat.

With Lt. Victor Steinman, a recent graduate of the Top Gun school, in the forward cockpit, we took off from the Lemoore Naval Air Station in California's Central Valley, climbed quickly out of the ground-hugging tule fog that often grips the valley in the winter, and flew in brilliant sunshine over the snow-mantled Sierra Nevada mountains.

As we flew, Steinman picked out other aircraft, mostly airliners, using the radar's air-to-air mode. Then he switched to air-to-ground by pushing a button on the instrument panel and demonstrated how the radar could zero in on a small island in the middle of Mono Lake.

In the training area south of the air station at Fallon, Nevada, we went through the "squirrel cage"—the loops and other maneuvers a pilot would use in aerial combat. For a minute or so, we flew upside down at 18,000 feet, looking at the world from a decidedly unfamiliar angle.

Then, at my request, Steinman demonstrated two of the maneuvers that distinguish the Hornet from most other planes.

First, he pulled back on the stick and engaged the afterburners until we hung virtually motionless, with the nose pointing almost straight upward and the tall vertical tails vibrating visibly in the vortex of air pouring back over the wings. It was a maneuver that would cause most other planes to stall and fall off into a spin, but the Hornet remained firmly under control.

Then we rolled over and dove down toward the desert floor. Leveling off at 200 feet, Steinman headed toward a target about six miles away at 600 miles an hour. Then he pushed the throttles full forward to engage the afterburners and pulled back on the stick. Up we streaked as we began the maneuver known as the Hornet high pop. Seconds later, at 10,000 feet, he rolled upside down, aimed the plane's nose at the target, rolled back right side up, pretended to drop his bombs, and then turned sharply to leave the area.

Sitting in the back cockpit, I suddenly learned what it is like to experience an almost total loss of situational awareness. The sky and the desert rotated before my vision, first one way and then the other. There was no up or down, just swirling confusion. Steinman, sensing my reaction, suggested we try it again. Again we screamed in close to the ground, zoomed sharply upward, and again went through our contortions. It wasn't until we were back on the ground, with paper and pencil, that I was able to follow through and understand the gyrations we had experienced.

Al Frazier was right: reporting on the F/A-18 has made my job a very interesting one, indeed.

BIBLIOGRAPHY ————————————————

1. THE BATTLE OF THE ADMIRALS

The description of the Backfire bomber that caused so much concern to the American military is based on *Jane's All the World's Aircraft, 1988–1989,* Jane's Information Group Limited, Coulsdon, Surrey, U.K.

The account of the roles played by Vice Adm. William Houser and Vice Adm. Kent Lee is based on interviews with the two officers, both of them now retired. The rivalry between the two men to shape the future of naval aviation was also described to me by others, especially Robert Thompson, who worked for Houser, and Rear Adm. Edward L. Feightner, who was involved in the early design studies of the F/A-18 and who is now retired.

Much of the background information on the advocates of the small, lightweight, wrap around fighter is based on my work as Pentagon correspondent for the *Washington Star* during the late 1960s and early 1970s.

Governor William H. Clements, Jr., of Texas, who was deputy defense secretary during much of the 1970s, gave me his account of his role in the development of the F/A-18 in an interview during one of his visits to Washington.

The language of the congressional restriction on the use of funds for a new plane that caused the navy so much trouble is taken from the Conference Report, H.R. Rep. No. 93-1363, 93rd Congress, 2nd Session (1974), page 27.

Throughout my research, I relied heavily on a series of General Accounting Office reports that monitored the early development of the F/A-18 and on several series of internal McDonnell Douglas publications that appeared under the names of "F/A-18 Status Report," "The Hornet

Nest'' and ''Team Talk.'' Also helpful for an overview was Mike Spick, *Modern Fighting Aircraft, F/A-18 Hornet* (New York: Arco, 1984).

2. WINGS OVER THE OCEAN

This brief review of military and, especially, naval aviation relies on a number of books as well as on interviews with fliers who served in World War II, Korea and Vietnam.

Especially helpful for their accounts of the beginnings of aerial combat in World War I were Arch Whitehouse, *Decisive Air Battles of the First World War,* (New York: Duell, Sloan & Pierce, 1963) and Quentin Reynolds, *They Fought for the Sky* (New York: Rinehart & Co., 1957). Also useful was W. R. Taylor and Kenneth Munson, *History of Aviation* (New York: Crown Publishers Inc., 1977). For a preview of aerial combat written early in the century, I found fascinating R. P. Hearne, *Aerial Warfare* (London: John Lane, 1909).

For an understanding of aerial combat through the years, I relied heavily on Mike Spick, *The Ace Factor: Air Combat & the Role of Situational Awareness* (Annapolis: Naval Institute Press, 1988).

Much of my description of the early development of naval aviation, from Eugene Ely's first landing and takeoff from a ship to the mid-1930s, is based on Lt. Harold Blaine Miller, *Navy Wings* (New York: Dodd, Mead & Co., 1937). Also helpful were Robert L. Lawson, ed., *The History of U.S. Naval Air Power* (New York: The Military Press, 1987); Capt. Edward L. Beach, U.S.N. Ret., *The United States Navy* (New York: Henry Holt & Co, 1986); Allan R. Millett and Peter Maslowski, *For the Common Defense: A Military History of the United States of America* (New York: Free Press, 1984); Anthony Preston, *Aircraft Carriers* (New York: Grosset & Dunlap, 1979), and Sandy Russell, ed., *Naval Aviation 1911–1986: A Pictorial Study* (Washington, D.C.: Government Printing Office, 1986), along with an article, Barrett Tillman, ''The Aircraft Carrier: A Brief History.'' *Soldier of Fortune*, June, 1983.

My accounts of the World War II battles that later influenced the thinking of those developing the F/A-18 were drawn from Stephen Howarth, *The Fighting Ships of the Rising Sun: The Drama of the Imperial Japanese Navy 1895–1945* (New York: Atheneum, 1983); Rear Adm. Edwin T. Layton, U.S.N. Ret., Capt. Roger Pineau, U.S.N.R. Ret., and John Costello, *''And I Was There: Pearl Harbor and Midway—Breaking the Secrets* (New York: William Morrow & Co., 1985); Gordon W. Prange, *At Dawn We Slept: The Untold Story of Pearl Harbor* (New York: McGraw

Hill Book Co., 1981) and Gordon W. Prange, *Miracle at Midway,* Donald M. Goldstein and K. V. Dillon, ed. (New York: McGraw Hill, 1982.) Layton and Prange each saw the Pacific war from a different perspective and it is useful to read their books in tandem.

The way in which the F6F Hellcat was adapted to serve as a strike-fighter was described to me by both Admiral Lee and Adm. Frederick H. Michaelis. Admiral Houser told me of his service as a squadron commander, using the F4U Corsair as a fighter and bomber in Korea. He also urged me to read Tom Blackburn, *The Jolly Rogers: The Story of Tom Blackburn and Navy Fighting Squadron VF-17* (New York: Orion Books, 1989), in which Blackburn describes how the Corsair fighter was first jury-rigged as a bomber.

For my description of the development of the American maritime strategy—and its rediscovery in the 1970s and 1980s—I relied on Michael A. Palmer, *Origins of the Maritime Strategy: American Naval Strategy in the First Postwar Decade* (Washington, D.C.: Naval Historical Center, 1988).

3. "HOLY MOLY! WE ARE IN TROUBLE!"

My account of the early development of the Northrop fighters and the fly-off between Northrop's YF-17 and General Dynamics's YF-16 is grounded in my experience covering those developments as Pentagon correspondent for the *Washington Star* and *U.S. News & World Report* magazine. This included several interviews with Thomas Jones over the years.

For the navy's reaction to the decision to "navalize" the air force choice for a new fighter, I relied on interviews with Thompson, Houser, Lee, and others involved in those events.

Much of the background information on the choice of the McDonnell Douglas-Northrop team to build the new navy plane is contained in a thick book of legal documents compiled by Harvey J. Wilcox, who was then general counsel for the Naval Air Systems Command, and who has since become deputy general counsel of the navy. Kent Lee was kind enough to loan me his copy of the book.

An interview with Wilcox and Charles J. McManus, then counsel for the F/A-18 program, was invaluable in helping to recall this period and put it into perspective.

The reaction of Northrop and McDonnell Douglas to their joint production of the new plane was described to me by Thomas Burger, Northrop's program manager for the F/A-18, and by John Capellupo, R. D. Dighton, and Donald Snyder, all of them involved in the project for McDonnell Douglas for many years.

The testimony of Joseph Gavin, of Grumman, and George Spangenberg before a Senate Armed Services subcommittee on 17 September 1975 was taken from a transcript of that hearing.

Governor Clements told me of his choice of the name Hornet for the new plane and also described his relationship to Houser and Lee.

G. W. Lenox, whom I had known when he was program manager for the F/A-18 during the development phase, recalled that difficult period during an interview in San Diego, where he now lives, and in telephone conversations.

Paul Hollandsworth, who plays a bigger role in chapter six, met with me at Oceana Naval Air Station where, as a civilian, he works for a navy contractor.

I interviewed Rep. William V. Chappell, Jr., (D-Fla.) about the F/A-18 before his recent death. Although one of the most outspoken critics of the plane for many years, he became a booster of the Hornet after seeing it perform in the fleet.

Admiral Feightner, who was involved in the early studies that led to the F/A-18, explained the rule of thumb known as the "fuel fraction" that is used to determine how much fuel a plane should carry.

Both Michaelis and Will Willoughby told me of Willoughby's influence on the F/A-18 program in separate interviews, and, in fact, whenever I visited aircraft or radar or engine factories, Willoughby's name was always mentioned with something approaching awe.

R. D. ("Bob") Dighton, chief operations analyst for McDonnell Aircraft Co., who spent more than ten years working on the F/A-18, provided a wealth of background on the development of the plane, including the emphasis on reliability and maintainability, during a lengthy interview in St. Louis. This was supplemented by R. D. Dighton, McDonnell Aircraft Co., "Designing the Hornet for Improved R&M," AIAA 19th Aerospace Sciences Meeting, 12–15 January 1981; and by Donald Malvern, executive vice president, and John Capellupo, chief program engineer, McDonnell Douglas Aircraft Co. "New Look in Assurance Technology—The Hornet." AIAA 14th Annual Meeting and Technical Display, Washington, D.C. 7–9 February 1978.

Admiral Thomas Hayward, the former chief of naval operations who now lives in Hawaii, taped a very useful response to my written questions about his experiences when the F/A-18 was in the formative stages.

4. ONE PLANE, ONE MAN

Admiral Lee told me of his conviction—shared by few in the navy—that it would be possible to develop a plane that would be capable of both air-to-air combat and attacks on surface targets. It was he who stressed the key role of the programmable radar.

Most of my information on the development of the programmable radar came from three officials of Hughes Aircraft Radar Systems Group in Los Angeles. They are John L. Conklin, manager of the advanced programs staff, Robert L. Salisbury, assistant manager, and Cecil K. Cumpton, manager of the system design laboratory, all in the F/A-18 program division.

Members of the F/A-18 team at McDonnell Douglas told me of their concern about the placement of the gun right on top of the radar, and Mike Tkach told me of his worry that he might shoot himself down while testing the gun for the first time in flight.

Lenox told me of his close relationship with Vice Adm. Forrest S. Petersen, and Petersen expanded on that account in a taped interview sent to me from his retirement home in South Carolina.

Much of my account of the development of the "glass cockpit" came from several interviews with Eugene C. Adam, who developed the concept and is now a senior fellow at McDonnell Douglas. Both Robert Thompson and Lenox described how they, within the navy, became advocates of the new cockpit.

My understanding of how the cockpit design aids the pilot was helped immeasurably by the time I spent in simulators at Cecil Field under the tutelage of Lt. Casey Albert, and by my flight in the F/A-18 with Lt. Victor Steinman at Lemoore.

Much of my information about how the computers work to control the plane—and, generally, about the development of the F/A-18—came from a series of reports presented at technical engineering meetings and published by the American Institute of Aeronautics and Astronautics (AIAA) and by the National Air and Space Administration (NASA). The McDonnell Douglas library provided many of these to me in microfiche form. Particularly helpful were the following:

The Hornet's flight control system was described in H. E. Harshburger, B. Glaser and J. R. Hammel, McDonnell Aircraft Co. "Backup Modes for the F/A-18 Digital Flight Control System," paper presented at 6th Digital Avionics Systems Conference, Baltimore, Maryland, 3–6 December 1984. This paper described the elaborate testing done to minimize the possibility of catastrophic software errors.

The plane's avionics are described in R. C. Drummond and J. L. Looper, McDonnell Aircraft Co. ''Advanced F/A-18 Avionics,'' presented at the conference on Advanced Concepts for Avionics/Weapon System Design, Development and Integration of the NATO Advisory Group for Aerospace Research & Development, Ottawa, Canada, 18–22 April 1983.

The computers and the development of software for the Hornet are described in T. V. McTigue, branch chief, McDonnell Aircraft Co. ''F/A-18 Software Development—a Case Study,'' at a conference on Software for Avionics by the Advisory Group for Aerospace Research and Development of NATO at Neuilly-sur-Seine, France, in January 1983, and in J. A. Bosch and P. Briggs, General Electric Co. ''Software Development for Fly-by-wire Flight Control Systems,'' presented at AIAA Guidance and Control Conference, Palo Alto, California, 7–9 August 1978.

The importance of providing the pilot new clues to what his aircraft is doing is emphasized in Lt. Col. J. M. Loh and A. H. Lusty, Jr. ''Display of Energy Maneuverability Performance Information for Fighter Aircraft,'' at the AIAA Mechanics and Control of Flight Conference, Anaheim, California, 5–9 August 1974.

Lt. Tom Chapin's brush with death was described to me in an interview aboard the *Coral Sea* by Chapin, his squadron commander, Comdr. J. T. Morris, and another member of VFA-132, Lt. Comdr. Richard O'Hanlon.

5. ''EXCESS ENERGY'' TO FLY AND FIGHT

The background in this chapter on General Electric's development of the F-404 engine for the F/A-18 is based primarily on a series of interviews conducted at the company's Lynn, Massachusetts, jet engine plant.

Those interviewed were Burton A. Riemer, general manager of the advanced turbo fans department, who was program manager for the engine selected to power the Hornet; Frank E. Pickering, vice president and general manager of the aircraft engineering division; George Rapp, now retired, who was involved in work on the F-404 engine and its predecessors for more than fifteen years; William Rodenbaugh, manager of product planning for the small aircraft engine division; and Frederick A. Larson, F-404 aircraft programs manager. Rodenbaugh and Larson were particularly helpful in providing the basic description, contained in this chapter, of how a jet engine works.

Again, several papers presented at technical conferences aided in my understanding of the development of the F/A-18's engine.

The difficulty of designing the engine inlet to avoid stalls is described in N. F. Amin, Northrop, and D. J. Hollweger, McDonnell Douglas, "F/A-18 Inlet/Engine Compatibility Flight Test Results," presented at the AIAA, SAE and ASME Joint Propulsion Conference, Colorado Springs, 27–29 July 1981. My interview with Rapp was enhanced by George Rapp, "The F-404 Development Program. A New Approach," presented at the AIAA/SAE/ASME 18th Joint Propulsion Conference, Cleveland, Ohio, 21–23 June 1982.

At McDonnell Douglas, Paul M. Doane described the development of the almost miraculous engine monitoring system that records engine problems beginning five seconds before the problem occurs. This interview was supplemented by P. M. Doane, McDonnell Aircraft, and W. R. Kinley, General Electric, "F/A-18 Inflight Engine Condition Monitoring System," presented at the AIAA, SAE and ASME Joint Propulsion Conference, Seattle, Washington, 27–29 June 1983.

A good overview of the entire propulsion system is provided by B. R. Williams, McDonnell Douglas, and C. J. Wendel, General Electric, "F/A-18/F-404 Propulsion System Integration," presented at AIAA/SAE/ASME 20th Joint Propulsion Conference, Cincinnati, Ohio, 11–13 June 1984.

Master Chief Don Leap, Comdr. Larry Crane, and AMS-1 Larry A. McCullough, all involved in maintenance of Hornets at VFA-125, the training squadron at Lemoore, told me of their favorable impressions of the F-404 engine.

The engine failure and crash that occurred on 8 September 1980 were described to me by Riemer and, in an earlier interview, by Jack Krings, at the time of the accident the chief McDonnell Douglas test pilot and later a Pentagon official in charge of testing new weapons.

John F. Lehman, Jr., describes his string-pulling effort to be named secretary of the navy in his *Command of the Seas* (New York: Charles Scribner's Sons, 1988). He also devotes a chapter to the F/A-18, focusing on his effort to push down the price and to force McDonnell Douglas to replace the plane lost in England.

J. C. Waldner, general manager of McDonnell Douglas's F/A-18 program at that time, told me of the decision to give the navy a new plane.

Vice Adm. Robert F. ("Dutch") Schoultz, who was deputy chief of naval operations for air warfare at the time, described to me the reaction from G.E. when Lehman suddenly decided to establish Pratt & Whitney as a second source for the F-404 engine.

G.E.'s winning of the contract to provide all F-404 engines during 1990 was announced in Pentagon and General Electric press releases on 18 August 1989.

The engine failure and loss of a plane on 4 June 1987 is described in an accident report made available to me by the office of the navy judge advocate general.

Adm. Wesley L. McDonald, who also served as deputy CNO for air warfare, described his differing reactions to engine and airframe problems during an interview.

6. WHEN WEIRD THINGS HAPPEN

The many bottlenecks preventing a rapid increase in aircraft production are described in Col. Joe G. Cabuk, Jr., Capt. Thomas J. Duncan, Lt. Col. Irving L. Hoffman and Lt. Col. David V. Nowlin, "Identification of Bottlenecks and Capacity Constraints in F-14, F-15, F-16 and F/A-18 Aircraft Production," a research report submitted to the faculty of the Industrial College of the Armed Forces, April 1983.

The decision to equip the F/A-18 with the Sparrow missile and, in the process, complicate design of the main landing gear, was described to me by Robert Thompson, cited above.

Details of the accident that took the life of Captain Kleemann were provided by the report of the official navy accident investigation.

Marine Lt. Col. (later Col.) Peter B. Field described the day he learned of the Hornet's roll rate problem during an interview at Patuxent, where he was then stationed. Technical details of the roll rate problem and a description of the way it was dealt with are contained in E. R. Shields, McDonnell Aircraft Co. director, F/A-18 Test and Evaluation, "F/A-18 Flight Test Program Overview," a paper delivered at the IAAA, SETP, SFTE, SAE, ITEA and IEEE 1st Flight Testing Conference, Las Vegas, 11–13 November 1981.

The extraordinary memo in which navy undersecretary R. James Woolsey invited the secretary of defense to kill the F/A-18 program in 1977 was obtained and published by *Armed Forces Journal International,* in an article by its editor, Benjamin F. Schemmer, in March 1978. I discussed this memo both with Woolsey and with Russell Murray II, the assistant secretary of defense whose four-page counter-memo supporting the Hornet was accepted by defense secretary Harold Brown.

Northrop's Thomas Burger described to me the difficulties that caused production problems with the F/A-18. John Capellupo, at McDonnell Douglas, told how he was called in to help deal with the problems.

Tom Jones's "Dear Davy" letter to Gen. David C. Jones was one of a number of documents made public during some of the peripheral skirmishes in the lawsuit between McDonnell Douglas and Northrop, although the record of the case itself was sealed by the court.

The sudden $5.1 billion jump in the estimated cost of the F/A-18 was detailed in testimony by Lenox and other navy officials in a number of appearances before congressional committees in the first five months of 1980.

Capt. (later Rear Adm.) John C. Weaver told me in an interview of his efforts to deal with the sharply rising costs he inherited from Lenox when he became program manager in 1980.

I interviewed Vice Adm. Richard Seymour, commander of NAVAIR during the period in the early 1980s when the F/A-18 had more than its share of cost and technical problems, shortly before his death early in 1989.

The incident in which Lt. Travis Brannon was forced to eject after his plane went into a flat spin was described to me by both Brannon and Colonel Field, who was involved in the test program at the time. Denny Behm, who conducted the tests that duplicated Brannon's spin, described his experiences to me in an interview at McDonnell Douglas in St. Louis.

The contentious period of operational test and evaluation of the Hornet was described to me by a number of those involved—or vitally interested in the outcome. They included Lenox; Rear Adm. Edward Carter III, the test commander; Hollandsworth, skipper of one of the test squadrons; Admiral Schoultz; Admiral Hayward; Rear Adm. Paul T. Gillcrist, and Rear Adm. George Strohsahl, Jr., who succeeded Weaver as program manager.

7. "A TREMENDOUS AMOUNT OF GRIEF"

The navy's insistence on a design that would permit inspection of the interior of the plane is described in Robert A. Weinberger, head, structures branch, Naval Air Systems Command; Allan R. Somoroff, technology administrator for structures, Naval Air Systems Command; and B. L. Riley, unit chief, strength technology, McDonnell Douglas Co., "U.S. Navy Certification of Composite Wings for the F-18 and Advanced Harrier Aircraft," presented at a conference on Aircraft Composites: The Emerging Methodology for Structural Assurance, in San Diego, 24–25 March 1977. This paper also includes a detailed description of the use of composites in the wings and tail.

The anguished reaction to the discovery of cracks in the vertical tail was described to me in interviews in St. Louis by John Capellupo; Robert Dighton; Donald Snyder, who was McDonnell Douglas's director of engineering on the F/A-18 from 1982 to 1985; F. Alan Frazier, the experimental test pilot who tested the LEX fence; and Len Impellizzeri, vice president of the engineering technology division. I also discussed the tail problem with Thomas Burger at Northrop.

The tail was also a major subject of discussion in my talks with the program managers, Lenox, Weaver, Strohsahl and Capt. John A. ("Spider") Lockard.

8. "A DEEP-SEATED DRIVE TO KILL"

My description of what it is like to land on a carrier is derived in part from my own clumsy attempts at such a landing in the simulator at Cecil Field. (I managed to get aboard on the second try.) I also witnessed many landings, both night and day, during my visit to the U.S.S. *Coral Sea*. The most useful information on carrier landings came from my interviews with Lt. Kevin Miller and Lt. Steven Sullivan, two landing signals officers in VFA-106 at Cecil Field, who teach pilots to land the F/A-18 on a carrier.

The process of introducing the F/A-18 into service with the marines and the navy was described to me by Rear Adm. James W. Partington, commander of Strike-Fighter Wings, Atlantic, at Cecil Field. The training of pilots and the way they would be expected to perform in combat was also the subject of interviews at Cecil Field with Lt. Casey Albert, Lt. Scott Speicher, Lt. Dennis Fitzpatrick, marine Captain Fred Martin ("Marty") Wilcox, Lt. Comdr. Dave Jones, Comdr. W. O. King, Jr., commander of VFA-106, and Comdr. John Matlock.

Albert, my guide at Cecil Field, patiently spent hours with me in the three different types of simulators, helping me understand what it is like to land and take off from a carrier, to engage in aerial combat with pilots of different levels of skill, and to go through the various maneuvers involved in attacking surface targets.

Development of the simulators is described in Thomas C. Santangelo, Naval Air Test Center, Patuxent River, Maryland, and R. Thomas Galloway, Naval Training Equipment Center, Orlando, Florida, "Flight Fidelity Testing of the F/A-18 Simulators," presented at the AIAA Flight

Simulation Technologies Conference, Niagara Falls, New York, 13–15 June 1983.

The Pilot Training Manual used by VFA-106 at Cecil Field was an invaluable aid in writing this chapter. It compares Oswald Boelcke's eight rules for aerial combat with subsequent lists of rules, contains a thick appendix of descriptions of aerial combat by pilots in a number of wars, compares the performance of American fighters against Soviet and other planes, and includes detailed how-to-do-it descriptions of the proper way to fly the F/A-18 and employ it in combat.

Also very helpful was Mike Spick's, *The Ace Factor,* cited in the notes on chapter two, and Capt. Thomas K. Mascot and Capt. Mark G. Beesley, "The Bandit's Alive at the Merge . . ." *USAF Fighter Weapons Review,* Winter 1985.

The account of the air battle on May 10, 1972, was taken from the appendix of the VFA-106 Pilot Training Manual.

The account of the accident at Patuxent River in October 1986 is taken from the report of the navy's investigation of the accident.

The discussion of the problems of sudden loss of gravity is based on the physiology training I received at Patuxent and my interview with Al Frazier, the McDonnell Douglas test pilot who has done a good deal of research in this area.

Admiral Gillcrist, who is now retired, told me of his experiences fighting the F/A-18 against an F-15 and provided me with a written account of that dogfight.

Two of the pilots who made the first deployment with the F/A-18 aboard the *Constellation* were Comdr. Tom ("Smooth Dog") Vaughn and Comdr. Bill Shepherd, both of whom I interviewed during a visit to the Fallon Naval Air Station in Nevada. They were also the sources of the account of the first experience with a broken tail hook that almost cost the loss of an airplane.

Adm. Leon Edney, the vice chief of naval operations, described, in an interview, his experiments to determine the useful range of the F/A-18 during that first deployment on the *Constellation*.

Admiral Partington, whom I interviewed at Cecil Field, was kind enough to write me a letter describing the experiments using the F/A-18 and the F-14 in mixed sections.

9. "IT STARTS RAINING F/A-18S ON YOU"
Most of my account of the raid against Libya in 1986 is drawn from the videotape of a presentation made at a meeting of the Association of

Naval Aviation by Rear Adm. Jerry Breast, who was commander of Carrier Group Two aboard the *Coral Sea* at the time of the operation.

During my visit to the *Coral Sea,* I was able to talk with Chief Petty Officer Kurt Benson and other members of the crew about their recollections of the night of the raid. The ship's public affairs office had a videotape taken that night, showing bombs and rockets being readied. Earlier, at Cecil Field, I had interviewed Commander Matlock and Lieutenant Commander Jones, who were aloft in their F/A-18s that night to protect the attacking planes from enemy aircraft and to protect the fleet from air and surface attack.

A good summary of the operation is contained in "U.S. Demonstrates Advanced Weapons Technology in Libya" and "Reagan Ordered Air Strikes to Preempt Libyan Terrorists." *Aviation Week & Space Technology,* 21 April 1986.

Lehman tells of his vigil with the chief of naval operations during the raid in his book, cited above.

The automatic carrier landing system is described in detail in J. M. Urnes, section chief, guidance and control mechanics, and R. K. Hess, lead engineer, both of McDonnell Douglas Co., "Integrated Flight Control Systems Development—the F/A-18 Automatic Carrier Landing System," presented at Guidance and Control Conference, Gatlinburg, Tennessee, 15–17 August 1983.

My account of the way the Hornet is flown, how it is maintained, and how it would be used in combat is based on interviews with many pilots and ship and ground crew members.

At Lemoore, I spoke with Lt. Mark Hunter and Lt. Comdr. Bob Norris. Norris, who was learning to fly the F/A-18, had spent more than two years flying the F-15 with the air force and another two years as an F-14 instructor, and was able to provide an unusual personal comparison of the F/A-18 with those other two planes.

Aboard the *Coral Sea* I visited with Lt. Comdr. Jack Stuart, operations officer of VFA-137, the Kestrels, and Lt. Comdr. Rich Thayer, the squadron administrative officer; marine Maj. Terry R. Dugan, executive officer, and marine 1st Lt. Tom Clark, quality assurance officer of VMFA-451, a marine F/A-18 squadron; Comdr. Steven Counts, the ship's combat direction center officer; Lt. Matthew ("Shoe") Laiden of VFA-132, the Privateers; Aviation Fire Control Chief Randall J. Sherwood, in charge of intermediate level maintenance for avionics equipment; marine S. Sgt. Howard Villar, in the jet engine maintenance shop, and AD-1 James

Jordan, engine test cell supervisor; First Class Metalsmith Rory Stanwood; MMC Jerry R. Hudson, in charge of the ship's propulsion system; AMS-1 Charles Elliott; and Tony Espinosa, a technical representative from the Naval Aviation Service Unit, in the composite repair shop.

At Fallon, I was fortunate enough to find two exchange officers, one from Australia and one from Canada. They were Squadron Leader Murray Gardner of the Royal Australian Air Force and Capt. Dean Rainkie of the Canadian Air Force.

While aboard the *Coral Sea,* I interviewed Rear Adm. William A. Dougherty, Jr., commander of the Atlantic Fleet's Carrier Group Four. We discussed both the use of the automatic landing system and the way a major war would be conducted.

One of the best recent accounts of how a war with the Soviet Union might unfold at sea is contained in Lt. Comdr. James A. Winnefeld, Jr., "Winning the Outer Air Battle." *U.S. Naval Institute Proceedings,* August 1989.

Figures on costs and the comparison of the reliability of the F/A-18 with other aircraft were provided by Captain Lockard, the program manager for the Hornet.

An interesting analysis of the cost and the cost growth of the F/A-18 is provided in Lt. Comdr. Joseph Wendell Dyer, "An Analysis of Cost Growth in the F/A-18 Airplane Acquisition Program," Naval Post Graduate School thesis, December 1981.

My discussion of how the F/A-18 fits into the navy's future is based on interviews with Vice Adm. Robert F. Dunn, who retired as deputy CNO for air warfare in the spring of 1989, and his successor, Vice Adm. Richard M. Dunleavy. As a result of a reorganization, he is known now as an assistant rather than a deputy CNO.

INDEX